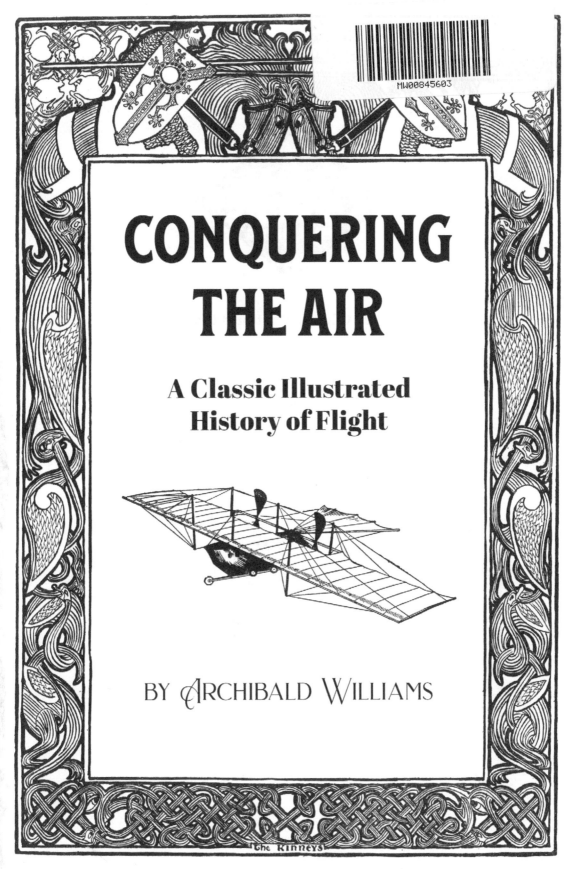

CONQUERING THE AIR

A Classic Illustrated History of Flight

BY ARCHIBALD WILLIAMS

Conquering the Air: A Classic Illustrated History of Flight

Written by Archibald Williams

More books at
CGRpublishing.com

The Aeroplane Speaks: Illustrated
Historical Guide to Airplanes

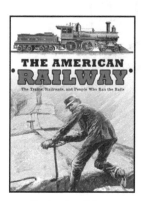

The American Railway:
The Trains, Railroads, and People
Who Ran the Rails

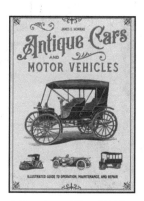

Antique Cars and Motor Vehicles:
Illustrated Guide to Operation,
Maintenance, and Repair

PLATE I

A remarkable photograph of an aviator jumping with his parachutes from an aeroplane. The parachute in front is for use should that on the back fail to open. The aviator is seen pulling at the cord which releases the parachute. [*Photo, Pacific and Atlantic Photos, Ltd.*

CONQUERING THE AIR

THE ROMANCE OF THE DEVELOPMENT AND USE OF AIRCRAFT

BY

ARCHIBALD WILLIAMS

Author of
"ENGINEERING FEATS", ETC.

LONDON: T. C. & E. C. JACK, LTD.
35 & 36 PATERNOSTER ROW, E.C.
AND EDINBURGH
1926

CONTENTS

CONTENTS

INTRODUCTION

THE author of the Book of Proverbs, writing two thousand and more years ago, gives "the way of an eagle in the air" as one of the four things that seemed most wonderful to him. No doubt he had often watched the great bird in the mountains of Judæa, climbing up the invisible staircase of the air on outspread, motionless wings, without effort, far up into the blue. Have we, too, not often felt the same admiration of the flight of birds, whether of rooks or gulls floating upward like the eagle on a rising air-current, or of the migrating flock passing far overhead on tireless wings, or of the swifts, screaming as they chase one another round the church steeple, or of the lark towering vertically into the sky, or of the kestrel "hovering" on the breeze and darting off to a new station? And is there not some envy mixed with our admiration? Don't we feel hopelessly clumsy and slow by comparison with the birds, which can reach in a few minutes a point accessible to us only after as many hours of tramping and climbing, or cross in a few seconds a river or chasm impassable to us?

This envy of "the way of an eagle in the air" has existed since the dawn of civilization. Why otherwise should beings of superhuman nature have been credited and represented with wings, from the Assyrian man-headed bull to the angel of the Christian era? Why else should legend, mythology, Northern saga, Eastern romance, the poetry of all nations, tell us of flying gods, flying men, flying horses, magic carpets, and so on? Having no wings of his own, man clapped them on to an Icarus or a Pegasus, and let his fancy do what he could not do himself. Flying thus by the proxy of the imagination was eminently safe, though somewhat unsatisfying, but until very recent years it had to suffice. If mediæval tradition and stories founded upon a rather shadowy basis are to be trusted, a few daring spirits, whose courage greatly exceeded their science, tried to imitate the birds with the crudest of apparatus, and, in most cases, with fatal results. But nothing—absolutely nothing—of practical value was achieved till the end of the eighteenth century, though monks in their cloisters, and a few secular scientists gave the problem of human flight a great deal of consideration, and indulged in prophecies and a number of unpractical suggestions, with which we need not concern ourselves.

When at last a definite advance was made towards navigating the air it was on unexpected lines. The flying *machine*, heavier than air, had been aimed at; but the lighter-than-air balloon first carried men through the clouds. The first balloon ascents, made in 1783, aroused most extraordinary enthusiasm—a regular frenzy of excitement—throughout France, the country in which they took place. It is perhaps difficult for us to appreciate, in these days of huge airships and swift aeroplanes, the hopes that people of the time based upon the spherical balloon. The great French astronomer, Arago, noted that, whereas the compass and steam-engine, both of them inventions of the first importance to mankind, had been greeted at first with contempt, or at least with indifference, the balloon attracted as much attention in the closing years of the 18th. century as had the discovery of America at the end of the 15th. The sight of a man rising into the air filled the onlookers with the most extravagant ideas and expectations. They thought that the balloon literally opened new worlds to them, that the moon and planets were now accessible:

that, just as in the past navigators had explored with their ships untraversed oceans, so balloonists would be able to explore the furthest recesses of space. Such hopes, it need hardly be said, were founded on a complete ignorance of the character of the atmospheric stratum enveloping our globe, and were therefore doomed to failure. Even the more modest anticipations, such as the exploration of the earth's surface and the carrying of passengers from place to place at their desire, fared likewise. The more ballooning was practised, the more evident it became that a balloon resembled an oarless boat set adrift in the ocean, completely at the mercy of the currents.

For a hundred years after the appearance of the first balloon no actual progress was made towards aerial navigation, except for some rather feeble experiments with dirigible balloons.

"Our age," wrote a Frenchman in 1870, "is the most renowned for its discoveries of any that the world has seen. Man is borne over the surface of the earth by steam; he is as familiar as the fish with the liquid element; he transmits his words instantaneously from London to New York; he draws pictures without pencil or brush, and has made the sun his slave. The air alone remains to him unsubdued. The proper management of balloons has not yet been discovered. More than that, it appears that balloons are unmanageable, and it is to air vessels, constructed more nearly upon the model of birds, that we must go to find out the secret of aerial navigation. At present, as in former times, we are the sport and the prey of tempests and currents, and aeronauts, instead of showing themselves now as the benefactors of mankind, exhibit themselves mainly to gratify a frivolous curiosity, or to crown with éclat a public fête. . . . The balloon is not the master of the atmosphere; on the contrary, it is its powerless slave."

Disillusion indeed! Yet within thirty years of these words being written the really navigable balloon was a reality; and five years later still men were cleaving the air with a machine kept aloft by its own power. Slowly, but surely, during the seemingly wasted years progress had been made in fields apparently unconnected with human flight; and when the time was ripe man flew.

Human invention is a chain, the links of which must be forged and attached in an inevitable sequence. If a link be begun before its time it must remain unfinished until the preceding links are in place. The evolution of the "dirigible" and the flying-machine really began in the laboratory of the chemist who discovered how to distil petrol from petroleum, and how to produce light gases in bulk; in the workshop of the engineer who invented the internal-combustion engine; in the furnaces of the metallurgist evolving light alloys of aluminium; in the testing room of the physicist. Until all of these had done their work, controlled flight necessarily remained a closed book.

When, however, the book was opened the leaves were turned at a remarkable speed. The practical dirigible balloon is but a quarter of a century old, while flight in heavier-than-air machines has barely attained its majority. Yet what astounding progress has been made in this short time! The airship bids fair to equal the largest sea ship in bulk. Its speed exceeds that of the fastest train; it can hold on a course for thousands of miles on end, fighting or circumventing storms if it meet them. The aeroplane's record is yet more astonishing. Its speed has risen to over four miles a minute, far eclipsing that of the swiftest bird. It has soared to heights exceeding that reached by the balloon, far above the loftiest mountain peaks. It has remained in the air nearly two days without alighting; has crossed the Atlantic; has flown from England to the Antipodes; has even encircled the world. Aeroplanes ply daily to regular schedules along many routes, carrying passengers, mails and goods. You may leave London for Paris in the morning, and be back at home in the afternoon. You may order an aeroplane like a taxicab, to take you to any place within its range. Weather hardly counts nowadays, for even if it be bad enough to keep ships in port, the aeroplane will face it.

Ten years ago to take a flight was an adventure, not without appreciable risk. Today air travel is practically as safe as other modes of locomotion and more comfortable than most. Aircraft are rapidly extending their uses and becoming a convenience of everyday life, giving hitherto unattainable facilities.

Far as we have progressed, we are still in the comparatively early stages of human flight. Though much has been done—and that within but a dozen years or so—there remain wide fields to be explored, and the most vivid imagination can hardly picture what aeronautics will be like twenty years hence. We have still much to learn about using air currents as does a bird, though men already have remained aloft in engineless machines for hours at a stretch. There are already signs of revolutionary changes in the design of aircraft, which may increase efficiency greatly and make flight even safer and more convenient than it is at present. One of these changes is in the direction of a machine which will be able to alight vertically in a space no larger than the back garden of a small suburban villa, or on a flat roof.

This book is, however, concerned more with the past history of aeronautics than with future possible developments. In the rush of present progress we must not forget the work of the pioneers of aeronautics, who, like pioneers in other fields, had to break the trail for those that have come after. The difficulties to be overcome were great, the courage shown in overcoming them even greater; and the story of the men who opened the paths of the air to their kind is surely worth telling, for their success heralded a new era for humanity. As the nineteenth century was the century of the railway and the steamship, so the twentieth will be that of the world-wide extension of aerial transport.

We shall devote our attention first to the origin of spherical balloons and to the most notable voyages made in them. Next, we shall see how the balloon was altered in form, provided with motive power of its own, and converted from a mere gas-container into a self-directing aerial ship. Then follows an account of the experiments which led up to the production of the first practical flying-machine; to be succeeded by a series of chapters devoted to those flights, of successively increasing length, which, as first exemplifying the conquest of the air on the grand scale, may justly be termed epoch-making. Some failures, too, will be described, not less dramatic than the successes. The part that aircraft took in the Great War, and the influence of the war in speeding up their development, then come under review, also the post-war application of aircraft to peaceful uses, and the organising of aerial transport on commercial lines. As a fitting conclusion comes a consideration of the lines along which aeronautics are likely to develop and a short flight into that future when humanity will really have taken to the air.

Just one more word to the young reader. Keep this book. In time to come you will be glad to have it by you to read over again.

CHAPTER 1

THE FIRST AERIAL VOYAGE MADE BY MAN

WE do not know, and we never shall know, the name of the bold spirit who first dared the perils of the open ocean, entrusting himself to the deep and heading for what lay beyond the horizon. The beginnings of marine navigation date back very, very far into those dim periods which preceded the earliest chapters of graven or written history.

Anything that will float on water—the rudest of rafts, or even a tree trunk—suffices for attempting a sea voyage. In modern times the oceans have been crossed by flimsy open boats, in the face of storms and raging seas. Given a certain amount of seamanship, and a modicum of luck, marvellous voyages may be made with apparently the most inadequate craft. Columbus dared his famous expedition into the unknown reaches of the Atlantic in a 200-tonner, badly found, and seriously overcrowded, but able to float more or less securely on the waves of stormy seas. As regards aerial navigation we have a definite starting date in 1783, about a century and a half ago. Many attempts at human flight had been made before that memorable day, but they had all ended in the same disastrous manner, the length of the flight being strictly proportionate to the height of the eminence from which the "flight" started. Man was revealed as quite unable to sustain himself in the air by his muscular power acting on or controlling movable wings or fixed surfaces.

But science and observation by men interested in the fascinating subject of conquering the air gradually evolved a solution of the first problem—that of successfully sustaining oneself in the atmosphere against the force of gravity, though without control of direction. In the early part of the eighteenth century coal gas had been discovered, and a few years later the English experimenter, Cavendish, had established methods of preparing hydrogen, the lightest of all gases. So that things were in train for the preparation of a "balloon" capable of raising human beings aloft by enclosing a body of gas that displaced a much greater weight of air. But the first balloon contained, strange as it may seem, nothing but air, differing from ordinary air only in one respect—that it had been heated.

In the later half of the eighteenth century, there lived at the small town of Annonay, in Auvergne, two brothers, Stephen and Joseph Montgolfier. They owned a prosperous paper-making business, which had been in the family for many generations, and so had at their disposal plenty of material for making fire balloons. They had noticed the manner in which clouds hang poised in the atmosphere, and it occurred to them that, if a body of "vapour" were enclosed in a large bag, the bag might be able to lift itself and objects fastened to it. The clouds suggested smoke, so we find them presently constructing a small paper balloon, open at the bottom, and lighting pieces of paper below it, "upon which," we read, "it began to distend itself, and in a few minutes sustained itself by being held at its lower part; when, on being released, it ascended to the ceiling of the chamber, where it remained a few minutes, much to the joy and astonishment of its projectors. Moved by this pleasing experiment, they next tried it in the open air. Here again, after it was inflated and released, it ascended, reaching a height of about 70 feet."

THE FIRST AERIAL VOYAGE MADE BY MAN

The Montgolfiers attributed their success to some peculiar quality of the "vapour" given off by the burning paper used to heat the balloon. They had not grasped the fact, which the proverbial schoolboy of today could have put before them, that the balloon owed its buoyancy merely to the hot air inside it being lighter than the cold air outside. The circumstance of the balloon descending after a short time should, we might expect, have set them on the track of the truth. But for the time at any rate they remained in ignorance of it.

Their success, however, spurred them on to further efforts. "The experiment was repeated on a much larger scale. For this purpose an envelope with a capacity of about 600 cubic feet, and of a spherical shape, was made. Upon trial this experiment far exceeded their most sanguine expectations. The balloon, after being inflated in the same manner as the first, became so strong that it broke the strings by which it was to be held a certain distance above the earth, and ascended to a height of about 600 or 700 feet, and alighted soon afterwards upon the adjoining ground."

The next step was to make a really large balloon, 35 feet in diameter, and having a capacity of 23,000 cubic feet. To increase its strength, the paper was lined with fine linen. At the bottom was a short neck, held open by a light frame. On the 25th of April, 1783, the balloon was given a trial, during which it rose to a height of 1,000 feet and travelled most of a mile before it came to earth again.

The Montgolfiers now decided to make a public exhibition of their invention. They accordingly issued invitations to the notabilities of the district to watch an ascent of the great fire-bag. On June 5, 1783, people flocked into the marketplace of Annonay from all the country round, to witness a novel and extraordinary sight. Much the same excitement held them as was experienced by tens of thousands of people still living who crowded Brooklands to witness the first public ascent of an aeroplane from British soil. The Montgolfiers were well known to those present as level-headed business men; but, in spite of this, few of the spectators believed that the huge bag which, heated by a fire of straw and wool lighted in a pit under its neck, slowly expanded as they watched it, would make the promised flight skywards.

Imagine the general surprise, therefore, when, on the signal to cast off being given, the balloon shot upwards to a height of 6,000 feet before it began to descend. It reached earth at a point a mile and a half from the marketplace.

The excitement caused by the ascent spread all over France, and even into countries outside. The Montgolfiers became the heroes of the hour. Stephen was summoned to Paris and invited to lecture before the Royal Academy of Sciences as well as to repeat his experiments for the edification of its members. Accordingly he built a new balloon, considerably larger than its predecessor. It was 72 feet high, 41 feet in diameter, and weighed about 1,000 pounds. The outside was very finely decorated with elaborate designs—for folk of that day threw themselves whole-heartedly into their work. On test it raised 8 men from the ground.

On September 12, 1783, the balloon was exhibited before members of the Academy, and took up a load of between 400 and 500 pounds, thereby proving its ability to lift human beings into the air. During the descent it was damaged somewhat seriously. Balloon No. 3 was soon put together. This had a small wicker-work basket attached to it, so that it might carry a load.

Royalty had by this time become interested in balloons, and on September 19 the balloon was inflated at Versailles in the presence of the King, Queen and Court, and ascended with a freight of a cock, a duck, and a sheep. It reached a height of 1,500 feet and landed two miles away without injury to the animals, so justifying the principle of "trying it on the dog."

The next obvious step was for a human being to make an ascent. The King at first was strongly opposed to any of his subjects taking the risk, but he ordained eventually that a couple of convicts should be experimented with,—and pardoned, if they came down alive! The honour of being the first human being to go up in a balloon was, however, too great to be cheapened in this way, and an enthusiastic young Frenchman, François Pilâtre des Roziers volunteered for the enterprise, and succeeded in obtaining the King's permission.

Montgolfier constructed a special balloon for the purpose. It was 74 feet high and 48 feet in diameter. The bottom opening was 15 feet across, and surrounded by a wickerwork gallery three feet broad, with a balustrade 3 feet high on the outside. In the neck were holes through which the aeronaut could throw fuel on to a brazier suspended from the balloon by iron chains. It was now realised that, to keep the balloon in the air, the supply of hot air must be maintained.

By way of preliminary practice, M. des Roziers made several "captive" ascents to heights of up to 300 feet. Having satisfied himself as to the buoyancy of the balloon, he prepared for a "free" flight, in which he was to be accompanied by a friend, the Marquis d'Arlandes. The twenty-first day of November, 1783, was fixed for this epoch-making event. As contemporary accounts are more vivid than the mere statement of facts, let what happened be given in the words of the official account.

"Today, November 21, 1783, at the Château de la Muette [in the Bois de Boulogne] took place an experiment with the aerostatic machine of M. de Montgolfier. The sky was partly clouded, the wind north-west. At 8 minutes after noon a mortar gave notice that the machine was about to be filled. In 8 minutes, notwithstanding the wind, it was ready to set off, the Marquis d'Arlandes and M. Pilâtre des Roziers being in the car. It was at first intended to retain the machine awhile with ropes to judge what weight it could bear, and see that all was right. But the wind prevented it rising vertically, and directed it towards one of the garden walls. The ropes made some rents in it, one of six feet long. It was brought down again and in a short time was set right. Having been filled again, it set off at 54 minutes past one, carrying the same persons. It rose in the most majestic manner and when it was about 270 feet high, the intrepid voyagers took off their hats, and saluted the spectators. No one could help feeling a mingled sentiment of fear and admiration. The voyagers were soon indistinguishable; but the machine, hovering above the horizon, and displaying the most beautiful figure, rose at least 3,000 feet high and remained visible all the time. It crossed the Seine below the barrier of La Conference; and, passing thence between the École Militaire and the Hôtel des Invalides, was in view of all Paris. The voyagers, satisfied with this experiment, and not wishing to travel further, agreed to descend; but seeing that the wind was carrying them upon the houses of the Rue de Sêve, they preserved their presence of mind, increased the fire, and continued their course through the air till they crossed Paris. They then descended quietly on the plain, beyond the new Boulevard, opposite the Mill of Croulebarbe, without having felt the slightest inconvenience, and having in the car two thirds of their fuel. They could, then, if they had wished, have gone three times as far as they did go, which was 5,000 toises [about 1¾ miles], done in from 20 to 25 minutes."

Even more graphic is the personal account of the voyage given by one of the aeronauts, the Marquis d'Arlandes, in a letter to a friend. This is worth reproducing in full. "We set off at 54 minutes past one o'clock. The balloon was so placed that M. des Roziers was on the west and I on the east. The machine, says the public, rose with majesty. I think few of them saw that, at the moment when it passed the hedge, it made a half turn, and we changed our positions which, thus altered, we retained to the end. I was astonished at the smallness of the noise and motion among the spectators occasioned by our departure. I thought they might be astonished and frightened and might stand in need of encouragement, so I waved my arm, with small success. I then drew out and shook my handkerchief, and immediately perceived a great movement in the yard. It seemed as if the spectators all formed one mass, rushing by an involuntary motion towards the wall, which it seemed to consider as the only obstacle between us. At this moment M. des Roziers called out: 'You are doing nothing, and we do not rise.'

"I begged his pardon, took some straw, moved the fire and turned again quickly, but I could not find La Muette. In astonishment I followed the river with my eye and at last found where the Oise joined it. Here then, was Conflans; and, naming the principal bends of the river by the places nearest them, I repeated Poissy, St. Germain, St. Denis, Sêve; then I am still at Poissy or Chaillot. Accordingly, looking down through the car, I saw the Visitation de Chaillot. M. Pilâtre said to me at the moment:

"'Here is the river, and we are descending.'

"'Well, my friend,' I said, 'more fire,' and we set to work.

But instead of crossing the river, as our course towards the Invalides seemed to indicate, we went along the Ile des Cygnes, entered the principal bend again, and went upstream till we were above the barrier La Conference. I said to my brave associate:

"'Here is the river, which is very difficult to cross.'

"'I think so,' said he. 'You are doing nothing.'

"'I am not so strong as you,' I answered, 'and we are well as we are.'

"I stirred the fire, and seized a bundle of straw, which, being too much pressed, did not light well. I shook it over the flame, and an instant after I felt as if I had been seized under the arms, and said to my friend:

"'We are rising now, however.'

"'Yes! We are rising,' he answered, coming from the interior, where he had been seeing that all was right. At this moment I heard a noise high up in the balloon, which made me fear it had burst. I looked up, and saw nothing; but, as I had my eyes fixed on the machine, I felt a shock, the first I had experienced. The shock was upwards, and I cried out, 'What are you going—are you dancing?'

"'I am not stirring.'

"'So much the better,' I said. 'This must be a new current, which will, I hope, take us over the river.' Accordingly, I turned to see where we were and found myself between the École Militaire and the Invalides, which we passed by about 600 yards.

"M. Pilâtre said: 'We are in the plain.'

"'Yes,' I said, 'we are getting on.'

"'Let us set to work,' he replied. I heard a new noise in the machine, which I thought came from the breaking of a cord.

I looked in and saw that the southern part was full of round holes, several of them large. I said: 'We must get down.'

" 'Why?'

" 'Look!' said I.

"At the same time I took my sponge and easily extinguished the fire which was enlarging such of the holes as I could reach, but on trying if the balloon was fast to the lower circle I found it easily came off. I repeated to my companion: 'We must descend.' He looked around him and said, 'We are over Paris.'

"Having looked to the safety of the cords, I said: 'We can cross Paris.' We were now coming near the roofs. We raised the fire and rose again with great ease. I looked under me and saw the Mission Étrangères, and it seemed as if we were going towards the towers of S. Sulpice, which I could see. We rose, and a current turned us south. I saw on my left a wood, which I thought was the Luxembourg. We passed the Boulevard, and I called out: 'Pied à terre!'

"We stopped the fire, but the brave Pilâtre, who did not lose his self-possession, thought we were coming on to some mills and warned me. We alighted at the Butte aux Cailles, between the Moulin de Merveilles and the Moulin Vieux. The moment we touched land I held by the car with my two hands. I felt the balloon press my head lightly. I pushed it off and leaped out. Turning toward the balloon, which I had expected to find full, to my great astonishment it was perfectly empty and flattened."

Surely one of the most interesting letters ever written, telling as it does of man's first voyage through a hitherto unsailed element. The twenty-first day of November, 1783, may well be regarded as one of the most memorable in human history, since it opened a new era of locomotion which, in spite of strides made in recent years, still has many developments in store for us.

It is interesting to note here that the word 'chauffeur'—which means a warmer-up, a stoker, a fireman—might have been applied to an aeronaut with more correctness than to the driver of a motor-car; for, as we have seen, the first aeronauts literally had to warm the balloon by feeding its grate with combustibles.

CHAPTER 2

FURTHER ASCENTS IN FIRE-BALLOONS

THE experiments described in the preceding chapter, created a craze for the new science. The inhabitants of the important city of Lyons appear to have been especially bitten by it, since they contributed funds liberally for the purchase of a balloon which should eclipse that which had astonished the citizens of the metropolis. The elder Montgolfier was called in, and a prospectus soon announced the construction of a Montgolfière —the name given to fire-balloons generally—of extraordinary size, warranted to ascend to a height of several thousand feet with a load of animals, the total weight of balloon and cargo being set down at about four tons.

The balloon was actually begun before M. des Roziers made his historic ascent. Money came in freely—we are told that there were 360 subscribers of £12 each—so that nothing stood in the way of making good the promises of the prospectus, at any rate as regards size. Eventually Montgolfier's staff produced a truly enormous bag, 126 feet high and 100 feet in diameter, with a capacity of nearly half a million cubic feet. Its "gores" had two layers of cotton cloth with paper sandwiched between them to prevent the passage of air, and were reinforced by ribbons and cords. The Flesselles balloon, as it was named after the promoter of the subscription list, had its exterior painted in a very artistic manner with representations of winged figures and mythological persons, and must have presented a very fine appearance.

CONQUERING THE AIR

The original purpose of the balloon was to raise animals into the air, but news that the King, by permitting the ascent of des Roziers, had cleared the way for other of his subjects doing the same thing, decided Montgolfier to trust himself to his great "machine." Applications from people wishing to accompany him poured in. Des Roziers, who had arrived in Lyons on the day after Christmas, was accepted without hesitation, and at his suggestion a number of alterations, to render the balloon more suitable for carrying human passengers, were carried out.

On January 7, 1784, the parts of the balloon were transported to the field, some distance from the city, selected for the scene of the ascent, which was to take place three days later at the chilly hour of five o'clock in the morning.

But the cumbersome bag proved so difficult to handle that the 15th. arrived before the balloon could be inflated, and the gallery, designed to carry six persons, be attached. By the time everything was complete, the day had advanced too far for an ascent to be undertaken, and the fire of alder wood, consumed at the rate of 5 lbs. per minute, was extinguished.

At the next attempt the balloon suffered damage by fire, and after repair it received further injuries from snow and rain. But on the 19th. the great bag was fully distended with hot air, and as it strained at its mooring ropes four young "bloods,"—Prince Charles de Ligne, and the Comtes de Laurencin, Dampierre and Laporte—sprang into the car, and, drawing their swords, dared anyone to try to remove them. Montgolfier and des Roziers were still on the ground, and as the latter particularly wanted to make a high ascent, he suggested that the six should draw lots and the number be reduced to three. On the principle that occupation in such a case was nine-tenths of the law, the spirited, but ill-mannered, occupants of the car cut the ropes with their swords, and the other two gentleman had to scramble aboard as best they might. At the last moment a certain M. Fontaine, who had taken a leading part in the construction of the balloon, and therefore considered himself to have a good claim to be included among the aeronauts, hurled himself into the gallery, so that when the balloon rose it carried a crew of seven persons.

The excitement of the 100,000 spectators on beholding the Montgolfière ascend as if by magic was unbounded. Men waved handkerchiefs and threw their hats into the air; women burst into tears and many, following the fashion of the time, fainted away.

The aeronauts themselves were in the highest spirits on finding that they could keep the balloon afloat with a slow consumption of fuel. At the rate they were burning it the supply ought to last until evening. But they had been in the air barely fifteen minutes, when a rent, four feet or more long, developed in a part of the bag which had previously been damaged by fire and imperfectly repaired. The hot air escaped rapidly, and the balloon fell at a speed that alarmed the passengers. In spite of the balloon striking the earth rather violently, the voyagers escaped uninjured, to find themselves acclaimed as the heroes of the hour. At the opera that evening they were publicly crowned; all the night through serenaders gathered under their windows; and when, a few days later, des Roziers left for Dijon, he made a triumphal departure, escorted by a large cavalcade of the most distinguished young men of Lyons. The citizens of Paris, whose noses had presumably been put out of joint by the ascent of "Le Flesselles," affected to regard the whole affair as fit only for ridicule.

About a month after the ascent at Lyons the first balloon ascent in Italy was made by three Italians at Milan. The balloon had hardly been released when it began to drive horizontally towards a large building, which threatened its destruction. The aeronauts hurriedly piled on fuel, and to the amazement, as well as the relief, of the onlookers the balloon leaped upwards and floated safely over the obstruction. The wind now carried the aeronauts towards a range of high, rocky hills, which they could not hope to surmount, as their fuel supply had run short. So the fire was let down and the balloon settled earthwards. Unluckily, it struck the top of a large tree and for some time hung poised, as it were, between heaven and earth, to the great peril of the aeronauts. These managed to keep their heads and stoke vigorously, with the result that the balloon freed itself from the branches. Willing hands then seized ropes that had been let down and drew the balloon into safety.

The most considerable flight made by a fire-balloon was probably that of the *Marie Antoinette*, which ascended from Versailles on June 23, 1784, with M. des Roziers and a friend, M. Proust, aboard. Des Roziers, as has already been mentioned, was anxious to experience a really high ascent, and on this occasion his wish was gratified. Striking an upward current of air, the balloon soon reached the clouds, charged with snow, which completely shut off the view. Eager to know how high the balloon could go, the aeronauts piled on the fuel, and eventually floated at an elevation of 11,732 feet, probably the greatest height ever reached by a balloon of this type. The "ceiling" of the Montgolfière—that is, the maximum height to which it could climb—had now been attained, and after "wandering about for a time in regions which we felt were now visited by man for the first time, isolated and separated entirely from nature," the voyagers decided to return to earth. Slowly the balloon sank through a glorious cloudscape and suddenly quite another scene revealed itself. "The extensive plains appeared under our eyes in all their glory. Except in the far distance, no snow nor clouds were now visible. In a moment we had passed from winter to spring. The boundless earth seemed covered with towns and villages, which, judged from our great height, might have been as many solitary houses standing in their gardens. The rivers winding about in all directions seemed mere streamlets designed to beautify the land round these houses; large forests appeared as mere clumps of trees; meadows and broad fields as garden plots. . . . In our lofty balcony we felt as secure as on that of a mansion, and could enjoy the ever-changing scenes below without any of that giddiness to which many persons are prone. The wind blew freshly, but caused us no anxiety. We could gauge our rate of progress only by the speed with which villages seemed to fly past below us. We often wished to descend, to learn what people were shouting up to us; and we were able to rise, fall, move horizontally or obliquely at will as often as we thought fit, without actually coming to earth."

Thus M. des Roziers seems to have combined with his enthusiasm for aerial navigation a considerable capacity for graphic description. Forty miles from the starting-point the balloon landed safely, accomplishing a truly remarkable voyage. For the first time man had been above the clouds without having his feet on the ground.

We may conclude references to Montgolfières with an account of a trip made in August, 1784, by the Abbé Carnus in the "City of Rodez," named after the town about 100 miles from the southern frontier of France. He was accompanied by a M. Louchet.

The day was sunny, calm and windless, when, at 8.20 a.m. the balloon left the ground amid the cheers of the assembled multitude. As on another occasion, many women fainted, perhaps through mistaking the fire used to heat the balloon for a conflagration of the fabric itself. In 12 minutes the balloon reached a height of 6,000 feet above sea level, and by stoking hard the elevation was increased to 7,000 feet. A magnificent view delighted the aeronauts, who could now see for many miles in all directions. What appeared like a small group of stones a few feet high was identified as the Cathedral of Rodez. Detail had been lost. The country below appeared perfectly circular, a little raised in the middle and marked with green patches—forests—and seemingly uninhabited. The distant Pyrenees were but a long line of snow piles, connected at their bases.

So far the balloon had moved almost vertically, hovering over the field from which it started. Then a slight breeze began to carry it south-eastwards. By nine o'clock the fuel was exhausted but for two bundles of straw, reserved for landing, and the balloon began to settle. When 600 feet above the ground the aeronauts threw the remaining straw on the fire to reduce the speed of descent. The Abbé alighted, but, as he released his hold on the balloon, this shot upwards again, carrying M. Louchet with it to a height of 1,500 feet. M. Louchet, however, managed to effect a safe landing, after which he experienced great difficulty in restraining the balloon, for the peasants near by refused to have anything to do with him or with the monster that had brought him among them. The Abbé meanwhile hastened up, and, to use his own words: "we then pressed out the hot air, folded up the envelope, put it on a small cart, and drove off with it."

Quite in the manner of the modern balloonist!

CHAPTER 3

THE COMING OF THE GAS BALLOON

The hot-air balloon of Montgolfier had two things in its favour: it could be inflated both quickly and cheaply. On the other hand, it was characterised by some serious disadvantages. An open fire close to the fabric of the bag was a decidedly dangerous travelling companion; yet upon the maintenance of this fire depended the ascensive powers of the balloon. Range of flight therefore centered largely on the amount of fuel that could be carried. Another adverse feature was its necessarily large size, relatively to its lifting power, as the difference in weight between a given volume of cold air and of air heated to the very moderate degree practicable, is small. The history of ballooning would, it is safe to say, have been very different had experimenters been limited to the use of the Montgolfière.

Shortly after the first Montgolfière had made its ascent at Annonay, as already described, a young Professor of physics at Paris, Charles by name, constructed a small balloon of light fabric, rendered it air-tight with a coating of India-rubber, and filled it with hydrogen, which, as the reader probably knows, weighs but one-fourteenth as much as air of the same temperature. The gas was produced by the action of sulphuric acid on iron filings.

The balloon, quite a small affair, held but 940 cubic feet, yet its inflation took several hours. The Parisians, who had got wind of the experiment, showed so much curiosity that when, on August 26, 1783, the partly-inflated bag was transported to the Champ de Mars, great precautions had to be observed to prevent damage by the crowd which accompanied it. Though the transfer took place at night, troops were needed to guard the strange object from the many people who desired to inspect it at close quarters.

Next morning, M. Charles and his assistants, the brothers Robert, completed the inflation of the balloon, now attracting the eyes of an excited and gaping multitude. At five o'clock the balloon was released, at once shot up into the clouds, and soon was lost to sight. As the neck of the bag had been tied up to prevent escape of gas—it was not yet realised that this should be left open to allow for expansion—the bag presently burst and descended in a village some distance from Paris. The astonished villagers, believing it to be some monstrous animal, and encouraged in this belief by two monks, fell upon it with pitch-forks, stones, scythes, and—if certain old prints are reliable—firearms, so that when a search for it was made, nothing remained but a few fragments. This incident caused the issue of a Governmental document, solemnly warning all and sundry against interfering henceforth with strange gasbags that might come sailing down from the skies.

Professor Charles and his assistants at once set to work on a much larger hydrogen balloon, intended to raise a car and one or two passengers. This balloon had a valve in the top which, on the pulling of a cord running up inside through the neck, would allow gas to escape when a descent had to be made. In all essentials it closely resembled the modern balloon.

December 1, 1783, was fixed for the ascent. About 600,000 spectators—if we may credit contemporary accounts—assembled to witness a repetition of des Roziers' feat of ten days earlier. A rumour ran round that the King had forbidden the ascent; but it was presently known that M. Charles, urging how he had pledged his word to the public, had finally obtained permission.

Soon after midday the discharge of a cannon signalled that the great moment had come. Before entering the car with one of his assistants, Charles handed to Montgolfier, who was present, a small balloon. "It is for you, monsieur," he said, "to show us the way." This well-calculated compliment did a great deal to allay the partisanship of the crowd, which had divided itself into Montgolfierites and Charlesites, and was showing considerable feeling.

The car contained a good amount of ballast, for Charles' idea was to use this in combination with the valve to control elevation, as is done today. We learn that friends had also stocked it with wine and much warm clothing. A large blanket was jettisoned soon after the balloon began to ascend.

Among the onlookers was the aged Maréchal Villeroi, a confirmed disbeliever in innovations such as balloons. His friends with much difficulty persuaded him to watch the ascent, and led him to the window. When Professor Charles rose into space the old Maréchal was instantly converted. Falling on his knees, and with tears in his eyes he exclaimed: "Yes! It is a fact! They will even discover how to avoid death; but only after I am gone!"

At an elevation of 1,800 feet, as shown by the barometer, the valve and ballast were used to keep the balloon on a horizontal course, in order that it might be seen by the Parisians as long as possible. The therometer was now between 10 and 12 degrees above zero Centigrade. The wind, however, kept the balloon moving, and about an hour after the start the faintly-heard report of a cannon informed the aeronauts that they had passed out of sight. The sound was not unwelcome, as they could now cease watching the barometer and turn their attention to what was below them. In all directions people were seen scurrying after the balloon, and occasionally the aeronauts could recognize words shouted up to them. The ballast being nearly exhausted, coats, muffs, and other things went overboard, and finally a descent was made in the plain of Nesles. Here they were quickly surrounded by country folk, eager to show their admiration; and they prepared a short account of the voyage which was duly signed by the clergy and magistrates present.

Soon afterwards up galloped the Duke of Chartres, who embraced them both and asked for details. Seeing how greatly interested the Duke was, Charles told him that he would make a second ascent alone. M. Robert then got out of the car, and the balloon rose quickly 3,000 feet. M. Charles records that in ten minutes the temperature fell from that of spring to that of winter, but without causing him any great discomfort. Also he notes how the sun, which had set while he was on the ground, now came into sight again on the horizon; so that probably he was the first man to see the sun set twice in the same day!

The Professor, who had promised to return to the Duke within the half hour, opened the valve and dropped earthwards. When close to the ground he threw out the rest of the ballast, and so made a good landing.

Thus ended the second aerial voyage. It is rather surprising that Professor Charles never repeated his experiment. His description of the trip betrays no suggestion of nervousness, and nothing seems to have occurred that might have prejudiced him against taking further risks. But it was his, and not Montgolfier's, method of ballooning that has been followed ever since the very early days of aerostation. The use of hydrogen gas, however, was abandoned as being much too expensive, when an alternative was available in the coal gas used for lighting. This, though several times heavier than hydrogen, is cheap and can be obtained readily in large quantities from any gas works, where many thousand cubic feet are always kept stored in the gasometers for providing the district served with light and heat.

The first ascent with coal gas was that made by the celebrated English aeronaut, Charles Green, on August 19, 1821, the coronation day of King George IV. Since then hydrogen gas—though it can be produced very much more cheaply now than 100 years ago—has been employed, with few exceptions, only for dirigible balloons.

CHAPTER 4

THE FIRST BALLOON ASCENTS IN BRITAIN

THE credit of first rising from the British territory in a balloon appears to belong to a Mr. J. Tytler, who made an ascent in a fire-balloon on August 27, 1784. He started from the Comely Garden, Edinburgh, and alighted at a spot a mile away. The shortness of the journey may be accounted for by the fact that no apparatus for keeping the air in the balloon warm was carried. Consequently, when the original heat had been dissipated the aeronaut had to land. It is not to be wondered at, therefore, that the ascent attracted little general interest.

Very soon afterwards all London was agog to witness the ascent, in a hydrogen balloon, of an Italian, Vincent Lunardi, secretary to the Neapolitan Ambassador. In the face of many difficulties he constructed a balloon, 33 feet in diameter, varnished with oil, but having no escape valve. When exhibited at the Lyceum, in the Strand, the balloon—which must have been a somewhat gaudy object with its alternate stripes of blue and red—attracted, we are told, over 20,000 people. Lunardi's intention was to ascend from the grounds of the Chelsea Hospital. Unfortunately, a recent abortive attempt by a Frenchman to go up in a fire-balloon from a garden in the same district had led to a riot. The crowds of that time seem to have shown little mercy to failures, though ready to applaud success. The authorities therefore put obstacles in Lunardi's way, fearing further trouble, but eventually he got leave to rise from the grounds of the Honourable Artillery Company.

To make the occasion more impressive, Lunardi was to take up a companion, one Mr. Biggin. On the morning of September 15, 1784, the balloon was in course of inflation, and a large crowd impatiently awaited the start. As the aeronaut himself has left a somewhat quaint account of what happened, we cannot do better than make some extracts from it.

"A little before two o'clock on Wednesday, Mr. Biggin and myself were prepared for our expedition. His attention was allotted to the philosophical experiments and observations, mine to the conduct of the machine and the use of the vertical oars,[1] in depressing the balloon at pleasure.

"The impatience of the multitude made it inadvisable to proceed in filling the balloon, so as to give it the force it was intended to have. On balancing the force with weights, it was supposed incapable of taking us up. When the gallery was annexed and Mr. Biggin and I got into it the matter was beyond doubt, and whether Mr. Biggin felt the most regret in relinquishing his design, or I in being deprived of his company it may be difficult to determine. But we were before a tribunal, when an instantaneous decision was necessary; for hesitation and delay would have been construed into guilt, and the displeasure impending over us would have been fatal, if in one moment he had not had the heroism to relinquish, and I the resolution to go alone.

"This event agitated my mind greatly, a smaller gallery [car] was substituted, and the whole undertaking being devolved on me I was preparing accordingly when a servant brought

---

[1] Lunardi had great confidence in the utility of the oars with which the balloon was provided, but there is little reason to think that they had any effect in controlling the balloon.

me word than an accident had befallen the balloon, which would prevent my intended voyage. I hastened down, almost deprived of my senses; and though I was instantly convinced that the injury was trifling I could not recover the shock in time to recollect that I should supply myself with those instruments for observation which had been appointed to Mr. Biggin. I threw myself into the gallery, determined to hazard no more incidents that might consign me and the balloon to the fury of the populace, which I saw was on the point of bursting. An affecting testimony of approbation and interest in my fate was here given. The Prince of Wales and the whole surrounding assembly almost at one instant, took off their hats, hailed my resolution, and expressed the kindest and most cordial wishes for my safety and success.

"At five minutes after two the last gun was fired, the cords divided, and the balloon rose, the company returning my signals and adieu with the most unfeigned acclamation and applauses. The effect was that of a miracle on the multitude which surrounded the place, and they passed from incredulity and menace into the most extravagant expressions of approbation and joy.

"On discharging part of the ballast the balloon ascended to a height of 200 yards. As the multitude lay before me, all the 150,000 people who had not seen my ascent from the ground, I had recourse to every stratagem to let them know I was in the gallery, and they literally rent the air with their acclamations and applause. In these stratagems I devoted my flag, and worked with my oars, one of which was immediately broken and fell from me. A pidgeon [Lunardi's spelling] too escaped, which, with my dog and cat, were the only companions of my excursion."

Lunardi himself relates, as a proof of the great interest taken in him personally—he seems to have had a fairly good opinion of himself—that the oar which fell was mistaken by a lady for the aeronaut, and the shock affected her so much that she died a few days later. His grief at this unfortunate occurrence was mitigated by learning that he had saved a life. For it so happened that, as the balloon passed overhead, the jury of a court trying a young man who undoubtedly would have been condemned to death, were so anxious not to miss the fun that they hurriedly found a verdict of "not guilty," and rushed out, leaving the prisoner a free man. Surely one of the most lucky escapes from justice on record!

The aeronaut presently became so cold that he "found it necessary to take a few glasses of wine. I likewise eat the leg of a chicken, but my bread and other provisions had been rendered useless by being mixed with the sand which I carried as ballast."

At 3.30 p.m. Lunardi descended in a cornfield in South Mimms, and landed the cat, which was suffering greatly from the cold. Possibly he himself would have preferred to end his journey at the same time, but as people had collected, thus putting him on his mettle, he threw out ballast and continued on his way. A letter was written, tied to a corkscrew, and thrown overboard; to be followed soon by plates, knives, forks and an empty bottle—a proceeding which, we fancy, would be severely frowned upon by a present-day aeronaut!

At Standon, near Ware in Hertfordshire, the balloon finally came to rest, on a spot subsequently marked by a stone. "Some labourers were at work in it (the field). I requested their assistance; they exclaimed they would have nothing to do with one who came in the Devil's house, or on the Devil's horse—I could not distinguish which of the phrases they used—and no entreaties could prevail on them to approach me. I at last owed my deliverance to the spirit and generosity of a female. A young woman, who was likewise in the field, took hold of a cord which I had thrown out, and calling to the men, they yielded that assistance to her request which they had refused to mine."

Lunardi, whose name but a few days before had been coupled in a very feeble pun with "lunatic," was now the lion of London. His voyage became the sole topic of conversation. The balloon was exhibited at the Pantheon, in Oxford Street, where thousands paid to see it; ladies would have nothing but "Lunardi" bonnets and "Lunardi" garters. The King received the aeronaut; a public testimonial was subscribed; and a medal was struck in his honour. There followed a very successful series of ascents in Scotland, during one of which Lunardi travelled more than 100 miles. Then he returned to Italy, where, sad to relate, he died 12 years later in great poverty. We owe Lunardi a debt, for it was he who awoke in the English an interest in a new science to which they had previously been quite indifferent, and presently led them to produce some of the most famous of balloonists.

The inscription on the stone at Standon is worth recording, if only as an example of the whole-hearted way in which our ancestors lauded any noteworthy person or achievement. It runs thus:

Let Posterity Know
And Knowing be Astonished
That
On the 15th Day of September, 1784,
VINCENT LUNARDI, of Lucca, in Tuscany
The First Aerial Traveller in Britain
Mounting from the Artillery Ground
In London

THE FIRST BALLOON ASCENTS IN BRITAIN

And
Traversing the Regions of the Air
For Two Hours and Fifteen Minutes
In This Spot
Revisited the Earth.
On This Rude Monument
For Ages be Recorded
That Wondrous Enterprise
Successfully Achieved
By the Powers of Chemistry
And the Fortitude of Man
That Improvement in Science
Which
The Great Author of All Knowledge
Patronizing by His Providence
The Invention of Mankind
Hath Graciously Permitted
To Their Benefit
And
His Own Eternal Glory.

CHAPTER 5

THE FIRST CROSSING OF THE ENGLISH CHANNEL BY AIR

Among the most daring exploits of the early balloonists a high place must be given to that of Jean Pierre Blanchard, a Frenchman, and Dr. John Jeffries, an American, who together crossed the English Channel on January 7, 1795.

Blanchard had already attracted attention in England by making a series of balloon voyages, the longest of which measured over seventy miles. On one of these he took Jeffries with him—in consideration of a fee of £100. When the Doctor, a fairly wealthy man and "bitten" by ballooning, heard afterwards that Blanchard proposed to cross from England to France in a balloon and so win the glory of being the first person to trust himself over the open sea, he at once offered to meet all the expenses of the trip—amounting, he tells us, to £700—if he were given a place in the car. To this Blanchard agreed, though apparently doubtful as to the balloon's ability to carry two persons safely. So eager was the Doctor, however, that in his agreement with the aeronaut he actually bound himself "that, in case of necessity on our passage, I would get out of the Car for his preservation," and what more, indeed, could a man promise?

The balloon was taken to Dover during the last days of December, 1784, together with the materials and apparatus for inflating it. But for a fortnight or so the weather and wind prevented anything further being done. During the wait Blanchard, whether from a selfish aversion from sharing the glory with anyone else, or at the instigation of his compatriots, anxious to confine the honour to their own country, put difficulties in Jeffries' way. He even had the meanness to increase his weight artifically by means of a loaded belt, in order to prove that the balloon would not carry two persons in addition to a reasonable amount of ballast.

Dr. Jeffries very properly held Blanchard to his bargain, calling in the aid of the Governor of Dover Castle. On January 7 weather and wind were favourable, though the cold was intense. Blanchard decided to start as soon as possible and had the balloon inflated. "The balloon being filled a little before one o'clock, we suffered it to rise, so as to be disengaged from the apparatus, etc., for filling it, and to be drawn down again right to the edge of the cliff, where we attached the oars or wings with the moulinet and gouvernail to the car. Exactly at one o'clock (having in the car with us three sacks of sand ballast of ten pounds each, a large parcel of pamphlets, two cork jackets, a few extra clothes of M. Blanchard, a number of inflated bladders, with two small anchors or grapnels, with cords affixed, to assist our landing) we rose slowly and majestically from the cliff, which being at the time of ascent from it almost covered with a beautiful assembly from the city, neighbouring towns and villages, with carriages, horses, etc., together with the extensive beach of Dover, crowded with a great concourse of people, with numbers of boats, etc., assembled near the shore, under the cliffs, afforded us, at our first arising from them, a most beautiful and picturesque view indeed."

Thus the good Doctor in the account which he has left of this eventful voyage. Thirty pounds of ballast was indeed a small amount to carry, and the event showed that Blanchard had some reason on his side. The "wings or oars" which he

mentions seem to have been a regular part of Blanchard's ballooning kit, though probably quite useless; and as for the
"moulinet and gouvernail," we can only guess at their purpose.
The second may have been a drag rope, and the first a winch
for winding it on: or perhaps the things were connected with
the working of the oars.

When the balloon was about one-third of the way across the
Straits, it began to descend so fast that half the ballast had
to be thrown over. For a time it rose again, but soon recommenced to sink. The aeronauts now jettisoned the rest of the
ballast and part of the pamphlets. Midway between the two
coasts the remaining pamphlets were sacrificed, but without
much effect; and the position began to look serious, though
Jeffries philosophically found some comfort in a magnificent
view of the French coast.

"At about half past two," writes the Doctor, "I found we
were descending very rapidly. We immediately threw out all the
little things we had with us, such as biscuits, apples, etc., and
after that one of our oars or wings; but still descending, we
cast away the other wing and then the gouvernail; having likewise had the precaution, for fear of accidents, while the balloon
was filling, partly to loosen and make it go easy, I now succeeded in attempting to reach without the car, and, unscrew-
ing the moulinet with all its apparatus, I likewise cast that
into the sea. Notwithstanding all which, the balloon not rising, we cut away all the lining and ornaments, both within and
on the outside of the car, and in like manner threw them into
the sea. After which we cast away the only bottle we had taken
with us."

The bottle, somewhat to the Doctor's surprise, appeared to
strike the water directly under the balloon. Though of a
scientific turn of mind, he did not realise that the bottle would

travel forward with the same velocity as the balloon while falling.

Even further sacrifices were demanded. The anchors and cords went overboard—and the sea still seemed to come nearer and nearer. The aeronauts accordingly began to strip themselves and discard their clothing. M. Blanchard disposed of his overcoat; and the Frenchman capped this by parting with his "trowsers." Which done, both men donned their cork jackets and prepared for the worst.

The French shore was now four or five miles away, and the balloon approaching it fast. At one time the car almost touched the sea, and then, just when the position appeared to have become quite desperate, the balloon encountered an upward current, which carried it at a good height over the French coast-line at 3 p.m.

The aeronauts, deprived by necessity of much of their clothing, were now almost numb with cold, though well satisfied at having performed the most dangerous part of their task. The cork jackets being needed no longer, they were taken off and kept handy as ballast, for the balloon now began to sink towards a large forest, the tree-tops of which looked very uninviting. Casting away the jackets improved things a bit, but only momentarily.

At last the aeronauts caught hold of a high tree, and, working from one branch to another, manœuvred the balloon over an open space. The escape valve was then pulled and the balloon came gently to earth in the Forest of Guines, near Calais.

A number of people who had been watching the course of the balloon now came up and gave the aeronauts a most enthusiastic welcome. The next day a fête was held in their honour at Calais, where Blanchard received the freedom of the city. Later, he was summoned to Versailles, and received by the

King, who, in addition to a gift of £500, bestowed on him a pension of £50 a year, besides other rewards. Jeffries had to be content with the freedom of Dover. Though he does not say so in as many words, he evidently thought that he had not received his fair share of recognition. We may hope that, as time passed, he was able to console himself with the reflection that he had played a leading part in a noteworthy adventure; one which at the time created as great a sensation as did Blériot's aeroplane flight 124 years later in the reverse direction.

Blanchard and Jeffries were more fortunate than Pilâtre des Roziers, who tried to emulate them the same year. His intention was to travel from Boulogne to England in a double balloon, the arrangement of which indicates either amazing courage or an inability to appreciate the risks involved. Having obtained from the French Government a grant of £1,600, he constructed a hydrogen balloon, from which hung a fire-balloon carrying the car. His idea no doubt was that, by varying the lift of the second, he could dispense with the need for throwing out ballast or allowing gas to escape from the hydrogen balloon. Friends urged him to abandon the experiment, among them Professor Charles, who told him plainly that he was simply putting fire beside powder. But des Roziers would not listen, and for many weeks he waited impatiently at Boulogne for favourable conditions. Eventually on June 15, 1785, des Roziers and his brother left the ground in the strange combination. A nobleman, at the moment of departure, threw a purse containing 200 louis into the car, to pay for a seat; but happily for himself the offer was politely declined.

The balloon rose to a height of 700 feet, and then met a contrary current which carried it inland. About half an hour

PLATE II

Vickers-Vimy-Rolls biplane leaving St. John's, Newfoundland, June 14, 1919, on the successful transatlantic flight to Ireland. [*Photo, Messrs. Vickers, Ltd.*

The start of the London–Australia flight from Hounslow Aerodrome.   The Vickers-Vimy gathering speed.   [*Photo, Messrs. Vickers, Ltd.*

after the start the occupants of the car were seen to be doing something with the fire-basket under the Montgolfière, and to the horror of the spectators a blue flame suddenly enveloped the balloon. The last fell like a plummet, and by a strange coincidence struck the earth only a few yards from the spot where Blanchard and Jeffries had landed safely a few months earlier. Des Roziers was already dead when found; his brother lived but a few minutes.

The first man to ascend in a balloon thus was the first victim of the new science.

CHAPTER 6

SOME NOTABLE LONG-DISTANCE VOYAGES IN BALLOONS

THE limitations of the spherical balloon and the cost of its inflation caused ballooning to become a profession rather than a hobby, as soon as the first wave of interest aroused by its introduction had spent itself. Balloon ascents became a common feature of fêtes and entertainments, the aeronaut recouping himself by exacting a fee from the organisers of the fête in which he took part.

Among the earliest professional balloonists was Mr. Charles Green, who has already been mentioned as the first user of coal gas for filling balloons. During his aeronautical career Mr. Green made hundreds of ascents, without meeting with any serious accidents. He had constructed for himself a very large balloon, named the Nassau balloon on account of a voyage made in it which is famous in the history of ballooning.

On November 7, 1836, the balloon ascended from the Vauxhall Gardens, London, having on board, besides Mr. Green, a Mr. Robert Hollond and Mr. Monck Mason, the author of "Aeronautica," one of the leading books on the early history of ballooning, in which is given a full account of the voyage now to be described briefly.

The object of the expedition was to fly eastwards as far as the balloon could carry its passengers. Green, being well aware of the uncertainties of ballooning as regards both direction and distance, had stocked the car with a good supply of provisions, and had provided himself and his companions with passports to all the countries of Europe, so that, wherever they might land, their "papers" should be found in order.

About four hours after the start, the balloon, which had passed over Canterbury—where a message to the Mayor of the town was dropped in a parachute—reached the sea near Dover. Dusk was now coming on, and the white cliffs behind offered a striking contrast to the great dark masses of clouds in front, resembling a gigantic barrier crowned with battlements and towers. The breeze soon carried the balloon into the clouds. Everything was blotted out by the darkening fog, and, now that the coast-line had been left some distance astern, no sounds of any kind could be heard. The balloon seemed stationary in a lightless, soundless world.

Presently the balloon emerged from the clouds and below them the voyagers saw the lights of Calais, whence rose the sounds of military drums. The first night balloon voyage to be described in print proved very interesting to the aeronauts, though the cold was severe enough to freeze solid all the water and oil aboard. But for the absence of any sensible wind— since the balloon was travelling at the same pace as the breeze—the three men might have suffered considerable discomfort. In the depths beneath, the watchers saw here the isolated lights of lonely houses and hamlets, there the massed lights of towns. At times it was easy to imagine that the sky was below, and not above them. As a large centre of population was approached, the massed lights appeared to spread themselves out until, when the balloon was directly overhead, the lay-out of a city, with its streets and squares, stood revealed by the glittering lines of lamps.

For a considerable time the aeronauts could only guess at their position. But about midnight the glare from many furnaces told them that they had reached Liége, the great iron-smelting district of Belgium. The balloon floated on, over country in which lights became fewer and fewer as people retired to bed, and by midnight only the stars remained to keep the aeronauts company. "Nothing could exceed the intensity of the night which prevailed during this part of the voyage," writes Monck Mason. "A black profound abyss surrounded us on all sides, and, as we attempted to penetrate into the mysterious deeps, it was with difficulty that we could beat back the idea of the apprehension that we were making a passage through an immense mass of black marble, in which we were enclosed, and which, solid to within a few inches of us, appeared to open up at our approach."

The balloon moved along at a speed of nearly 30 miles an hour, about 2,000 feet above the ground. Suddenly, what sounded like an explosion was heard, and the balloon and car shook violently. This happened three times, and at each occurrence the travellers feared that something was seriously amiss. But their fears were groundless, for the jerks came from the sudden yielding of ropes frozen stiff by the cold when the gas in the balloon expanded as the balloon rose.

At times the travellers got glimpses of snow-covered plains, and at others they were above masses of clouds hardly less white than the snow, so that it was difficult to say whether they saw land or clouds. Occasionally the sounds of falling water were heard, or what imagination easily interpreted as the noise of waves. Had they been driven northwards over the Baltic? What would they see below when daylight returned? With the dawn came relief from any fears, for under them stretched a cultivated country, traversed by a noble river—the Rhine.

They had now travelled quite as far as they wished, and, as this neighbourhood appeared a good one for a descent, some gas was allowed to escape and the balloon dropped low enough to cast its anchor. People came running up on all sides, and from their language they were evidently Germans. A few words of German converted them from somewhat mistrustful watchers into useful helpers, so that in a very short time the travellers were safe on the ground. The place they had landed on was a part of the Duchy of Nassau—hence the name given to the balloon in commemoration of its 500-mile voyage made in 18 hours.

The balloon having been packed and put in a cart, the party adjourned to Weilburg, a couple of miles away, where the statement that they had left London only on the previous day aroused a great deal of interest, mixed, at first, with some incredulity, for the voyage had been one of quite unprecedented length. Then followed a good deal of feasting and lionising of the aeronauts, who returned to England well satisfied with the success of what at the time was a feat requiring considerable courage.

The Adventures of the "Giant" Balloon

In the "sixties" of last century there lived at Paris a photographer, Felix Tournachan, better known under the assumed name of Nadar. He wrote for the newspapers, drew rather clever caricatures, and had a taste for aeronautics. M. Nadar thought he saw money in ballooning. He founded an Association for navigating the air by means of machines heavier than air, and had the idea of building a gas balloon of record size, the exhibition of which was calculated to raise funds sufficient to put the Association on its legs financially. Accordingly, he had "Le Géant," otherwise "The Giant," constructed. It was worthy of its name, for it held 200,000 cubic feet of gas and carried a huge two-story wickerwork car. The lower part of the car formed an enclosed cabin, the upper part an open observation platform with low sides. We are told that it included a dark-room, a restaurant, a small printing office, and other conveniences. No fewer than 22,000 yards of silk, costing over five shillings a yard, went to the making of the bag, so that it is not surprising that the total cost of the balloon exceeded £8,000. As a money-maker it proved a failure, for it brought in only £3,300 before it was destroyed.

The "Giant" made but two ascents. The first took place from the Champ de Mars, Paris, on October 4, 1863, in the presence of hundreds of thousands of people. M. Nadar was in command; two experienced aeronauts, named Godard, acted as his lieutenants; and the passengers, ten in number, included some very distinguished persons.

As the huge balloon with its thirteen souls aboard rose from the Champ de Mars, a roar of cheering went up also—cheers such as had greeted Pilâtre des Roziers eighty years before. For a time the passengers seem to have enjoyed themselves greatly. We read of a quite sumptuous supper taken in the "cabin," at which ham, fowls, and dessert disappeared with a rapidity that testified to the appetite-provoking effects of ballooning. Later on, however, when the balloon was enveloped in the darkness of night and thick fog, conditions became far less pleasant. The moisture condensing on the balloon trickled down and found its way into the car, adding to the already general moistness there. Then something appears to have gone wrong with the valve rope, or with the valve, for the balloon began to descend with great rapidity in spite of the hurried dumping of ballast. The car struck the ground with a violent shock, at Meaux, only 25 miles from the starting point. A very tame ending to a flight which had been advertised as going to break records!

A fortnight later the "Giant" went up again, with the same

crew, but having four fewer passengers aboard than on the first occasion. This time there was no feasting, but the balloon made much greater progress. After nightfall, the course was north-eastwards, across Belgium to Malines. Then, amid total darkness, the balloon headed almost due north, and presently some shimmering reflections from below told the travellers that they were over the canals and lakes of Holland.

The wind was now increasing in violence, and there seemed to be a real danger of the balloon being swept out to sea. The coming of the dawn was awaited with great anxiety. When at last the growing light allowed them to see what lay underneath them, the balloonists, to their great relief, beheld not the dreaded sea, but green fields and highly cultivated country, studded with flocks and herds and farmhouses.

The balloon was now moving at a great speed. The pilot opened the valve, allowing some of the gas to escape, so that he might reconnoitre the ground for a landing-place. The descent was so rapid that the earth appeared to leap upwards towards the balloon. There was plenty of ballast aboard, but either this was not thrown out fast enough, or the pilot lost his head and forgot it. A collision with trees, whose tops were bending under the force of the gale, seemed imminent when the direction of flight flattened out into a horizontal path and for the moment a catastrophe was avoided.

At last the car struck the ground so violently that the occupants were flung against its sides. Then it bounded upwards, and each passenger scrambled back to his or her seat and hung on for dear life. Over fields and villages sped the balloon. An anchor was dropped, but its cable snapped like a piece of thread when the anchor got a hold. The second anchor proved equally unable to arrest the headlong career. Then followed bump after bump, as the car struck and rebounded repeatedly, sometimes rising forty or fifty feet into the air. The travellers had now huddled together on one side of the car, which naturally kept striking on that side, so that the unfortunates were well bruised and shaken, besides being half-paralysed by fright. A solitary tree standing in the path of the balloon went down with a crash. Then the car narrowly missed collision with a train moving along an embankment. The driver shouted a warning of the telegraph wires some distance ahead. The car struck these and continued its way at a reduced speed, trailing wires and some telegraph posts behind it.

Finally the balloon came to a standstill in a wood near Rethem, in Hanover, being arrested so suddenly that one of the balloonists had his arm broken, and nobody escaped without serious bruises. They all had reason to be thankful for getting out of the affair with their lives. Some compensation for the damage done to nerves and bodies may have been derived from the fact that the journey totalled up the very respectable figure of 400 miles.

The Highest Balloon Ascent on Record

From time to time ascents were made in balloons by scientific men anxious to collect information about the temperature and moisture of the atmosphere at different heights, the thickness of cloud strata, and wind-currents. Very little systematic work of this kind was done, however, until 1862, when the British Association voted a grant to defray the cost of making high ascents to explore the upper strata of the atmosphere.

A professional aeronaut, Coxwell, constructed specially for the purpose a balloon of 90,000 cubic feet capacity, and James Glaisher, a member of the Association, volunteered to take the observations.

LONG-DISTANCE VOYAGES IN BALLOONS

The most famous of their ascents took place on September 5, 1862, from Wolverhampton. The balloon cast off at three minutes past one o'clock in the afternoon. It rose two miles in 18 minutes, three miles in 25 minutes, 4 miles in 36 minutes, and 5 miles in 46 minutes. So far Glaisher had been able to attend to the various instruments and keep records of their readings without feeling any discomfort. His sight then began to fail him and he asked Coxwell to help him read the instruments. But the aeronaut was busy in the rigging above the car, adjusting the valve rope, which had become twisted, and did not hear. The barometer at this time indicated a height of 29,000 feet,—that of the summit of Mt. Everest. "Shortly afterwards," wrote Glaisher in his Report to the British Association, "I laid my arm upon the table, possessed of its full vigour, and on being desirous of using it I found it powerless— it must have lost its power momentarily. I tried to move the other arm, and found it powerless also. I then tried to shake myself, and succeeded in shaking my body. I seemed to have no limbs. I then looked at the barometer, and whilst doing so my head fell on my left shoulder. I got my head upright, but for an instant only, when it fell on my right shoulder, and then I fell backwards, my back resting against the side of the car, and my head on its edge; in this position my eyes were directed towards Mr. Coxwell in the rigging. When I shook my body I seemed to have full power over the muscles of my back, but none over either my arms or my legs. As in the case of the arms, all muscular power was lost in an instant from my back and neck. I dimly saw Mr. Coxwell in the ring, and endeavoured to speak, but could not; when in an instant intense black darkness came: the optic nerve lost power suddenly. I was still conscious, with as active a brain as at the present moment whilst writing this. I thought I had been seized with asphyxia, and that I should experience no more, as death would come unless we speedily descended: other thoughts were actively entering my mind, when I suddenly became unconscious, as on going to sleep."

Meanwhile Coxwell had become so numbed by the cold that he could not grasp anything with his hands, and dropped into the car. Glancing at his companion, at first he thought him to be merely resting, but soon realised that he was insensible. On trying to go to him he found himself unable to move and fast lapsing into unconsciousness. If the balloon continued to ascend, death was certain for them both. As he could not use his arms he managed to grip the valve-cord in his teeth and pull it by bending his neck. The slight escape of gas that followed sufficed to check the balloon and make it descend. Glaisher soon recovered consciousness when the air-pressure increased, and was able to resume his observations. The balloon dropped at a great speed—3 miles in nine minutes—for a time, then was checked and alighted gently at Cold Weston. The two men were so little the worse for their trying experiences that they were able to walk 7½ miles to Ludlow.

The exact height attained by the balloon will never be known, owing to the observers' inability to take observations. But calculations which were probably fairly correct placed it at from 36,000 to 37,000 feet—say 7 miles—the greatest altitude ever reached by a human being until recently, when it was exceeded by an aeroplane.

Escapes from Paris by Balloon

Some of the most exciting voyages ever made in balloons were those of the daring aeronauts who flew balloons from Paris after the investment of the French capital by the Germans in

LONG-DISTANCE VOYAGES IN BALLOONS

September, 1870. So tight was the blockade that the escape of individuals or the sending out of news by land became practically impossible. To maintain communication with the outside world the Government instituted a balloon service, which of course operated mainly in one direction only. Balloons were constructed out of calico made airtight by dressing with oil or paint; the two chief workshops being at the Northern and the Orleans railway stations. M. Nadar, whose exploits with the "Giant" form part of this chapter, was in charge of the service.

Hardly a day passed without one balloon at least leaving Paris. M. Nadar himself had an exciting experience while endeavouring to enter Paris from Tours by balloon with Government dispatches. He left Tours at 6 a. m. and five hours later was near the capital, at a height of about 10,000 feet. He now sighted another balloon, which he challenged by showing the French tricolour. The other aeronaut at once replied with the same flag. The two balloons, caught in the same air-current, approached each other, until but a small distance apart. The strange aeronaut then ran up his true colours—German—and opened fire on Nadar, to the dismay of onlookers below. The Frenchman, however, returned the fire in what was probably the first aerial duel ever fought, and, to use a phrase often employed since in military despatches, drove his attacker down. Whether the last or his balloon was hit, is not known; but M. Nadar got the better of the exchange of compliments, and was able to land safely.

On October 27, 1870, a large balloon, "La Bretagne," started from Paris with the intention of reaching London, if possible. A strong wind carried it north-eastwards at first, then veered to the west and blew straight towards territory occupied by the Prussians. Thick clouds enveloped the balloon, so that the aeronauts—four in number—had no idea of their whereabouts, and suddenly, through an opening in the clouds, they saw some Prussian detachments marching along. Ballast was promptly thrown out, and the balloon rose into the clouds again. When it was judged to have passed the Belgian frontier, the chief aeronaut released some gas, and the balloon fell very quickly, striking the ground with a crash. One of the men, fearing that the collision would be fatal to all aboard, jumped out while the car was still 40 feet above the earth, but fell in a newly-ploughed field and escaped uninjured, though he was promptly captured by Prussians who happened to be there.

The balloon shot up again amid a hail of bullets, some of which probably holed it, for it soon struck again, near Verdun. Two of the three men left jumped out, and they also were captured. Once more the balloon rose with the one survivor, M. Manceau. The great reduction in weight sent it quickly to an elevation of 10,000 feet. Rain fell heavily and M. Manceau became so dizzy that he released gas, and quickly came to earth. Leaping out before the car touched, he fell in a quagmire, dislocating his right ankle. In spite of his injury he managed to conceal the balloon, and then crawled on all fours to the house of the local *curé*.

This gentleman smuggled his dispatches across the Belgian frontier, but M. Manceau himself was betrayed by a villager to the Germans, and, like his companions, spent the rest of the war in captivity.

Perhaps the most extraordinary flight from Paris was that of two aeronauts who left for Tours on November 24, 1870, but were caught by a strong southerly gale and carried north-eastwards over the sea. At last they landed in a strange, snow-covered country, in which wolves seemed to be the only living creatures. When they finally reached a habitation they discovered themselves to be in Norway, and found that in 13 hours they had travelled over 600 miles.

A Remarkable Escape

The American aeronaut, John Wise, was a contemporary of the Englishman, Charles Green, and his counterpart as the most famous balloonist of his time in his own country. He made many ascents and had a variety of exciting experiences, the most memorable of which is worth recording. On May 4, 1843, he was engaged to make an ascent from Hollidaysburg, Pennsylvania, where a large crowd had assembled to see the balloon go up. A strong wind blew during the process of inflation, knocking the great bag about in such a way as to damage the netting, so that the fabric began to protrude through a rent in it. Fearing that further inflation would make matters worse, Wise decided to start at once. He soon found himself being swept along by a gale at 60 miles an hour, and as he gained height and the gas expanded, the balloon threatened to burst the netting and explode. To relieve the strain, the aeronaut seized the valve rope and hung on with all his weight, with the result that the balloon descended very fast. An anchor let fall caught in a fence, broke loose, caught another fence and broke loose again. Wise tried to jump out, but caught his feet in the rigging, and hung head downwards. He managed, however, to seize the valve rope in his teeth and pull on it. The balloon swooped down into a high tree, a branch of which Wise gripped. The balloon tugged at his feet until he thought he would have to let go and be carried away. But fortunately the balloon tore itself adrift, leaving the aeronaut perched nearly 100 feet above the ground. He got safely to earth, little the worse for his adventure, though sad at the loss of his balloon. A day or two later he heard that it had been captured some distance away and, though a self-styled expert had cut it up into several parts for transport, he was able to use it again.

We may conclude this chapter with a reference to the longest balloon flight ever made—in 1914, from Bitterfeld in Germany to Bittersk in Siberia, 1,895 miles.

CHAPTER 7

THE COMING OF THE DIRIGIBLE BALLOON

WHEN you have been blowing soap-bubbles with a pipe you have doubtless noticed that the slightest movement of the pipe, or the least draught of air, causes a bubble to distort itself into queer shapes: whereas, as soon as it is free from the pipe, the bubble at once becomes a true sphere and remains so if blown about.

Similarly with the big spherical balloon. So long as it is free it moves at the same speed as any air-current in which it is floating, without being deformed in any way by the wind. Anyone travelling in a balloon swept along by a gale might, with his eyes shut, imagine himself to be floating in a dead calm, since he is moving with and at just the same speed as the gale.

Ballooning is able to provide many very pleasurable sensations, and, so far as mere movement is concerned, is about the most ideal means of locomotion at our disposal. As a method of transport, however, it has the very serious defect of depending for speed and direction entirely on the vagaries of the air-currents travelling over the face of the earth. An aeronaut may start off eastwards in the morning and find himself drifting westwards, or southwards, in the afternoon.

The helplessness of the balloon, combined with a natural desire to use it as a ship rather than a mere sailless, oarless, and rudderless raft, led the earliest aeronauts to endeavour, by means of oars, sails and other devices, to propel their balloons in the desired direction, or at least to direct their flight in some degree. It was a hopeless task, since, in the first place, the spherical balloon offers so enormous a surface to the wind that very powerful apparatus would be needed to overcome the wind; and, in the second place, even could the wind be more than neutralised, the balloon would at once be deformed and collapsed by the two antagonistic forces.

It soon became apparent that a spherical shape was as unsuitable for a dirigible balloon as a circular hull would be for a ship. A form approximating to that of a ship was needed; and the elongated bag must be driven endways through the air. Various attempts were made with hand-propelled elongated balloons, such as those of the Comte de Lennox (1834) and Hugh Bell (1848), but they all proved fruitless. In 1852 Henri Giffard, the inventor of the steam injector used for feeding boilers with water, built at Paris a spindle-shaped airship, holding about 80,000 cubic feet of gas, and suspended from it a car containing a 3-h.p. steam-engine, which drove two propellers. At the stern was a triangular rudder. This airship travelled at about 4 miles an hour in still air. What may be considered the first voyage of a "dirigible" was made with this airship on September 24, 1852. A larger ship, built three years later, was destroyed while landing. Though Giffard cannot be said to have achieved a great triumph, he at least succeeded in interesting the public and encouraging other inventors.

During the siege of Paris M. Dupuy de Lôme, a French naval architect, began work on a dirigible ballon which was not completed till 1872. It had a capacity of 120,000 cubic feet, and an enormous propeller, turned slowly by eight men aboard. The propeller gave it a speed of about 5 miles an hour above that of the wind, but it was navigable only in a calm. In 1881 and 1884, Gaston Tissandier, another Frenchman, made use of electric motors to drive balloons shaped like

PLATE II

Front view of the biplane that flew from London to Australia in 1919. The members of the crew are standing in front of the aeroplane.

A Vickers-Napier " Vulture " Amphibian, with boat body and wheels, which enable it to start from, and alight on, either land or water.

those of Giffard. Current was supplied from bichromate batteries. Another and a more successful electrically propelled airship was that of the French army officers, Captains Renard and Krebs, experimented with during the years 1883 and 1884. This balloon had a better shape than any made previously, being on the lines of a torpedo or fish, with fairly blunt nose and tapering tail. A car, of girder form, and more than half as long as the balloon itself, was suspended from the last by a large number of ropes, so that its weight, and that of the machinery and crew, should be distributed over the length of the envelope. Inside the balloon was a smaller balloon or ballonet containing air. If the gas in the balloon expanded, air would be driven out of the ballonet; and if it contracted, air could be forced into the ballonet to maintain the pressure and prevent the envelope becoming flabby. The motor derived the current needed to drive it and an airscrew at the front of the car from a primary battery, and when running at full load developed about 9 horsepower. A weight sliding fore and aft was used to maintain longitudinal balance.

A successful trial of the vessel took place on August 9, 1884, when for the first time a complete circle was made in the air. The airship had quite a good turn of speed, being able to hold its own against a head wind blowing at 11 miles an hour. Captains Renard and Krebs carried out several short trips with their airship, which was far the most successful of any yet built and aroused a great deal of enthusiasm throughout France, where it was regarded as definitely opening the era of aerial navigation.

Further progress was delayed, however, until the petrol engine had been developed to a stage at which it became suitable for acting as the power plant of an airship. Not only is it much safer than a steam-engine, but much more powerful, weight for weight, than either it or the electric motor, when all the accessories needed for a long voyage are brought into calculation. Consequently, nothing of any great importance was done in the direction of perfecting the airship until 1898, when two experimenters began work on entirely different lines. At Paris the young Brazilian, Alberto Santos Dumont, busied himself with the construction of the first of his many navigable balloons, which were all of the non-rigid type; that is, they depended for maintaining their shape entirely on being kept inflated. In Germany Count Ferdinand von Zeppelin set to work doggedly that same year on building the first "rigid" airship, the form of which was maintained independently of the condition of the gas-containers. Whereas Santos Dumont took to ballooning as a sport, the German aimed at producing an airship which should have great military value, and add to the armed might of his Fatherland. Both men had in common a dogged perseverance and a determination not to acknowledge defeat; and thanks to this quality the names of both have become famous in connection with aeronautics.

Santos Dumont, who appears to have taken an interest in human flight from the time when he was a small boy, had the good fortune to be born with a silver spoon in his mouth, for his father was a wealthy coffee-planter owning large and prosperous estates. In 1891 young Alberto left Brazil for Paris, where he had a spherical balloon made for him, and with it gained practical experience of aeronautics. The balloon was a one-man affair, and the smallest that had ever been used for lifting human beings, since it held but a little more than 4,000 cubic feet of gas. To cut weight down to the minimum, Santos Dumont selected thin Japanese silk as the material for the bag—far too flimsy for the purpose, professional balloon-makers said, but in practice amply strong enough.

THE COMING OF THE DIRIGIBLE BALLOON

The next step was to construct a dirigible driven by a petrol motor. Here he could get no help from professionals, so he decided to do the work himself. After overcoming many difficulties in collecting and training workmen, he managed to produce a balloon 82½ feet long and holding 6,300 cubic feet of gas. From this he hung a wickerwork car containing a 3½-h.p. motor; also two bags of ballast, one fore and one aft, which could be drawn by cords towards the car to trim the balloon.

The first attempt at flight with his No. 1 took place in September, 1898, in the Jardin d'Acclimation, Paris. Owing to mismanagement, the airship, immediately after rising, was driven against some trees and damaged. Santos Dumont repaired it and tried again. This time he had better luck, and, made bold by success, he threw out ballast till he attained a height at which a considerable amount of gas escaped by expansion. On descending again the envelope began to fold up like a V; and those of the suspension cords which now had to carry all the weight threatened to tear adrift. Santos Dumont got to the ground safely, however, though he had a narrow escape.

The following year he built a rather larger airship, which was destroyed at the end of its first flight. Nothing daunted, he constructed the much larger No. III, on which he made at least one successful voyage in 1899. No. IV behaved even better, and he carried out quite a number of trips with it over the Bois de Boulogne.

In 1900 M. Henri Deutsch, a member of the French Aero Club, offered a prize of £4,000 to the first person who should make a journey in the air from the Aero Club Park to and round the Eiffel Tower and back to the starting-point. The time allowed was half an hour.

CONQUERING THE AIR

Santos Dumont built his No. V with the intention of using it in an attempt to "lift" the prize. Though the airship failed him, it at least gave him some exciting moments. On July 13, 1901, he got as far as the Tower, rounded it, and was returning, when the motor jibbed, and the airship ran into some trees, fortunately without damaging itself or its pilot.

During another attempt made on August 8, he had completed more than half the journey when, as he beat his way back against the wind, the propeller got foul of some of the suspension ropes and snapped them. Santos at once switched off the engine, leaving the balloon at the mercy of the wind, which swept it over some high buildings. One of these it struck, and a man got hold of the trailing guide rope and made it fast. The rope broke, and the balloon drifted on till it collided with a hotel roof and was wrecked. Fortunately, both ends of the long girder carrying the car were supported on buildings, and in spite of its fragile appearance the girder stood the strain. Firemen got on to the hotel and threw a rope to Santos Dumont, whom they pulled up into safety quite uninjured.

The airship had made its last voyage. The same day Santos Dumont ordered another, No. VI, which was completed within two months. Of larger capacity than any of its predecessors, it carried a 16-h.p. motor. After having tested it and found it to answer the helm well, the young Brazilian prepared for a further attempt on the Deutsch Prize. About midday, on October 18, he suddenly decided to start. At half-past two the balloon rose and, with a gentle breeze astern, headed for the Eiffel Tower at a good pace. The guide rope caught on a house and pulled the balloon up with a jerk, causing it to swing in an alarming manner. People rushed up and unhitched the rope, allowing the airship to resume its journey.

THE COMING OF THE DIRIGIBLE BALLOON

Rising to a height of about 800 feet, Santos Dumont circled the Tower at a respectful distance, and 9 minutes from the start was heading for home in the face of the breeze. The motor now began to fire irregularly and for a time things looked as if the airship would be swept backwards against the Tower with disastrous results. At the critical moment the engine picked up again till the danger was past, though soon it recommenced misfiring, with the result that the balloon lost height quickly, and narrowly escaped hitting the grand-stand of the Auteuil racecourse. As the balloon approached the Aero Park the motor got into its stride again, and some of the time lost was made up. Great excitement prevailed among the spectators, for it had now become evident that, if the prize were won, it would be won by seconds only. With three-quarters of a minute in hand the airship crossed the mark, but at such a height that the guide rope was just out of reach, and a minute and a half more elapsed before it could be caught. The huge crowd of onlookers raised hearty cheers for the plucky aeronaut as he stepped from his car; and a few seconds later were uttering loud cries of protest when the President of the Aero Club informed Santos Dumont that he had *not* won the Prize, as the time elapsed between the letting go of the rope at the start and the seizing of it at the finish had exceeded the prescribed 30 minutes. A fortnight later, however, the Aero Club pronounced the Prize to have been won. Santos Dumont accepted the £4,000 and distributed it among his workmen and the poor of Paris; but he resigned his membership of the Aero Club as a protest against what he considered to be the unsportsmanlike behavior of some of its members.

After his great success Santos Dumont built several more airships, and made many flights. In No. IX, which was very little longer than No. I, he used to wander about Paris. One day he would steer it down the Champs Elysées; on another anchor it by his own house while he went in to luncheon. His exploits attracted a great deal of attention, especially in military circles. In fact, to Santos Dumont may be attributed the beginnings of the aerial fleet of France.

In spite of his achievements with the dirigible balloon, the Brazilian aeronaut did not regard it as the only possible means of navigating the air, and in 1904 we find him building the first of his several aeroplanes, in one of which he made the first flight, or one of the very first, in Europe on a heavier-than-air machine propelled by a petrol motor. He was thus a pioneer in aviation as well as in the development of the steerable balloon.

The Zeppelin Airships

Count Ferdinand von Zeppelin, whose name acquired an ominous import during the war, retired from the German Army in 1891, after a somewhat distinguished career. As a soldier he had done some military ballooning and had acquired a great enthusiasm for aeronautics. On his retirement he devoted the whole of his energies and most of his money to the production of a practical airship on what he considered to be the proper lines. He regarded the non-rigid single-chamber balloon as not giving sufficient security or efficiency. If partly deflated, it lost much of what rigidity it had; if punctured in any part it was bound to lose its gas; and deformation of its shape by air pressure made it more difficult to drive through the air.

He therefore set to work on designing an airship which could not change its external shape, and would derive its buoyancy from a large number of independent gas-containers that need not be kept taut. The maintenance of shape under all conditions would render an airship more easily propelled, while distribution of the gas among a series of bags, one or more of which might become entirely deflated without destroying the airship's buoyancy, would increase safety very greatly.

To bring about this desirable state of things the gas-bags must be housed inside a rigid frame-work, covered externally by tightly stretched fabric. By the use of aluminum alloy, it was possible to build a framework having great strength relatively to its weight. Even so, the weight would be considerable, and an airship built on this principle be heavier than a non-rigid of equal size. A rigid airship must therefore essentially be a very large one, to take advantage of the fact that the weight of a framework of the necessary strength would form a smaller proportion of the total weight of the airship, the larger the airship were made.

A rigid hull offered further advantages. In the first place, it could be given a more tapering stern than a non-rigid—and a "fine run aft," as a naval architect would term it, has a very important effect on speed, by lessening "drag." Also, the engines and propellers could be placed quite close to the hull, and exert their push much nearer the centre of the balloon than those of a non-rigid. And the rudders, being attached to a stiff framework, could be put hard over without deforming or endangering the ship.

In short, Zeppelin aimed at producing an aerial ship which would resemble a sea ship much more closely than did the other type; and, thanks to the inclusion of a rigid framework, might be much larger than any non-rigid, without sacrificing safety. The correctness of his views cannot be disputed, for the largest airships yet built or building are "rigids," and for commercial transport the big rigid has things much to itself.

Experimenting on a large scale is notoriously expensive, and Zeppelin appealed to his Government for assistance. The German War Office, though ever on the lookout for novelties of military value, contributed nothing, regarding the inventor as a visionary rather than as a practical genius. Balked here, the Count formed a limited liability company, with a capital of 800,000 marks (£40,000), in which the King of Wurtemburg is said to have been a large shareholder. With the funds provided he engaged two engineers to help him get out designs for an airship, and built his first airship shed. This was a floating structure, moored near Friedrichshafen, on Lake Constance. The shed, which had one end closed in, served also as workshop. The central part of the floor was a long pontoon, which could be drawn out of the shed, bearing the airship with it. The shed was moored by the closed end, and automatically turned this towards the wind, so that the airship when leaving the shed would always have the wind with it.

Zeppelin's first airship, though small by comparison with some of his latest productions, was much larger than any yet projected. It measured 420 feet in length and 39 feet in diameter, and the sixteen gas-bags held between them 400,000 cubic feet. The driving power was relatively small—only 32 horsepower, developed by two motors, one in each car, and each turning two propellers on brackets projecting from the sides of the ship. LZ1 (Luftschiff Zeppelin 1) made its first trial over Lake Constance in July, 1900. It was an anxious time for the inventor, and, in spite of every precaution in handling, the huge structure received injuries which put it in dock for some months. Though the speed never rose above

8½ miles an hour, Zeppelin at least had the satisfaction of knowing that his airship steered well both vertically and horizontally.

Further trials, of a more successful kind, were carried out the following October, when LZ1 attained a speed of 17 miles an hour,—by far the greatest yet reached by an airship. Zeppelin now became a popular hero, and Germans everywhere regarded him as the conqueror of the air. But he knew only too well that he had a long way to go before he could lay a sound claim to the title. LZ1 was very far from perfect, and a better design was needed. But the money for carrying on experiments had now come to an end. The company went into liquidation.

Zeppelin appealed to the public and collected sufficient money to proceed with a second airship, LZ2. This was rather shorter than the LZ1, but very much more powerfully engined with two 85-h.p. motors. It made some very successful trips; and then came to a bad end. Owing to failure of the engines and the steering gear, a descent had to be made in a meadow. This was effected without damage, but during the following night a strong wind arose and wrecked the balloon in the course of a few minutes.

This was a great blow to the Count, who at one time announced that he would retire from aeronautics. But he soon was building again, and within nine months of the disaster had LZ3 in the air. This airship proved a great success, and was, in fact, the model on which subsequent ships were based. The German Government took it over after it had undergone some alterations, and attached it to the German Army as the first item of an aerial fleet. It remained in use for several years—at least until after the outbreak of war.

With the aid of a parliamentary grant of £25,000 Zeppelin

now began work in 1907 on LZ4, a larger ship than its predecessors and provided with two 110-h.p. motors, each driving three propellers. The Government agreed to buy LZ4 for £100,000 provided that it flew for 24 hours without descending, and proved able to land and rise again without assistance. On July 1, 1908, the new airship made a memorable cruise over Switzerland, much the longest yet carried out by a dirigible balloon; and a month later started on her 24-hours trial. On August 4, she left Friedrichshafen at 6.02 a. m. and, following the course of the Rhine, passed over Basle, Colmar, Strasburg, Carlsruhe and Mannheim, to Mayence. At the last place, reached at 6 p. m., she remained a few hours to repair a defect in one of the motors. The outward journey of about 300 miles had now been completed, and when the airship started off again at 11 p. m., it was headed southwards for Friedrichshafen. All went well till the loss of gas compelled a descent, which was made at 8 a. m. next morning at Echterdingen, after 440 miles had been covered. A huge number of gas cylinders were hurried up to inflate the gas bags, but while operations were in progress a sudden squall struck the airship. Two engineers leaped into one of the cars and started up the motor, but the ship was driven along the ground, bumping heavily, until one of the petrol tanks burst and in a moment the airship was in flames.

This overwhelming catastrophe won Zeppelin the sympathy of the whole nation in a most practical form. People of all kinds subscribed liberally to a Zeppelin fund, which reached £300,000 in a few weeks; and to this the Government added another £25,000. This financial help enabled the Count to continue his work without fear of running short of money. For a time fortune smiled on him. The Kaiser publicly embraced him and conferred on him a knighthood; and next to that of the War Lord his became the best-known face in Germany, thanks to the many photographs and busts of him that appeared in shop windows.

But his troubles were by no means over. In June, 1909, he set out in a new airship from Lake Constance with the intention of flying, if possible, to the capital, where a Zeppelin had not yet been seen, though every Berliner was extremely anxious to have a sight of one. Starting off late on a Saturday evening, the great vessel flew northwards all night and till late next day, arriving at Bitterfeld, about 70 miles from Berlin, at 7.10 p. m. In spite of a head wind, good progress was made, and at Leipzig Zeppelin dropped a telegram to the airship battalion at Berlin, asking assistance if he should be able to land there. On hearing of this, the Kaiser at once ordered a general mobilisation of all the local troops in the Tempelhof Field, to give the Count a fitting welcome—and the public one of those displays which it, and the Kaiser, delighted in. Vast crowds of people waited patiently for hours, and then the news leaked out that the airship had been compelled by shortage of petrol to head south again. During Sunday night it passed over the Thuringian Forest and the Swabian Alps, and at 9.30 a.m. on Monday was welcomed by the population of Stuttgart, which turned out *en masse* to watch it circle round the Crown Prince of Wurtemberg's palace. Then it continued on its way to Goppingen, within 50 miles of Friedrichshafen, where an attempt was made to descend and replenish the fuel supply.

Unfortunately, as the great ship neared the ground, a strong gust blew it against a pear tree, and it sustained severe damage, which took weeks to put right. But in spite of its unhappy ending, the flight had been a very notable one, as nearly 1,000 miles had been covered in a continuous journey lasting 38 hours, and it thus quite eclipsed all previous records.

In 1910 Zeppelin completed his first passenger airship, LZ7. This was also the first "rigid" to have three motors—of 120-h.p. each—a central cabin, luxuriously equipped, and a restaurant. The "Deutschland," as it was named, made a large number of successful trips, and people paid high prices to participate in the experience of rushing through the air at 45 miles an hour. As the first airship built for pleasure purposes, the "Deutschland" attracted a great deal of attention, so that the world in general, and Germany in particular, learned with regret that misfortune had overtaken the great vessel while making a voyage in June, 1910, over the Teutoburger Wald.

The "Deutschland" left Düsseldorf in the morning for a round trip of a few hours, carrying 23 passengers. For a time all went well. Then the wind began to rise, and one of the motors broke down. As it would have been dangerous to turn and run with the wind, the captain endeavoured to drive the ship against it to Münster, where there was a suitable ground and a large garrison to help in the landing operations. But the remaining engines were not able to make any headway, and for hours the airship just held its own, tossed up and down and swerving wildly. Heavy rainstorms blew up, shutting out the view; and everyone aboard began to realize that, when the petrol gave out, a disaster must occur. The passengers and crew were therefore in much the same position as the occupants of a sinking ship without boats and far from help.

When at last the motors ceased running for lack of fuel, the gale seized the airship and hurled it down into a forest, the trees of which it struck with a mighty crash. The airship was a wreck, but everyone aboard escaped uninjured, reaching the ground by means of a rope ladder.

In spite of this and still other disasters, Zeppelin continued to build ship after ship for passenger, naval, and military use. By 1914 the total had reached twenty-six, capacity had risen to nearly a million cubic feet, and speed to 50 miles an hour. Also, great improvements had been made in design, construction, machinery, and steering arrangements. Public confidence in the rigid airship led to the formation, in 1910, of the German Air Travel Company, called for short the D. E. L. A. G. after the initial letters of the words forming the Germany title. This Company was managed by the Hamburg-Amerika (steamship) Line and ran passenger excursions, as well as a few regular town-to-town services, during the years 1910 to 1914. During the first three years the four air liners "Schwaben," "Viktoria Luise," "Hansa" and "Sachsen" made 760 flights, totalling nearly 100,000 miles, and carried 14,000 passengers. The "Viktoria Luise" is credited with 200 flights in 250 consecutive days, a record which shows that airships were now not merely fair-weather craft. It may be added that, during the 760 voyages referred to, no mishap occurred, and not a single passenger was injured.

The airships named had spacious passenger saloons fitted up in a most luxurious style, with beautiful carpets and comfortable wicker chairs, and closely resembling a railway Pullman car. Lunch and tea were served from a buffet as required. The Company built large airship sheds at Potsdam (near Berlin), Hamburg, Leipzig, Gotha, Baden Baden, Frankfurt, and Düsseldorf, and made a profit in addition to a subsidy from the Government for the use of the airships in training military crews.

The principles for which Count von Zeppelin contended may

be considered to have been justified before the outbreak of war. His airships had, in length and duration of voyages, beaten anything done by other airships, or by aeroplanes; and in regularity of service had far outdistanced other aircraft. They had made it plain that aerial transport was a practical proposition, though of course a great deal remained to be done before anything in the way of world services could be established. During the war intense activity prevailed at Friedrichshafen and other Zeppelin factories, and airships of up to 2,000,000 cubic feet capacity and having a speed of 60 miles an hour appeared one after another. The activities of these ships will be referred to in another chapter, so it must suffice here to say that the Zeppelin was the only type of airship that carried out big-scale raiding operations.

Simultaneously with the development of the "rigid" dirigible balloon, the non-rigid and the semi-rigid types also made a great deal of headway as appanages of an army. The non-rigid airship, which can be quickly deflated and packed up for transport, had some obvious advantages for military use. The semi-rigid, which also has a collapsible balloon, differs from the non-rigid in having a long, stiff girder attached to the balloon, to prevent it bending upwards at the ends if partly deflated and to distribute the weight of car and machinery. While possessing neither the stiffness of the Zeppelin nor the portability of the non-rigid, it is a useful compromise between the two types, and as such has found considerable favour with the French and the Italian governments. Remarkable flights have been made with all three kinds, and it is not likely that any one type will entirely disappear, though the large rigid is undoubtedly marked out as the world air-liner of the future.

The spectacular disasters that have overtaken many airships, combined with the great loss of life and money resulting, have prejudiced the airship in the eyes of many people. But when these disasters are analysed they may in most cases be traced to causes—such as mechanical breakdown, shortage of fuel, and bad design—which can be avoided, and, as experience shows how to do it, will be avoided, though of course accidents are certain to happen to airships from time to time just as they happen to trains and ships. Its huge bulk is one of the great handicaps of the airship when it has to descend, as its enormous surface gives it great pulling power even in a light wind. The mooring mast, when perfected, will make it easy for the airship to descend, ride at anchor, ascend, and embark or disembark passengers and cargo, even in a strong wind.

Though airships do not possess the speed of the aeroplane, nor its general handiness, they have some great advantages over it. The first is that they do not depend on motion for staying in the air. Even should all its engines fail—a very unlikely occurrence—an airship can remain aloft, floating with the wind like a spherical balloon. Repairs, if not of a very serious nature, can be effected without landing. Speeds may be anything between zero and the maximum, and to be able to travel slowly has its uses at times—as when surveying or taking observations to ascertain position, or when fog is encountered. The fact that an airship is kept aloft by its own buoyancy and not by its engines enables it to travel almost as safely by night as by day: and, as its speed of descent can be made as small as desired, it can land in many places quite unsuitable for an aeroplane's descent. Since an airship requires power only for propulsion and not, as in the case of an aeroplane, for lifting also, it has a much greater range, weight for weight, while consuming a given amount of fuel. Compare a Zeppelin of 2,000,000 cubic feet capacity with one of the largest aeroplanes yet built. Both have engines of about the same power.

CONQUERING THE AIR

But whereas the airship could carry thirty to forty people several thousand miles without alighting, the aeroplane could transport a much smaller number of people only some hundreds of miles before it would run short of fuel; and the fuel consumption per passenger per mile would be far heavier.

The "endurance" in flight and economy of the airship therefore seems to mark it out for the long non-stop runs of commercial aerial transport, especially where the routes include wide expanses of water. The transatlantic flights of R34 are described in later pages. They were both remarkable examples of duration and weather-worthiness: though not individually the longest that have been made by airships. Two which exceeded them will now be noticed.

On November 21, 1917, a Zeppelin left Jamboli, in Bulgaria, to carry over 20 tons of medical supplies to the forces fighting the British in (then) German East Africa, under the leadership of von Lettow. After delivering her cargo she was to embark the German leader and bring him home. The airship crossed the Mediterranean, and followed the Nile as far as Khartoum. When over the Victoria Nyanza she picked up a wireless message from Germany ordering an immediate return to Bulgaria, as the place where she was to land had been captured by the British. She accordingly turned about, and retraced her route, arriving safely at Jamboli exactly four days after the start, having made a *non-stop* voyage of 5,500 miles at an average speed of 57 miles an hour.

Surely a very notable achievement!

The next longest flight stands to the credit of the ZR3, a German Zeppelin built after the war for delivery to the United States in part payment of reparations. It is the largest ship yet constructed, measuring 656 feet in length, 92 feet in diameter, and 102 feet in height. Its cubic capacity is 2,500,000 feet;

PLATE IV

[Photo, Airways.

Sectional view of a three-engined Caudron aeroplane, such as is used on French airways.

Within the image:

260 H·P SALMSON WING ENGINE

PILOT SEAT

PETROL TANK

ELECTRIC GENERATOR

REAR BAGGAGE COMPARTMENT

8 PASSENGER CABIN

BAGGAGE COMPARTMENT

CENTRAL 400 H·P LORRAINE ENGINE

ELECTRIC HEATING

SIGNAL LIGHTS

LANDING LIGHT

F-AGBK

F

and five motors of 400 h.p. each are able to drive it through the air at a speed of 80 miles an hour.

The ZR3 left Friedrichshafen in November, 1924, in dense fog, under the command of Dr. Hugo Eckener, the Managing director of the Zeppelin Airship Company. This gentleman, it need hardly be said, is a firm believer in the merits of the rigid airship and, since he confesses to having made more than two thousand aerial trips, not without good reason. Crossing France and Spain, the ZR3 flew straight for New York, favoured for half the voyage by good weather. While passing over the Gulf Stream the airship encountered a high wind, but wireless weather reports sent from American cruisers made it possible to avoid the worst of the storm which was crossing the route, and after passing the Newfoundland Banks— wrapped in fog as usual—ZR3 made a good run to the landing ground in Long Island. It took just 70 hours to cross the Atlantic, reckoning from the mouth of the Gironde to Sandy Hook.

The most striking proof of an airship's reliability is afforded by the adventure which the British R33 went through in April, 1925. This vessel was built in 1918-1919 as a sister ship to the R34,[1] both being close copies of the German L33, brought down in England in 1916. After lying idle for nine years she was reconditioned in 1925, a new outer cover being fitted, and apparatus installed to enable her to carry out various tests for strain and pressure during flight.

While she was riding at her mast at Pulham, after some tests, a strong gale arose, causing her to strain heavily on her mooring, and a crew was sent aboard with provisions and supplies as a precaution, so that she might be released at a moment's notice if the gale increased its violence. This was

[1] For details of R34 see p. 145.

a fortunate move, for some hours later the ship released herself by tearing away the couplings and at the same time bursting the covering at the nose and the two forward gas bags. Flight-Lieut. Booth, who was in charge, at once released some tons of water ballast, which made her rise suddenly and clear a shed towards which she was blown, and he got the engines going within a minute of the breakaway. There was a great danger of the wind entering through the breach and bursting the outer envelope, which would have meant disaster. The damaged gas-bags were promptly lashed athwart the hull to act as a bulkhead, which effectively excluded the wind. To run before the wind would have meant a calamitous landing somewhere in Europe when the fuel gave out, while to attempt to head for Pulham against the gale would have endangered the bulkhead. So the R33 was kept bows to wind, her engines running at such a speed that she drifted slowly backward across the North Sea. After 30 hours of steady battling the airship was over Holland; and then the gale abated sufficiently to allow her to make for home. As she circled round the Pulham flying-ground before landing, with nose all crumpled up and twisted girder ends projecting from the torn cover, onlookers marvelled that she had been able to fly at all in such a condition. That she weathered the gale is a testimony as much to the reliability of the airship as to the capacities of her crew.

CHAPTER 8

THE FIRST AIR-ATTACK ON THE ATLANTIC

MANY years ago the American aeronaut, John Wise, interested himself in plans for crossing the Atlantic in a spherical balloon. But the balloon constructed was so faulty that he abandoned the project.

Nothing more was done in the direction of conquering the Atlantic by air till 1910, when Mr. Walter Wellman, another American, made preparations for essaying a trip to Europe in a dirigible balloon. The balloon was of the non-rigid kind, and one of the largest of its kind ever built, for it had a capacity of 350,000 cubic feet, and a lifting power of about six tons. Underneath it were a long enclosed gangway, which served for living quarters, and a detachable lifeboat, to be used if it should become necessary to abandon ship in mid-ocean. Two motors, estimated to give a speed of 20 miles an hour, were provided.

The most original feature of the airship was a magnified guide rope, termed an equilibrator, which was to trail on the surface of the ocean and keep the airship automatically at the same height, thus doing away with the need for letting out gas or throwing out ballast. Through the centre of it ran a steel cable, more than 100 yards long, fastened at one end to the airship. On the cable were threaded a number of cylindrical wooden blocks, connected by ball-and-socket joints; and, nearer the upper end, a series of similarly-shaped petrol tanks, which could be drawn up to the car as required. The equilibrator weighed two tons at the maximum. Wellman attached great importance to this accessory.

A wireless receiving and transmitting installation formed part of the equipment. Everything that science and care could do to ensure a successful voyage was done; but, apart from Wellman and his small band of enthusiasts, experts had grave doubts as to the likelihood of the expedition achieving its object. It was felt that the science of aeronautics had not advanced far enough to warrant so ambitious an attempt.

The great airship started from Atlantic City at 8.05 a. m. on October 15, 1910. Mr. Wellman was in command; Capt. Murray Simon, an Englishman, was pilot; Mr. Melvin Vaniman acted as chief engineer; and Mr. Jack Irwin was wireless operator. Two mechanics completed the crew of six, and a black cat represented the passenger department.

A small motor boat towed the airship some distance out to sea; and when this cast off, the motors were started up and the "America" began her maiden voyage. The cat grew tired of the trip as soon as it commenced, and was quieted only by being put in a bag and suspended below the car. Afterwards it seems to have resigned itself to life aboard, though it refused all food except biscuits—strange provender for a cat!

A thick fog enveloped the airship for some hours after the start, but as the craft answered her helm well, no anxiety was felt. At 11 a. m. one of the motors had to be stopped, owing to sand in the bearings causing it to run hot. While the matter was being attended to the airship drifted northwards in a freshening wind. After being in action an hour the motor had to be stopped again, for the same reason as before, but was put right.

In the afternoon, which turned rather hot, the airship rose 100 feet above the sea, lifting thirteen tanks of the equilibrator above the water. The equilibrator, from which so much had been expected, now began to prove itself a nuisance, as some people had prophesied it would. When the waves rose, its drag, instead of being a steady pull, became a series of jerks, causing much discomfort to all aboard; and the check imposed on the airship made the last often descend perilously near the water.

As night came on, some of the gasolene had to be sacrificed to make up for the loss of buoyancy due to the contraction of the gas. About this time a steamer was sighted, but, as she carried no wireless, communication could not be established with her. Two hours later the airship narrowly missed colliding with another vessel; had the lookout not spotted the danger in time a serious disaster would have occurred.

Captain Murray, after being 20 hours continuously at the helm, was relieved by Mr. Wellman at 4 a. m. the morning after the start; and resumed his post two hours later. By 8 a. m. the "America" was over the island called Martha's Vineyard, lying between Nantucket lightship and the mainland, and about 250 miles N. E. of Atlantic City. The wind increased in strength as the day advanced, and with the wind the size of the waves and the vibrations of the equilibrator. The airship kept plunging downwards, until at times the lifeboat hanging below actually touched the water. To lighten ship more petrol had to go overboard. By 3 p. m. things began to look very serious, and all hands agreed that the "America" could not cross the Atlantic. After a conference it was decided to break up the larger of the two motors and jettison it, to keep the airship out of the sea. The motor was accordingly taken to pieces, and the parts were placed handy for throwing out when the need should arise. At sundown the airship sank so low that this costly ballast had to be dumped.

During the night the airship drifted helplessly before the

wind, sometimes at a speed of nearly thirty miles an hour, and the crew had nothing to do but keep their places and wonder how long their craft would hold together. Their position was now a perilous one, for the wind had changed direction and was carrying them south-eastwards into the open Atlantic. As the next day dawned their eyes were gladdened by seeing in the distance a steamer, the *Trent*, to which they signalled for assistance. The *Trent* at once headed for the airship, while Wellman and his party made preparations for launching the lifeboat—a very ticklish business in a heavy sea. The equilibrator proved a bugbear to the last, for it lashed about, knocked holes in the lifeboat, and injured two of the men. But after a long struggle and much manœuvring the entire crew and the cat were got safely aboard the *Trent*, and the "America," now greatly lightened, rose high in the air and disappeared from sight. What became of her is not known.

The rescue took place in latitude 35° 43' N., longitude 68° 18' W. If you work out the position on the map you will see that the "America" had drifted several hundreds of miles after her motors stopped.

Thus ended a voyage which had lasted three days all but half an hour. All chances of it being successful were, as Mr. Wellman himself afterwards admitted, wrecked from the first by the equilibrator, which imposed terrific strains on the structure of the airship, as well as on the nerves of the crew. Captain Simon, who kept a diary of the voyage, states that the irregular jerks caused by the equilibrator made it almost impossible to sleep, even the sleep of utter exhaustion. A few minutes' nap was all that could be managed before the sleeper found himself jerked back into consciousness.

Apart from the equilibrator the airship was a success. It held the gas well, and stood the strains well; and its motors behaved well as soon as the trouble with the bearings had been overcome. Had it been possible to make a trial trip before starting on the great adventure the outcome might have been different.

Faith in the possibility of crossing the Atlantic impelled Mr. Vaniman, the engineer of the "America," to build another airship, the "Akron," in which to repeat the attempt. While this was being tested it took fire, and Vaniman and his four assistants all perished.

CHAPTER 9

THE PIONEERS OF MECHANICAL FLIGHT

THE balloon has no counterpart in nature. The nearest approach to it, the thistledown, is able to keep aloft only if there be an upward current. In still or horizontally-moving air it inevitably comes to earth.

Birds, bats, and insects navigate the air by the exertion of muscular force combined with a very skilful use of the sustaining surfaces given them by nature. Proportionately to their weight, they are very much stronger than man; and human beings have long realised the futility of trying to fly without the help of forces other than their own.

The story of how the problems of mechanical flight were analysed, attacked, and finally solved forms one of the most interesting chapters in the annals of human progress; also one of the latest. Looking back, one can see plainly enough that successful navigation of the air by means of heavier-than-air machines depended ultimately on the provision of an engine of very great power relatively to its weight. Since such an engine did not appear until the early years of the present century, as the ultra-light internal-combustion motor, we cannot conceive of a practical aeroplane dating back to last century. When the proper motive power was available, mechanical flight—or aviation, for short—soon became an established fact, and developed with astounding rapidity: as mechanical transport on roads had developed a decade earlier. The last, be it noted, also owed its impetus to the internal-combustion engine.

But quite apart from the question of adequate motive power, there were other very perplexing difficulties to be overcome in connection with the design of apparatus to which the power should be applied. In the first place, the physical risks were enormous. Experiments with flying-machines are not comparable with trying out new methods of travelling through water or on land. A ship or a vehicle is at least securely supported, and runs practically no risk from the effects of gravity. Ordinarily, if anything goes wrong, it simply comes to a standstill.

A flying-machine, on the other hand, while flying, that is, while in the air, may be compared to an imaginary ship that would founder instantaneously if its steering were mishandled or any one of many parts broke or failed to do their duty. Safety during mechanical flight depends on the skilful handling of a machine that is well designed, carefully constructed of the best materials, and strong enough to withstand much heavier strains than are likely to be put upon it under normal conditions. That we can now use such a mode of transportation with but negligible risk to our necks is due to experience gained by the pioneers and their successors, at a heavy cost in life, limb, and money.

If ever there was a subject that demanded the utmost caution in experiment, surely we find it in mechanical flight. Every foolhardy attempt to rush matters ended more or less disastrously; even some of the most cautious pioneers had to pay with their lives for such success as they attained. Furthermore, the conditions made it unavoidable that advance towards the goal should at first be disappointingly—often exasperatingly—slow. Long waits for favourable atmospheric conditions, followed by flights to be measured in seconds and often ending in the destruction of apparatus—such was very commonly the lot of those who probed the secrets of the air and the birds.

Among the innumerable experimenters who have interested themselves in the problems of flight a few stand out whose names will never be forgotten. One of the very first was Sir George Cayley, a Yorkshire squire, who is known as the "Father of aerodynamics." About 120 years ago he published an article which showed him to have a very fair idea of what an aeroplane should be. Among other things he suggested the use of wings with curved, rather than flat, surfaces,—perhaps as a result of studying the wings of birds; and it is noteworthy that he championed fixed supporting surfaces as against the flapping devices which found favour with other investigators. He has left a record of a large "glider" on which he sailed from the top of a hill at a gentle angle: and he is even credited with having built an aeroplane driven by an engine of his own design, though no definite evidence on this head is forthcoming.

Cayley, who died in 1857, at least had set the ball rolling, and created in a good many people a desire to carry matters further. Among them were W. S. Henson and John Stringfellow,—the first a lace manufacturer and the second a very clever engineer,—who met at Chard, in Somersetshire, and together carried out some very interesting experiments. Henson had large ideas and actually floated a company which was to transport mails, passengers, and parcels through the air in a big machine designed by himself. This machine is described in a patent taken out by Henson as having "a very extended surface or plane of a light yet very strong construction, which will have the same relation to the general machine which the extended wings of a bird have to the body when the bird is skimming through the air; but in place of the power for on-ward progress being obtained by movement of the extended surface or plane, as is the case with the wings of birds, I apply suitable paddle-wheels or other proper mechanical propellers worked by a steam or other sufficiently light engine, and thus obtain the requisite power for onward movement to the plane or extended surface."

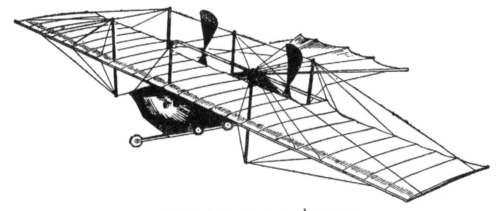

HENSON AND STRINGFELLOW'S MODEL.

We see from this that Henson had accepted Cayley's teaching, and that the general principles of the modern aeroplane were already taking shape. The words "or other sufficiently light engine" might be taken as an intelligent anticipation of the petrol motor.

The big machine never materialised, but Henson and String-fellow produced some very interesting models, one of which is to be seen in the South Kensington Science Museum. Whether any of them flew is doubtful, but we know that later on String-fellow, who had a genius for building very light miniature steam-engines, constructed, in 1848, a small self-propelled model which actually sustained itself in the air. It weighed only 8½ lbs. Another model, a triplane, was demonstrated in the Crystal Palace twenty years later, and subsequently found a home in the Smithsonian Museum, at Washington.

Stringfellow's models, though nothing but models, created a good deal of popular interest, and, what was more valuable, interested scientific men. Among these may be named F. H. Wenham, who experimented with long, narrow planes placed one above the other. Wenham proved that the longer, transversely to the direction of flight, a plane of given area was relatively to its fore and aft width, the greater lifting effect it had. This and other discoveries concerning the most efficient forms of lifting surfaces were his contributions towards the fund of knowledge needed before a satisfactory aeroplane could be built.

Passing over about twenty-five years, we come to a model aeroplane built by the Hon. Charles A. Parsons, famous for his development of the marine steam-turbine. His model, a monoplane, had a span of 11 feet and a total sustaining surface of 22 square feet. A tiny steam engine and boiler, working at about 50 lbs. to the square inch, supplied the motive power. The aeroplane, which weighed but 3½ lbs. complete, made flights limited to about 100 yards; for after a run of that distance the steam pressure became insufficient to keep the model in the air.

The next model worthy of special notice is that constructed by Professor S. P. Langley, Secretary of the Smithsonian Institution at Washington. For many years he devoted his spare time to the study of mechanical flight. After many experiments he convinced himself that the power needed to lift a given weight into the air was very much less than mathematicians had calculated it to be. To put his convictions to the test, he built a steam-driven model, to which he gave the name "aerodrome"—a word now applied only to the open spaces which aeroplanes start from or alight in. The model was a masterpiece of mechanical workmanship. It may be described as a double monoplane; that is to say, it had a large plane in front, and another, of almost the same size, behind and at the same level as the first. The span was 12½ feet. Below the framework hung a boat-shaped body to enable it to rise from and alight in water. The body housed an engine and boiler which weighed only 6 lbs. 10 ozs. between them, but developed from 1 to 1½ horsepower. The model, when ready for flight, scaled nearly 30 lbs. After many delays due to unfavour-

LANGLEY'S STEAM-DRIVEN MODEL.

able weather the model was launched from a houseboat on the Potomac River. It rose in the face of the wind and flew for half a mile at a speed of from 20 to 25 miles an hour. The flight terminated with the supply of steam from the boiler, and the model settled on the water. Many other successful trials followed. Professor Langley's experiments, by proving that one horsepower could maintain at least 20 lbs. in the air, and that balance could be assured by a proper arrangement of the planes, attracted a great deal of attention, and encouraged other investigators to persevere.

From models we may now turn to the more ambitious efforts

made by experimenters with man-carrying machines. The credit for having been the first person to build one that actually raised human beings from the ground belongs to Sir Hiram S. Maxim, of machine-gun fame. An engineer to his finger-tips, this gentleman approached the subject of mechanical flight in an eminently practical and methodical manner. Before attempting anything in the way of a flying-machine he devoted some years to experiments with propellers, lifting surfaces, and the air-resistance of struts of different sections. To make an efficient flying-machine it was obviously necessary to equip it with propellers which would convert a large percentage of the power transmitted to them into useful work, and with sustaining surfaces that would make good use of the push given by the propellers; while, to avoid waste of power, the struts connecting the various parts must be so shaped as to offer a minimum of resistance.

His researches put him in possession of a great deal of useful knowledge. The next step was to construct a boiler and engines which would develop a great deal of power relatively to their weight. The boiler—of water-tube type—weighed about 1,000 lbs., had 800 square feet of heating surface, and was heated by a burner using benzolene as fuel.

The boiler supplied steam to a pair of compound engines, weighing 320 lbs. each and capable of developing between them some 300 to 350 horsepower. The total weight of boiler, engines, fuel, and water came to about 7 lbs. per horsepower—an average probably far lower than that of any steam plant of equal power constructed up to that time.

The engines, etc., were mounted on a platform attached to a framework, which also had secured to it a great central upper plane with smaller planes projecting on each side. Two more small planes, fixed at a lower level—thus making the machine in effect a biplane—an elevating plane in front of the main plane, and a tail plane behind it, brought up the total sustaining surface to about 4,000 square feet. With three men aboard the machine weighed 8,000 lbs., or just 2 lbs. for every square foot of plane area.

Maxim's object was not to make a "free" flight, but to find out whether a really heavy machine could be made to rise from

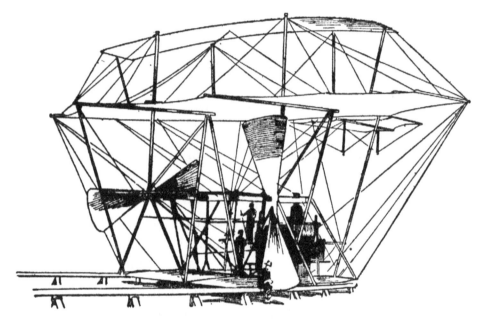

THE MAXIM MACHINE.

the ground. He laid down a steel railway 1,800 feet long, of 9 ft. gauge, for the aeroplane to run on: and outside this another of 35 ft. gauge, with reversed rails, against the under side of which flanged wheels, at the ends of long outriggers, would press if the narrow-gauge wheels rose one inch above their rails, so that the machine would still be "captive."

The engines drove two propellers, 17½ feet in diameter, which, at 400 revolutions per minute, exerted a thrust of 2,000 lbs. Apparatus was provided on board for measuring the lifting effort of the planes, and the pushing effort of the propellers.

The first run was made with a boiler pressure of only 150 lbs. to the square inch. All the lower wheels remained in contact with the inner track. For the second run the pressure was increased to 240 lbs., and the higher speed resulting made the aeroplane lift itself spasmodically. Maxim next had the machine tied to a dynamometer for measuring pull, and ran the pressure up to 300 lbs. When steam was turned on full, the propeller thrust rose to nearly a ton. On the word to let go being given, the machine rushed forward, nearly throwing the crew off their feet.

"The first part of the track," wrote Sir Hiram, "was up a slight incline, but the machine was lifted clear of the lower rails and all of the top wheels were fully engaged on the upper track when about 600 feet had been covered. The speed rapidly increased, and when 900 feet had been covered, one of the rear axletrees, which were of 2-inch steel tubing, doubled up and set the rear end of the machine completely free. . . . The rear end of the machine, being set free, raised considerably above the track and swayed. At about 1,000 feet the left forward wheel also got clear of the upper track, and shortly afterwards the right forward wheel tore up about 100 feet of the upper track. Steam was at once shut off, and the machine sank directly to the earth, embedding the wheels in the soft turf without leaving any other marks; showing most conclusively that the machine was completely suspended in the air before it settled to the earth. . . . The total lifting effect upon the machine must have been at least 10,000 lbs."

The trip, though less than a quarter of a mile in length, rendered July 31, 1894, a famous date in aeronautical—one may even say human—history. For on this occasion man was first lifted into the air on wings by mechanical power. Maxim had accomplished a feat which scores of able mechanics, and even men of science, had stated to be impossible. The inventor had spent over £20,000 on his experiments, and could not afford to continue them, or he very probably would have scored even greater successes.

The next name on our list is that M. Clement Ader, a French electrical engineer, who interested himself mainly in two things,—the improvement of the telephone, and artificial flight. He began constructing experimental flying machines in 1882, and built a number of models before undertaking anything

ADER'S "AVION."

large enough to carry a man. It is rather difficult to ascertain the facts about Ader and the performances of his machines. Apparently he began with flapping machines which proved a failure, and then tried fixed-wing machines with steam-driven propellers. In appearance these later machines suggested enormous bats, their wings being very arched and pointed at the ends. One of them is preserved in the Paris Museum of Arts and Handicrafts.

Ader succeeded in interesting the French military authorities, and received financial help from them in return for which he was obliged to conduct his experiments in secret; a circumstance which has wrapped his doings in a certain amount of mystery. It is generally accepted that his "Avion," weighing about half a ton, carried him some hundreds of yards through the air on October 11, 1897; so to Ader belongs the glory of making the first "free" flight on a flying-machine. The flight ended in the destruction of the apparatus, on which much money, time, and mechanical ingenuity had been expended. The military officials seem now to have lost faith in M. Ader, for they withdrew their support; and for want of the necessary means he, like Maxim before him, had to discontinue his investigations.

The experiments so far described showed the *possibility* of artificial flight. Machines had actually ridden the air for brief periods. But, as Maxim himself admitted, the steam-engine, on account of the great weight of fuel and water consumed, was useless except for very short flights, and must be superseded by something better before man could hope to make aerial voyages. He also recognised that the problem of controlling a machine when in the air had still to be solved, and that models, without any governing mind aboard, gave little help here. The fact is that Maxim and Ader might have continued to make and crash machine after machine without advancing much nearer to the practical aeroplane until the all-important matter of maintaining equilibrium or balance in the air had been cleared up. A flying-machine cannot sustain itself except when moving at high speed, when it has the qualities of a projectile. Therefore if it be not under perfect control, a man aboard it runs at least as serious risks as, for example, a man who had never before been on a bicycle would run were he suddenly to mount a cycle and endeavour to ride through traffic. It is evident that experience of balancing in the air can be gained safely only at low speeds and at small distances above the ground. And as a power-driven machine is essentially a high-speed one, something of another kind was required. This brings us to the man-carrying *glider*, which may be compared to a kite of special design and large size, unrestrained by a cord and kept aloft by the pressure of the air on its inclined surfaces. If the wind be sufficiently strong, the glider may remain more or less stationary for long periods —for hours even, as proved in recent trials: otherwise it must create a sufficient wind for itself, as it were, by advancing in a descending path under the pull of gravity.

The first systematic experiments made with gliders were those of Otto Lilienthal, a native of Anklam, in Pomerania. To this brave and persevering German we owe a mass of information which forms the foundation on which the science of practical aviation was subsequently built.

After long years of quiet scientific study and experiment, Lilienthal came to the conclusion that the first steps in the direction of human flight must be made with very simple apparatus, launched from elevated points, and allowed to glide downwards. Only by experiments with such apparatus would it be possible to learn the secrets of balancing, the best forms of supporting surfaces, and the area required to support known weights at known speeds. "Experiments in gliding by a single individual," he wrote in 1896, just before his death, "following closely the model of bird gliding, is the only method which permits us, beginning with a very simple apparatus and in a very incomplete form of flight, to develop gradually our proficiency in the art of flying."

Lilienthal was led to these conclusions by his observations of bird flight. He kept a number of young storks and watched closely their first attempts to fly. They did not fly naturally, that is, without practice. In fact, for a time they could not lift themselves from the ground at all, though provided with suitable wings and muscles. Instinct told them to practice facing the wind, never with it behind them. Days of experimenting were required before they succeeded in making anything worthy of the name of flight. Much more, argued Lilienthal, and rightly, did man need to practise; and he could not do better than take a hint from the birds as regards the wind.

He began his gliding experiments with a pair of rigid outstretched wings attached to each other and to a tail. The apparatus, which had an opening for the experimenter's body between the wings, had a sustaining area of 160 square feet and weighed about 50 lbs. The wings were slightly curved

LILIENTHAL GLIDER.

fore and aft, and consisted of cotton twill tightly stretched on a light framework of willow wood. Lilienthal passed his head and arms through the central opening, the edges of which he gripped to support the glider when not air-borne, or himself during flight.

Facing the wind, he ran with the glider till it lifted him off his feet, and as the slope of a hill somewhat steeper than the angle of descent was chosen for the take-off, he travelled a distance varying according to the strength of the wind and other circumstances, before touching ground again. At first he ventured to experiment in very light breezes only, for, as he says, "the mercilessness of the wind towards all flying machines is a difficulty in their invention." By dint of practice he mastered the art of "trimming" his craft and maintaining balance, swinging his legs in the direction needed to counteract undue rolling and pitching,—to use nautical terms.

As he acquired confidence, he faced stronger and stronger winds, and he confesses to having been tossed about at times in such a manner as to be rendered almost breathless.

One of his greatest difficulties was to find a suitable place for his experiments. Eventually, he had to form an artificial conical mound, about 50 feet high, which exactly met his needs. This sloped gently in all directions, so that, no matter from what quarter the wind blew he could use it.

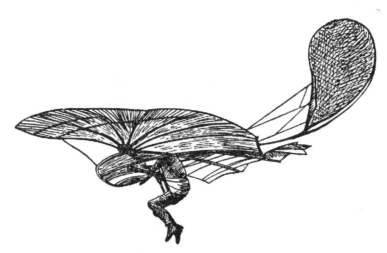

LILIENTHAL GLIDING.

By dint of perseverance Lilienthal succeeded in making flights of up to 300 yards in length. At times he soared to greater heights than the starting-point, and was able to deflect his course to right or left by moving his body about to shift the centre of gravity.

During five years of experiments Lilienthal was actually in the air only about five hours, made up of innumerable glides lasting from a few seconds up to a minute or more. These figures suggest how quickly a human being could learn to bal-

ance a glider if it would only keep in the air of its own accord!
To increase the length of his flights, he built a biplane glider,
having about 200 square feet of surface, and considerably
heavier than the monoplane. This, however, proved considerably more difficult to balance, and therefore more dangerous
to use: though Lilienthal seems to have remained master of it.

When he considered that he had advanced sufficiently in the
art of balancing, the experimenter decided to equip his monoplane with a small engine, driven by carbonic acid gas, to flap
movable parts of the wings up and down. The motor weighed
90 lbs. and developed 2½ horsepower,—a very poor showing

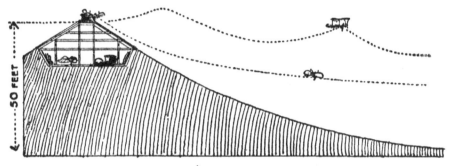

LILIENTHAL'S ARTIFICIAL HILL.

by comparison with modern aero engines, but, according to his
calculations, adequate for his purpose. Whether he would
have succeeded in flying with it can never be known, for, while
experimenting with a new rudder in a high wind, he lost his
balance and fell from a height of 100 feet, sustaining injuries
so serious that he died almost immediately—the first victim
to practical experiments. Before his death he had, fortunately, published the results of his labours, and so pointed the
way for further research.

While his sad fate undoubtedly discouraged many experimenters, others were encouraged by his achievements to persevere. Among the latter was a young English marine engi-

neer, Percy S. Pilcher, who had visited Lilienthal at Berlin and been infected with his enthusiasm. Pilcher built gliders of much the same form as Lilienthal's; but instead of hanging from them he sat between the wings, and as a safeguard he added an under-carriage with wheels. To start a flight his machine was towed by means of a fishing line and a multiplying gear until it rose into the air, when the line was disconnected. He proved that about two horsepower was needed to attain the towing speed which would raise him and the glider above the ground. The gear was fixed on a hill on one side of a valley; and the glider was placed on a hill facing it, so that it had gravity to help it while gathering velocity. Pilcher made glides of up to 250 yards in length with his aeroplane. Then, like Lilienthal, he built a double-decker, for which he constructed an oil-engine of 4 horsepower. But before he could put this to the test, the fate which had overtaken his predecessor overtook him also. While he was giving a display in a gentleman's park the tail of his machine broke, and Pilcher fell heavily, with fatal results. He had proved two things: the possibility of launching a glider like a kite, and the value of an undercarriage to absorb landing shocks. His death was a great misfortune for Britain, for, had he been spared, he might have won for her the honour that passed to America.

In that country a Mr. Octave Chanute of Chicago, an elderly engineer, had been interested in Lilienthal's doings by Mr. A. M. Herring, a pupil of the German flier. The two joined in carrying out glider tests, Chanute financing the experiments, and Herring doing the actual flying. Their greatest successes were obtained with a biplane, or double-decker, having a tail. This glider was constructionally an improvement on anything yet built, for the planes were connected by struts and wires in such a way as to stand rough usage without suffering injury.

CONQUERING THE AIR

The machines made by these two men, though balanced by movements of the pilot's body, were more easily managed than Lilienthal's, even in more violent winds than either the German or Pilcher had dared to face.

Among the people who read with more than casual interest the news of Lilienthal's death in 1896 were two young Americans, Wilbur and Orville Wright, of Dayton, Ohio. The brothers, who had previously done a good deal of kite-flying, and had made some model "helicopters" which screwed themselves through the air to the ceiling, were at the time running a cycle and engineering business in their native town. Having got hold of available literature on the subject of artificial flight, they determined to follow up Lilienthal's work, but if possible under conditions which would give them a larger percentage of time in the air. Their idea was to find some spot where winds of sufficient velocity blew frequently and steadily, and to practise with a glider attached kite-wise to a cord.

After two or three years of planning and experiment they built a double-decker machine of Chanute type, but embodying some very important modifications. In the first place, it was so arranged that the pilot could lie flat on it, thus exposing much less body-surface to the air than if he adopted the upright positions of previous experiments. Secondly, since the prone position made it difficult to shift the body about, a horizontal rudder, or small plane, was attached some distance in advance of the main planes. By tilting this as required, fore-and-aft balance might be maintained. Thirdly, to correct sideways balance, the main planes were so designed that, by pulling on cords, the rear edges of the planes could be drawn down towards their tips. In this way it would be easy to give the wings on one side a greater inclination from the horizontal than those on the other, and so increase their lifting effect and counteract any tendency to tilt. These innovations all proved to be of first-rate importance; since not only did they abolish the need for bodily gymnastics but they rendered a large machine as easily controllable as a small one.

In the early summer of 1900 the glider, which had a surface of 165 square feet, was taken to Kitty Hawk, in North Carolina, on the Atlantic Coast, where sea breezes blew with fair constancy. The brothers were disappointed with the results, for their machine appeared lacking in lifting power; and by

THE 1900 WRIGHT GLIDER (OPERATOR'S POSITION).

the end of the season the time spent in the air totalled but two minutes, as against the anticipated hours. The months had not been wasted, however, for the Wrights had discovered a satisfactory way of launching the glider, and some suitable sandhills from which to launch it.

The next year they returned to Kitty Hawk with a much larger machine of 308 square feet area, for which they built a suitable shed. At first the new apparatus behaved very erratically. But investigation showed that the planes were too much curved in section; and when they had been flattened somewhat the machine travelled very much better, and glides of up to nearly 400 feet were made. The second season as a whole was decidedly successful; so that the brothers began to consider the question of fitting a motor.

The machine used for the third season (1902) had about the same area as its predecessor, but the planes were longer and

WRIGHT MOTOR AND PROPELLERS.
A. Motor; B. Gear-wheels upon motor crank-shaft; C.C. Tubes carrying driving chains; D.D. Sprocket-wheels over which chains pass; E.E. Propellers.

narrower, and behind them two fixed vertical tails were fitted to hold the machine steady on its course. This glider did very good work, especially after the tail had been altered so as to be movable and act as a rudder. By the end of the summer the Wrights had made many glides and obtained a greater mastery of the art of balance than any earlier experimenter. The foundations of aerial navigation were now appearing above ground.

In 1903 began the first essays with a power-driven machine. This resembled the gliders in general design and appearance, but, as it had to carry a much greater weight, it was larger and more strongly constructed. A seat was provided for the pilot in front of the planes, and on each side of it was a lever for working the front elevator, warping the wings, or moving the steering rudder behind. Below the machine were two skids, rather like the runners of a sledge, for it to alight on.

No petrol-motor of suitable lightness being obtainable, the Wrights set about making one for themselves, and presently produced one of 25 horsepower, weighing, with its attachments, about 250 lbs.,—say 10 lbs. per horsepower. As compared with modern engines it was heavy and clumsy, but its makers were not interested so much in cutting weight down to the minimum as in having a reasonably light motor which they could depend upon to keep going. The engine was fixed between the planes the same distance away from the centre line as the pilot, so that the machine should be in balance sideways; and by means of chains it drove two large propellers revolving (about 500 time a minute) in opposite directions behind the planes.

The machine with pilot, weighed about 900 lbs. It was therefore much too heavy to be launched by hand like a glider. To get over the difficulty the Wrights laid down a single rail, some 20 yards long, on which ran a small trolley carrying the aeroplane. At one end of the rail rose a high wooden structure inside which a heavy weight could be lifted by gearing. A rope ran from the weight down the tower, along the rail, round a pulley at the far end, and back to the trolley. To launch the machine it was placed on the trolley and brought back to the weight end. Then the weight was raised, and the rope made fast to the carriage. The motor having been started up, the retaining catch was released, and the aeroplane darted forward partly by its own power and partly owing to the pull of the rope. By the time it reached the launching end of the rail its speed was sufficient for flight.

The first trials took place at Kitty Hawk, the scene of the gliding experiments. After many failures the day arrived—December 17, 1903—on which the machine actually flew for the

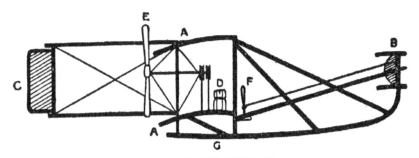

THE WRIGHT BIPLANE.

A.A. Main-planes; B. Double front elevator; C. Rudder (two narrow vertical planes); D. Motor; E. Propellers; F. Pilot's lever; G. Skids upon which machine landed.

first time. That day four flights took place, the last of them being one of 59 seconds, which easily beat anything done by Ader in 1897.

In 1904 the brothers removed to a field 8 miles from their home, and built a new machine, with which they advanced the duration record to 5 minutes 17 seconds, the distance covered being rather over 3 miles. During this year they succeeded in making a circular flight, on September 30. The machine still gave trouble in its handling, and at times behaved in an unexpected manner. But during 1905 the causes were tracked down and remedied, with results which the Wrights communicated to the Aeronautical Society of Great Britain in a letter. It ran thus:—

"We have finished our experiments for this year after a season of gratifying success. Our field of experiment has been very unfavourable for experiment a great part of the time, owing to the nature of the soil and the frequent rains of the past summer. Up to the 6th. September we had the machine out on but eight different days, testing a number of changes which we had made since 1904, and as the result the flights on these days were not so long as our own of last year. During the month of September we gradually improved in our practice, and on the 26th. made a flight of over 11 miles. On the 30th. we increased this to 12 miles, on 3rd. October to 15 1/3 miles, on 4th. October to 20¾ miles, and on the 5th. to 24¼ miles. All of these flights were made at about 38 miles an hour, the flight of the 5th. October occupying 38 minutes 3 seconds. . . . We had intended to place the record above the hour, but the attention these flights were beginning to attract compelled us to suddenly discontinue our experiments in order to prevent the construction of the machine from becoming public. The machine passed though all of these flights without the slightest damage. In each of these flights we returned frequently to the starting point, passing high over the heads of the spectators."

It is somewhat curious that the publication of these statements of the Wrights met with great scepticism, though the flights took place in an open field, with much-used roads on two sides of it, and must have been witnessed by hundreds of people. In France, where Archdeacon, Ferber, Voisin, Blériot, Santos Dumont, Farman and others had been experimenting for some years with gliders, little, if any, credence was given to the claims that long flights had been made before a single European power-driven machine (Ader's excepted) had managed even a short "hop." (The first European success was Santos Dumont's flight of 238 yards on November 12, 1906).*

The facts of the case are, however, beyond dispute and the Wright brothers are now universally recognised as the fathers of *practical human flight*. They raised it from an aspiration

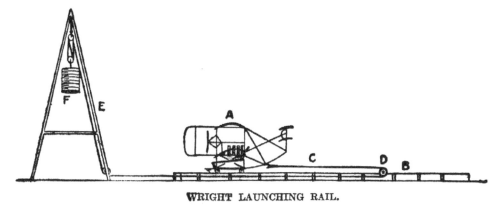

WRIGHT LAUNCHING RAIL.

A. Biplane; B. Rail; C. Rope passing from the aeroplane round the pulley-wheel (D) and thence to the derrick (E); (F) Falling weight.

to being an accomplishment. Owing to the secrecy maintained by the young Americans for the two years (1906 and 1907) following their greatest initial successes, while they were negotiating with Governments for the sale of their experience, French aviators attracted far more attention; and indeed in some ways got ahead of the Wrights in practice. But when, in 1908, the brothers brought their "White Flier" over to France, and, after a few trial runs, made a non-stop flight of 77½ miles,—unbeaten till seven months later—the truth of their claims was ungrudgingly recognised in all countries.

* A Dane, Ellehamer, is credited with having anticipated Dumont by a few days, but his effort appears to have been much less successful.

CHAPTER 10

THE FIRST CROSSING OF THE CHANNEL BY AEROPLANE

CROSSING the Channel is an aeroplane is now an everyday occurrence, forming part of the routine of various transport companies operating between London and the Continent. In fair weather or foul the aeroplanes detailed for the service rise at schedule time from Croydon, Brussels, or Le Bourget, as the case may be, and head for a distant capital. The actual passage of open water is a mere incident, occupying but a fraction of the total time taken by the flight. The business man anxious to save a few hours, or the tourist in search of a new sensation, takes his seat in the comfortable cabin of the air liner with, perhaps, a slight quickening of the pulse if it be his first experience of aerial travel, but certainly without any justification for pluming himself on a display of unusual daring.

In 1909, however, conditions were far otherwise. Flights across open water had not been attempted, and the English Channel, albeit but 21 miles across at the narrowest point, offered a formidable challenge to the imperfect aeroplanes of the time.

The challenge was one of exactly the kind most calculated to intrigue the courageous and enterprising men who, at great risk to life and limb, had won their spurs as aviators over land. The Channel represented not merely so many miles of water, but a stretch of sea having enormous geographical importance as separating England from the Continent of

Europe. For centuries, thanks to her navy, the "silver streak" had been England's safeguard. To cross it by air for the first time would not merely confer undying fame on the successful airman, but provide an object-lesson the importance of which could not be misunderstood.

Not that the British had any objection whatever to the Channel being flown. In fact it was a British newspaper, the *Daily Mail*, which encouraged attempts by the offer of a prize of £1,000 to the first man across. Excitement ran high in both England and France when the word went round that Hubert Latham, a young Frenchman with English blood in his veins, intended to try his luck. Latham was already well known for the skill and daring with which he handled his graceful Antoinette monoplane. His evolutions in a gale during a meeting held at Blackpool in the autumn of 1908 had impressed deeply everyone that witnessed them, besides proving that in capable hands an aeroplane was not merely a fair-weather machine.

In July, 1909, Latham took his aeroplane to Sangatte, not far from Calais, and waited impatiently for a favourable opportunity to essay the crossing. A French torpedo boat, the *Harpon*, had been detailed to follow his flight, if and when it took place, and to render any necessary assistance. Alighting in the water, should the engine fail, might not be in itself very dangerous under skilful control, but obviously the chances of the pilot getting safely to land without help would be small.

A week or more passed before M. Latham considered conditions to be such as to justify an attempt. Early in the morning of July 19, 1909, however, he decided that the moment had come. At 6.20 a.m. three gun signals announced that the aeroplane was about to start. The Antoinette raced down the gentle slope leading to the cliffs' edge, and took the air. A minute

PLATE V

A seaplane carrying a torpedo above and between its pontoons.   The " torpedoplane "
may prove a formidable weapon in any future naval warfare.

[Photo, Sport and General.

later, a wireless signal received in Dover, followed immediately by the firing of a maroon, brought into the streets
crowds of people straining their eyes in the direction of Calais,
in the hope that they would soon descry a small spot floating
high above the waters.

While motor boats and a tug put out from the English
port, the *Harpon* was speeding towards England in chase of
the aeroplane, which soon after leaving the cliffs had plunged
into a light cloud and disappeared from the sight of the
watchers on the French side. A little later it was seen
again, heading straight for Dover. Then it vanished altogether, and people began to wonder what had happened. Enquiries flew to-and-fro, under and over the Channel, and when
it became certain that something had gone wrong anxiety both
at Sangatte and at Dover rose to fever point.

At last the *Harpon* was sighted heading for Calais, where
a tumultuous welcome awaited the airman, who had been
rescued from the sea. He had travelled about 7 miles at a
speed of nearly 45 miles an hour, when the engine began to
misfire, a thing it had never done before after so short a flight.
The aeroplane quickly lost height and there was nothing to
do but glide down towards the water and meet it at as flat
an angle as possible. This he managed to do, and, though the
machine was travelling at a high speed when it struck, it
settled easily without injury and floated buoyantly on the
surface, held up by the hollow wings. M. Latham stuck up his
feet clear of the water, and lighted a cigarette, which he was
still smoking when the *Harpon* reached him. The torpedo
boat took the aeroplane in tow, and brought it to land in a
damaged condition, though the engine itself was none the worse
for the adventure.

Not at all discouraged by his bad luck, M. Latham hastened

off to Paris to procure a new aeroplane, which arrived at Sangatte a few days later. But meanwhile another Richmond had appeared in the field—Louis Blériot—who had recently

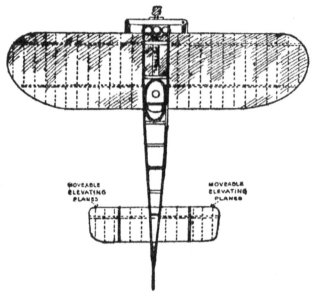

THE BLÉRIOT MONOPLANE SEEN FROM ABOVE, SHOWING ITS BIRD-LIKE SHAPE AND THE POSITION OF THE PILOT.

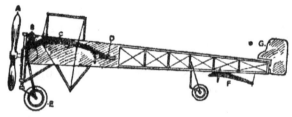

THE BLÉRIOT MONOPLANE.

A. Propeller; B. Motor;
C. Sustaining-plane;
D. Pilot's seat;
E. Landing chassis;
F. Combined tail and elevating planes;
G. Rudder.

made a cross-country flight of 25 miles—then a considerable feat—in a monoplane of his own design, one of the smallest and neatest that had yet appeared. It weighed only 484 lbs. when empty, and its engine was a three-cylinder rated at only 25 horsepower. As a precaution M. Blériot fitted a large air-bag inside the frame to keep the machine afloat if it should fare like M. Latham's.

Latham at Sangatte, and Blériot at Les Barraques, a few miles nearer Calais, anxiously watched the weather, and each his rival, lest he should steal a march on him. The weather had been stormy for several days, but when M. Blériot, rendered restless by pain in a foot which he had burned some time before, rose at 2.30 a.m. on the morning of July 25th. he found, somewhat to his surprise, that the wind had dropped. He at once left his hotel and motored off to the marquee in which his aeroplane was housed. As the dawn broke he had his machine wheeled out and made ready. At 3.30 a.m. he took it for a test trip, during which it behaved so well that he made up his mind to seize the opportunity.

"At 4.35," stated M. Blériot, "I gave my mechanics the order to let go. The machine rose splendidly. My course to the sea lay across the sand dunes, and then I had to surmount the telegraph wires which run along the coast. It was because I wished to be certain of clearing these that I started on the plain. I struck across the dunes and went over the telegraph wires at a height of about 180 feet. I could see the destroyer *Escopette* a few miles out at sea, and as she was to steam towards Dover I took my bearings from her. The destroyer was steaming at full speed, but I very quickly passed her. My machine was then travelling at about 45 miles an hour, the revolutions of the propellers being about 1,200 to 1,400 a minute. While travelling over the Channel my monoplane was at a height of about 250 feet. At times she dipped a little, but I always got her to rise again.

"For about ten minutes after I passed the destroyer I was able by looking back to steer my course by the direction in which she was steaming. Then I lost sight of the destroyer, and the English coast was not in view, so I decided that the

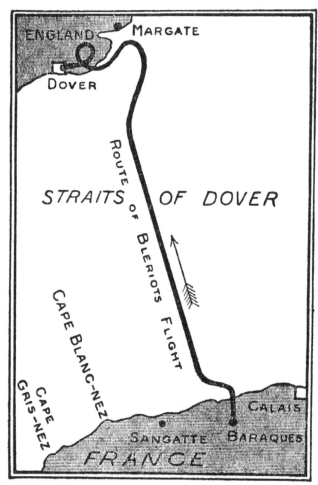

BLÉRIOT'S COURSE WHEN FLYING THE CHANNEL.

best thing to do was to set my steering gear for the point at which I had last seen the *Escopette* heading. The flight continued for about ten minutes with nothing in sight but sea and sky. It was the most anxious part of the flight, as I had no certainty that my direction was correct, but I kept my motor working at full speed and hoped that I would reach Dover all right. I had no fear of the machine, which was travelling beautifully. At last I sighted an outline of the land, but I was then going in the direction of Deal, and could see the long beach very plainly. In setting my steering I had overlooked for the moment the effect of the wind, which was blowing very strong from the south-west, and had therefore deflected me eastward. I could have landed at Deal, but I had started to come to Dover, and made up my mind to land there. I headed my monoplane westward, therefore, and followed the line of the coast to Dover about a mile or a little more out at sea. I could see a fleet of battleships in Dover Harbour, and I flew over these to a point where I could see my friend, M. Fontaine, with a large French tricolour, denoting the point where I was to descend. I flew in over the cliffs all right, but the descent was one of the most difficult I have ever made. When I got into the valley between the Castle and the opposite hill I found an eddying wind. I circled round twice to ease the descent, but I alighted more heavily than I had anticipated, and the monoplane was damaged." [1]

The exact spot on which M. Blériot completed this epoch-making feat in the Northfall Meadow is now marked by a permanent stone monument, reproducing in the flat the aeroplane which made the crossing. Owing to the earliness of the arrival it was witnessed by but a very few people, and the only person who actually saw M. Blériot reach the ground was a policeman, soon afterwards joined by two more policemen and some soldiers camping in the neighbourhood. These stayed to guard the machine, which had been damaged slightly in landing, from the people who soon began to crowd round it and congratulate the daring Frenchman.

Telegrams rained on the airman from all parts of the world.

[1] The *Times*.

CONQUERING THE AIR

In France, as may easily be imagined, the utmost enthusiasm was aroused by a success that took the public quite by surprise, since the victory had been won while most people were still in their beds.

In England, too, enormous interest was taken in the event. Blériot became the hero of the hour. His arrival in London suggested the return home of a victorious commander after a great war. Long before the train from Dover was due at Victoria a great crowd had gathered outside the station, filling the approaches and overflowing far along Victoria Street. The now famous aeroplane, placed on show at Selfridge's, in Oxford Street, was visited by 120,000 persons in the course of four days. Almost every one of the great British journals devoted "leaders" and columns of description on July 26 and 27 to what was universally acclaimed as an historical triumph; and the same may be said of the foreign press generally. For a month after the famous flight Blériot's was probably the most used name in the world.

If ever a man deserved success it was M. Blériot. He had always been fascinated by the idea of constructing a flying machine that really would fly. His earliest attempt, made in 1901, took the form of an ornithopter, that is, a contrivance with flapping wings in imitation of a bird. But neither this nor two further machines embodying the same ideas met with any success. Perceiving that he was working on the wrong lines, he applied himself, like the Wrights, to a serious study of the principles and science of flight. In 1906 he built, in co-operation with Voisin Frères, his first biplane. Then he contrived a monoplane of so peculiar a shape that it resembled a flying duck with long outstretched neck. The "Canard," as it was nicknamed, made one wobbly jump and crumpled up. Eventually, in 1907, M. Blériot on a new machine kept in the air for 120 yards. This short trip ended, however, in the wreck of his monoplane. But at least it had flown; and, encouraged by this fact, M. Blériot made and wrecked aeroplane after aeroplane, meeting, it is said, with no fewer than 50 accidents, from all of which he emerged without serious injury. In the course of his experiments he spent at least £20,000, so that, from a pecuniary point of view, his hobby was not a profitable one, in spite of the several prizes won. But after all, as the airman himself said, it was a greater thing to be first across the Channel than to win £1,000.

A humorous incident occurred a few hours after the landing at Dover. M. Blériot had just finished breakfast when three customs officers appeared at the hotel and inquired for him. Having asked him whether he had any dutiable goods on board they filled up the certificate as follows:

"I hereby certify that I have examined Louis Blériot, master of a vessel "monoplane," lately arrived from Calais, and that it appears by the verbal answers of the said master to the questions put to him that there has not been on board during the voyage any infectious disease demanding detention of the vessel and that she is free to proceed."

One of the first messages of congratulation to reach Blériot at Dover was from his rival, Latham. But for an extraordinary oversight or miscalculation on the part of his manager, Latham might have been the hero of the day. Latham had retired on the night of the 24th., after giving orders that he was to be called at 3 a.m. if the wind seemed light enough for a trial to be made. But though there was hardly any wind at all, the airman was allowed to sleep on until some 20 minutes after Blériot had actually left the coast. Latham's disappointment, when he knew what had happened, was cruel. He hurried on his clothes, had the monoplane brought out, and entered it. But by this time the wind had risen so much that a flight was too risky to be undertaken.

Two days later a good opportunity came, for the winds had gone to sleep for a time. Early in the morning, after a short trial flight, the Antoinette left the French cliffs, and at the same moment a message was wirelessed to Dover announcing the departure. The citizens at Dover, who had been metaphorically kicking themselves for having missed seeing Blériot come over, were assembled in their thousands on the cliffs, shore, and harbour works, despite heavy rain, to give the airman a welcome. When a special flag was run up near the Lord Warden Hotel, and the steamers in the harbour blew their sirens, everybody knew that Latham was in the air. Excitement grew intense, as eyes and fieldglasses searched the sky in the direction of the French coast. For ten minutes nothing could be seen. Then a dark speck revealed itself, becoming larger and larger every second, until it resolved itself into the shape of a gigantic bird. The delirious cheers of the delighted spectators mingled with the renewed screaming of the sirens as the glittering monoplane came gliding onwards at what seemed to be a terrific speed. "He'll do it! He'll do it!" was the verdict as well as the wish of the onlookers. Suddenly the monoplane, which was flying only a few hundred feet above the sea, began to circle round, for no apparent reason, and lost height. A dead silence fell on the crowd as it realized that Latham was in trouble. A few moments later the aeroplane struck the water with a splash, not a mile from the English coast. In a very short time a number of boats and vessels were on the spot, and M. Latham, whose face had been somewhat severely cut by his goggles being splintered against some part of the machine at the instant of entering the sea, was taken aboard a destroyer. The British dearly love a good sportsman, such as M. Latham certainly was, and when he landed he received a welcome which could not have been warmer had he been the first man to fly the Channel successfully.

The Channel was not flown again till the next year, when, on May 23, 1910, M. Jacques de Lesseps, the youngest son of the famous engineer of the Suez Canal, started from Les Barraques, and alighted 37 minutes later in a large meadow some distance inland from the South Foreland Lightship.

It still remained for a crossing to be made in the opposite direction. And this feat was accomplished soon afterwards by the Hon. C. S. Rolls, who had already won a name as an expert balloonist and driver of racing motor-cars. After the usual long wait for suitable weather which seemed to dog the heels of early aviators, the propitious moment for an attempt arrived on June 2, 1910. The Wright biplane with which the flight was to be attempted was brought out in the afternoon of that day and placed on its starting-rail in a meadow near Dover. At 6.30 p.m. Mr. Rolls took the air, and, after circling round in a bold sweep over the Castle, turned his machine for France, crossing the English coastline at 6.34½ p.m. at a good height. The aeroplane sped uneventfully over the Channel, and at 7.15 p.m. was over French ground. But Mr. Rolls' purpose being to return to England without alighting, he circled over the Channel Tunnel works near Sangatte, and dropped three envelopes containing greetings to the Aero Club of France. This done, he set his course for Dover and twenty minutes later he was sighted by the large number of spectators awaiting him. The flight ended close to the starting rail at 8.06 p.m.

In less than an hour and half he had covered over 50 miles, most of the distance being over water, thus surpassing by a good margin the more historic achievement of M. Blériot.

CHAPTER 11

THE RACE FROM LONDON TO MANCHESTER

In November 1906, the proprietors of the *Daily Mail* offered a prize of £10,000 to the first person who should fly in twenty-four hours from a spot within five miles of the offices of that paper to Manchester. The distance to be covered was 183 miles, and, as at the time when the offer was made only the Wright brothers had made flights in a heavier-than-air machine—excepting the short "jumps" of Ader and Santos Dumont, and those only over flat ground—most people, and certainly all not gifted with the power of imagination, thought that the offer entailed very little risk to the persons who made it. The idea of taking an aeroplane nearly 200 miles across railways, trees, buildings, telegraph wires, hills, and multitudinous other objects appeared somewhat fantastic to the mind of the ordinary citizen. The public attitude towards aviation was still the sceptical one usually entertained towards any revolutionary innovation; and hardly less reasonable than the later one of expecting far too much from a young and unfledged science.

A leading humorous paper made fun of the *Daily Mail* by declaring that it had decided to offer sums of £10,000 to the three persons who first should respectively fly to Mars and back in a week, reach the centre of the earth in a fortnight, and swim from Fishguard to Sandy Hook before the end of 1909. Another journal sarcastically offered £10,000,000 for any kind of flying machine that proved itself able to fly five miles out from London and back again.

The *Daily Mail* was undoubtedly unduly optimistic in declaring, at the time the offer appeared, that "We look with confidence to seeing our offer accepted within the next few months, when the flight of an aeroplane from London to Manchester will convince even the most sceptical, and prove that aviation is an accomplished fact." Three and a half years had to pass before the money was in danger.

The magnitude of the prize had without question a stimulating effect upon aviation, as the winner would be able to more than recoup himself for the heavy expenditure entailed in building or acquiring a machine capable of attempting the flight with a reasonable prospect of success.

The first active entrant for the prize appeared in 1910, in the person of Mr. Claude Grahame-White, who the year before had become interested in aviation and purchased a Blériot monoplane, on which he quickly became an expert flier. Soon afterwards he bought a Farman biplane, a type of machine that, if not particularly fast, was steady, reliable, and easy to handle. Its motor was a Gnome rotary engine of 50 horse-power, driving a propeller aft of the planes. The pilot sat in a kind of skeleton chair forward of the lower plane, and in front of him was an elevating plane, used in combination with a similar plane in the tail of the aeroplane.

With his "Farman" Mr. Grahame-White decided to make a bid for the big prize. The reader should realise that up to this time no cross-country flight of any length had been made in England, and a feat which would now be a mere bagatelle to quite a novice was then regarded by the best airmen of the day as a very serious undertaking. A fairly stiff breeze sufficed to keep aeroplanes on the ground, and engines were very much less reliable than they are today—as witness Latham's two failures.

On Saturday, April 23, 1910, Mr. Grahame-White rose from a field at Park Royal, near Willesden Junction. Though the time was a quarter past five on a cold, cheerless morning, so great was the interest taken in the Englishman's attempt that several thousands of people had gathered to witness his departure. Rounding the gasometer near Wormwood Scrubs that had been chosen as the official starting-point, he picked up

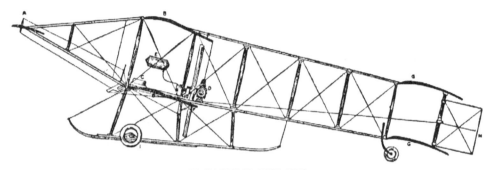

THE FARMAN BIPLANE.

A. Elevating-plane; B.B. Main-planes; C. Pilot's seat;
D. Motor and propeller; E. Petrol tank;
F.F. Hinged balancing-planes, or ailerons;
G.G. Tail-planes; H.H. Twin vertical rudders;
I. Landing wheels and skids.

and followed the (then) London and North-Western Railway, by which he would steer to Rugby. That place was reached at 7.20 a.m., at the end of a record-breaking cross-country flight of 85 miles. The reception awaiting the airman was as warm as he himself was cold,—for the rush through the morning air had almost frozen him stiff. About an hour after landing he set off again, heading for Crewe. Unfortunately the wind had risen and was now blowing fairly strongly, and this fact, combined with the engine not being in very good form, caused Mr. Grahame-White to make a second descent near

THE RACE FROM LONDON TO MANCHESTER

Lichfield, about 117 miles from London. It was a bit of very hard luck that the wind continued to freshen until all hopes of continuing the journey had to be abandoned for the day, and therefore of winning the prize at this attempt, since the flight had to be completed within 24 hours of the start. To make things worse, next day the aeroplane was turned over by the wind and sustained injuries which, by delaying a second attempt, possibly robbed Mr. Grahame-White of the prize.

While the machine was undergoing repair at Wormwood Scrubs, another competitor came on the scene,—M. Louis Paulhan, a young French airman who already had made a name for himself in flying circles. The prospect of there being a race between an Englishman and a Frenchman raised public excitement to fever point. Nothing but the London-Manchester flight was talked of in trains, trams, and omnibuses. Everybody who could find time went to the field near Hendon where M. Paulhan had his headquarters, or to Wormwood Scrubs. From all parts of the country came in enquiries for the latest news.

M. Paulhan's machine did not arrive at Hendon till the early hours of the morning of Wednesday, April 27, when the great packing-case containing it appeared at the shed after the impatient mechanics had begun to despair of its coming. Under the eyes of a crowd which swelled its numbers from hour to hour the Frenchman, unhurried and thorough, assembled his machine. He asked no questions about his rival, and gave no indication of his intentions, until the work was complete. At three o'clock the wind was light, and M. Paulhan decided that he would take advantage of this circumstance to start off at once, without even a trial flight. A message to this effect was therefore sent to the official observers. At 5 p.m., everything being ready, the French airman, after saying goodbye to his wife and to Mr. Farman, the maker of the aeroplane—that both competitors were using the same kind of machine added interest to the contest—climbed into his seat, and gave the word to let go. At 5.30 the aeroplane rose into the air and the news flashed in all directions, "Paulhan is off!"

Immediately after the start, Paulhan's wife and mechanics, and some friends motored to Willesden, where a special train was waiting to follow the flight, as it well could, since the railway, with sleepers specially whitewashed at junctions to guide the airman, was the course for him to follow, and an express engine had a higher speed than the aeroplanes of 1910. Things are very different today, when plenty of aeroplanes are able to turn off three miles in a minute!

Great was the excitement of those aboard the train on sighting, 75 miles up the line, the aeroplane flying strongly, a mile east of the railway and at a height of about 600 feet—but no greater than that of the railway staff and of the thousands who crowded the bridges and embankments on the lookout for the Frenchman. Near Lichfield the train pulled up suddenly, for Paulhan had alighted in a field close by. How he had fared up to this point may best be told in his own words, reproduced by the courtesy of the *Daily Mail*.

"I found the atmosphere rather disturbed when I rose; there were small, gusty puffs and tricky currents, and it was somewhat difficult to find just the altitude at which they would bother me least. I heard the cheering of the people as I circled over Hendon, and the enthusiasm delighted me, so I flew right over the heads of the crowd.

"I followed the line of the Midland Railway to Hampstead. Then I saw the cemetery and the white flag of the official observer. I went round it, high up in the air, and I knew then that I had fulfilled the conditions necessary for the start, so

THE RACE FROM LONDON TO MANCHESTER

I flew over the lake of the Welsh Harp and made directly for the North-Western Railroad.

"I had to fight the wind on the way from London. Not a moment's rest came to me in my battle against the gusts. Glance at my altitude chart, and you will see that I made rises and dips of as much as 320 feet, always with the object of flying in the steadiest level of air I could find.

"It was cold, very cold indeed, and the wind bit into my face. Fortunately for me, my eyes do not suffer while I am flying, though they burn terribly when I come down to earth again. . . . I started without gloves, for I hate to feel my hands encumbered while I am flying. The result was that at the end of my first flight the little finger of my driving hand was useless and without sensation: it was quite numbed with cold.

"I was going north for a long time before I sighted the special train which was accompanying me. But there was no mistaking it when it caught me up. The three loud hoots of the whistle and the big white signal cloth floating from the window of the rear coach—it looked like a handkerchief from such a height—told me all. I could see that things were going well. The wind whistled, and so did I.

"A pelting rainstorm lashed me for twenty minutes while I was in the neighbourhood of Rugby. Fortunately I am not unused to flying in the rain. Therefore, although it was uncomfortable, it had no effect upon my flight. I kept on flying at a steady pace, although my altitude varied remarkably.

"I flew until it was quite dark. All I could make out beneath me was the smoke of the train once in a while, and an occasional flicker of lights from a village. I came down rapidly from 300 metres to 100, so that I could be more certain of my direction.

"Then came the most existing incident of my flight. Darkness had fallen before me. I saw the lights of Lichfield. I decided to alight in some convenient meadow before reaching the town, and to do this I sank down to 150 feet. I was immediately above what looked like a large factory with a chimney. So, to alight safely in the field with no damage done, I made a fishhook turn, and my machine was now pointing towards London.

"Suddenly my motor stopped, every drop of petrol exhausted, and the machine swooped downwards almost like a stone dropping. What should I do? Beneath me was the brewery and a certain smash. Behind me was the narrow field which was almost a spider's web with a mesh of telegraph wires. I had an imperceptible fraction of a second in which to make up my mind, and I decided to risk the telegraph wires. As I sank I made a sharp twist right back on the line of my course, and was lucky enough to lift myself over the wires."

The Paulhan party now knew that the affair had developed into a race, for Grahame-White had given chase and was reported as having passed Bletchley. Let us return to London and review what had happened in the case of the Englishman.

At Wormwood Scrubs people had begun to pour into the great open space near the airship shed at an early hour. When Mr. Grahame-White arrived at 8.30 a. m. a huge crowd awaited him, and the crush became so great that the police had to be reinforced before a space could be cleared for the aeroplane to manœuvre in. About 2 p. m. the Farman emerged from its shed, and the airman climbed into his seat. The wind, however, was too gusty for a start to be advisable; and Mr. Grahame-White decided to wait a few hours in the hope of conditions becoming more favourable. The crowd increased; so did the wind, and finally it was decided to postpone the flight till the next morning. As the spectators streamed away from the field, the news came in, about 6 o'clock, that Paulhan had started from Hendon, and was now well on his way. Grahame-White awoke from a much-needed nap to learn the true state of things,—that the other competitor had stolen a march on him. Only half-awake, he stumbled out, exclaiming that he must go in pursuit at once. Willing hands rushed the aeroplane out from its garage, and the airman got aboard, taking no notice of friendly advice against starting in so gusty a wind. Just after 6.30 p. m. came the word to let go, and the aeroplane rose, rocking and swaying, until well away from the ground, when it was brought round, to circle over the gasworks which were the official starting mark. When the machine was turned towards Manchester its speed was seen to fall greatly, as it now ran obliquely into a strong breeze. The Farman reached Tring at 7.10 p. m., Leighton Buzzard at 7.30, Bletchley at 7.35. But the light was now failing, and at 7.55 the airman, whose machine still flew strongly, cut off his engine and settled in a field near Roade, 60 miles from the Scrubs, and 57 miles nearer London than the point at which his rival landed a quarter of an hour later.

The news that Grahame-White had started and that a race was fairly "on," raised public excitement higher than ever. That evening the late editions sold like hot cakes, not only in England but in France and Germany. Even in distant New York the bulletins posted outside the newspaper offices attracted large crowds. At Manchester and at intermediate places on the route still to be covered many people sat up all night to make sure of not missing the fun on the following day.

The rivals retired to rest with the intention of starting with daybreak. Grahame-White, however, later decided to take a heavy risk and try to reduce the gap by getting away before dawn. At 2.30 a. m. he was on his biplane again, much against the wishes of some of his friends. To ascend in the darkness had never yet been attempted by any airman. Mr. White carried no map,—it had been left behind in the rush of departure—and in any case it would have been useless. But nothing would dissuade him from his "night attack" on the enemy. In the glare of motor-car headlights he rose into the gloom overhead, and was soon invisible to the onlookers.

Immediately on rising the airman headed for the lights of the railway station. Let him now tell his own story.

"I could see absolutely nothing of the ground below me. It was all a black smudge. I went right over the railway station lights and then—fortunately only for a second or so—my engine missed fire. I began to sink towards the inky darkness below me. I could have picked no landing. It would become a swift, steep glide to—I know not what. And then, to my joy, my engine picked up again and I rose once more.

"A great difficulty presented itself in not knowing in the darkness whether I was ascending or not. I had done no night flying before, but I soon became accustomed to watching closely the movements of my elevating plane, which was silhouetted before me against the sky. I steered on for a spell with nothing at all to guide me after leaving the lights of Roade behind. The gleam from an occasional signal box far below helped me as well, and so I picked my way through the night to Blisworth. Here I felt surer of my ground, and bore away to the left for Weedon. The meadows below me I couldn't see at all. Faint lights shone here and there. Some, no doubt, were cottage windows, others I think were the headlights of motor cars.

"I passed over Weedon, my eyes becoming more accustomed to the darkness. On I flew. The weirdness of the sensation can scarcely be described. I was alone in the darkness, with the roar of my engine in my ears. As I glanced back, small, bright flashes of light—the discharge of the exhaust gases from the motor—flashed out in the night.

"Then I lost my way, with no railway lights to guide me. For a spell I steered off too much to the right. I wheeled and turned, wondering what I should do, but then a light to my left caught my eye, and I worked my way back to the railway line again.

"At a little inn by the roadside near the village of Crick my friend Mr. Frederick Coleman had promised to draw up his motor car, shining its headlights upon a wall to act as a guide for me. I was keenly on the lookout for this unmistakable night sign, and, sure enough, I saw it quite distinctly below me soon after I had left Welton station behind. I deviated a little from my course and headed for this patch of light. I saw the motor-car moving as I approached; then, with its headlights throwing a great path of light down the roadway, it set off at a breakneck pace, its driver evidently meaning to guide me on my way. Leaving the railway line on my left, I followed the light on the motor-car, and for a mile or so I hovered almost directly above it, allowing it to act as my pilot.

"But while I was doing so I chanced to glance over to the left again. Coming down the railway line I espied a goods train: it was making for Rugby. 'This,' I thought, 'will be a splendid guide,' and so I swung away from the lights of the motor-car and flew off till I was over the train.

"I saw the lights of Rugby, flew over the town, and forged ahead. The daylight began to come now, and from here on to the point of my descent in a field near Polesworth, my struggle was not with the darkness but with the wind. It was fierce gusts which eventually brought me down."[1]

[1] *Daily Mail.*

CONQUERING THE AIR

The aeroplane alighted at 4.14 a. m., and for three-quarters of an hour afterwards not a soul appeared, so that the airman had to wage a single-handed fight against the efforts of the wind to upset his machine. Then people began to gather, a small trickle developing into a steady stream of folk hurrying to get a sight of an apparatus such as many of them had not seen before. At 6.15 a. m. the news came in that Paulhan had reached Manchester, and it was his defeated, but sportsmanlike, rival who led the cheering, though the disappointment must have been bitter.

The night flight of Grahame-White certainly provided the most dramatic feature of the race. He had indeed made an extraordinarily plucky attempt to overtake the Frenchman, and with but a little good fortune to help him he might have succeeded. At the moment when he landed at Polesworth only a dozen miles or so separated him from Paulhan, who, being delayed by some necessary engine adjustments, did not leave Lichfield until 4.09 a. m.

After a few anxious moments while clearing the hedge surrounding the narrow field in which he had alighted the evening before, Paulhan set off northwards, following the railway, and keeping pace more or less with the special train in attendance. The wind, though favourable, blew very gustily, and the Farman was seen to pitch and roll about a good deal. More than once before he reached his destination the airman, who had not troubled to take his map with him for the second stage, went astray and had to circle about to pick up the guiding marks.

All along the line excitement ran high. Stafford and Crewe were alive with enthusiasts, and at one point was observed near the line a man in nightcap, nightshirt, and a pair of slippers, blue with cold but rendered quite unconscious of both discomfort and appearances by the sight of Paulhan speeding overhead.

At Didsbury, a southern suburb of Manchester, where the flight was to end, thousands of people had collected to witness the finish. It became known that Grahame-White had started in the dark; then that he had passed Rugby, Nuneaton, and Atherstone. Paulhan still lingered at Lichfield, so things looked like a level race between the Englishman and the Frenchman. What more was needed to put everyone on the tip-toe of expectation? Naturally enough, the majority wanted their countryman to win, all the more earnestly because of his determined and risky effort to make good the ground lost on the previous day. Presently the telegraph wires announced that Paulhan had started.

Excitement became almost painful. He was at Sandbach; at Crewe; but no further news of Grahame-White.

Suddenly, low down against the grey clouds to the south appeared a tiny speck, and about the same time steamed in the special train known to be accompanying the Frenchman. "Paulhan!" shouted the crowd, in which disappointment at the defeat of their favourite quickly yielded to the desire to give a rousing welcome to the victor, whatever his nationality might be. Over a wildly cheering mass of humanity the aeroplane swept; then it curved round and floated gracefully towards the earth, on which a perfect landing was made at 5.32 a. m. The 183 miles had been covered in 242 minutes of flying.

Thus ended what may perhaps be regarded as the most exciting episode in human flight. Its sporting character, combined with the fact that it began and ended in two great centres of population widely separated, probably did more to stimulate public interest in aviation and make nations realise the possibilities of mechanical flight, than all previous events in the history of aviation put together. Blériot's cross-Channel flight, witnessed by but a few, took the public by surprise: they cheered the aviator for his flight, not the flight itself. The London to Manchester contest, on the other hand, was witnessed by hundreds of thousands at one place or another, and could have been made more exciting than it actually was only by a neck-and-neck finish at the winning-post.

CHAPTER 12

A SPLENDID FAILURE

WHAT may without hesitation be written down as the most dramatic incident of aviation up to the present time was due to the offer, by the *Daily Mail*, in 1913, of a prize of £10,000 to the crew of the first aeroplane which flew the Atlantic. The flight was to be made from any point in the British Isles to any point in Newfoundland, Canada, or the United States or in the reverse direction; and it must be completed within 72 consecutive hours. Machines might not be changed during a flight, though repairs *en route* were permissible (this assumed that seaplanes might be used); and the flight had to be direct, not in sections by way of the Azores. Since an intermediate descent in mid-ocean would for an aeroplane mean the end of the attempt, and an aeroplane, on account of its greater lightness, would be preferred to the cumbersome seaplane, the feat practically resolved itself into a non-stop flight of at least 1,880 miles—the distance separating Newfoundland from the nearest point of Ireland.

The success of an attempt would depend mainly on three conditions. First, the engine, or engines, must be capable of running many hours on end. Second, the course steered must be approximately straight, as inaccurate navigation might easily add hundreds of miles to the journey. Third, the weather must be suitable, for the direction of the wind would be a very important factor; while calm, clear weather would make the chances of reaching the goal much better than would cloudy or stormy.

The third condition, being quite beyond human control, presented the greatest difficulties. The Atlantic is so vast that hardly ever is it entirely free from clouds, fog or storms, and reports wirelessed from one part of it may be quite at variance with reports from another region some hundreds of miles away. Furthermore, even if a report covering the whole of the route were obtainable, the duration of the flight would give ample time for change while the aeroplane was in the air. The pilot in any case would therefore have to take considerable risks as regards the weather.

The great weight of fuel needed for a crossing in one "leap" added considerably to the difficulty of the enterprise. Though this weight would decrease steadily during the journey, it fixed the power needed by the engines at the start, and during the earlier stages of the voyage especially would be an adverse factor.

Until after the Great War nothing was done to win the prize and at the same time achieve a feat which would, more than any aeronautical exploit yet carried through, bring honour and glory to the winners. Though aviation had advanced by leaps and bounds during the war, as regards both the quality of engines and aeroplanes and the capacity and skill of pilots, the great Atlantic still offered a worthy challenge to the most daring airman and the most perfect machine. To leap into the air on one side of the ocean, trust oneself to the even more boundless ocean of air and to the unnumbered chances of a flight that must be partly through darkness, and finally, if fortune favoured, to alight in another land nearly two thousand miles away—surely here was something to stir the blood and steel the determination of every first-class aviator!

A SPLENDID FAILURE

In 1919 entrants for the flight appeared. The first, or one of the first, was a young Australian, Mr. Harry Hawker, who already had to his credit many fine records, and held a leading place among the Empire's airmen. During the war he had been associated with the Sopwith Aviation Company, which, early in the year mentioned, offered to build an aeroplane specially for a transatlantic flight if Hawker would fly it. This offer was accepted.

The aeroplane, suitably named the *Atlantic*, was a biplane with a single 350-h.p. Rolls-Royce engine. Its weight at the start, with fuel, water, and crew of two aboard, was estimated at about 2¾ tons. The undercarriage, weighing about 450 lbs., was made detachable, so that it might be dropped as soon as the aeroplane had fairly got away from the land: while the upper part of the body took the form of a detachable boat of three-ply wood, inverted, which might prove useful if a descent had to be made into the Atlantic.

For his navigator Hawker selected Lt.-Commander Kenneth Mackenzie-Grieve, R.N. With him he made a trial non-stop flight of 1,800 miles at Brooklands Aerodrome, to prove that they and the machine could stay the distance. It must be admitted that flying round and round an aerodrome in good weather contained few of the risks lurking in a transatlantic journey.

Hawker and his companion, who decided to fly from west to east, arrived by ship with their aeroplane in St. John's Newfoundland, at the end of March, 1919. Their plan was to start on or about April 16, when the moon would be at the full. Leaving at 10 p. m. (Greenwich time) they calculated on reaching Ireland the following afternoon, if all went well. The country round St. John's was very unsuitable for establishing an aerodrome, and the mere transport of the machine to

CONQUERING THE AIR

Mount Pearl Farm, finally selected, proved a very difficult business, owing to the shocking condition of the roads. The ground of the aerodrome itself, being undrained, quickly became soft after a fall of rain or snow: and altogether conditions were very far from ideal. On one occasion the aeroplane narrowly escaped crashing on the trees surrounding the aerodrome.

While the two awaited favourable weather a rival machine, a Martynside, reached St. John's and prepared for making the transatlantic flight—a circumstance which rendered the first-comers all the more eager to be off. Each crew now had to keep a friendly watch on the other and maintain its machine in instant readiness for a start. Day after day passed, with the weather reports consistently unfavourable. The only prudent course was to be patient, as a heavy storm encountered in mid-Atlantic might well have disastrous results.

April 16 came, and with it a heavy fall of snow. On April 18 the morning opened well, but later on a storm blew up. Again and again, before the end of the month, hopes alternately rose and fell. When April gave way to May, and the aeroplanes still remained weather-bound, the public as well as the airmen became impatient, and the former began to doubt whether a flight would ever take place.

But everything comes to him who waits. By May 18 the weather had improved, though it might easily have been better, and Hawker determined to start at once, because three American flying boats had left the United States for Europe, via the Azores, on the 16th, and Lt.-Commander Read had actually reached those islands. A few days' more delay might rob the Empire of the chance to make the first flight from the New World to the Old.

At 3 p. m. Hawker and Mackenzie-Grieve got into their flying clothes, the outermost layer of which consisted of a rubber suit with inflatable air-bags back and front which would sustain the airmen if they fell into the water. In the boat already referred to had been stowed emergency rations of water, paddles, and coloured lights for signalling; while the body of the aeroplane itself contained coffee in thermos flasks, sandwiches, cheese, and various foods in compressed form. Aboard, too, were a small wireless transmitting set and a number of letters, including one from the Governor of Newfoundland to His Majesty King George V.

At 5.51 p. m. (Greenwich time) the Sopwith biplane rose from its aerodrome, speeding down the slope of Mount Pearl Farm for the last time. Heavily weighted with the full load of 350 gallons of petrol it narrowly escaped hitting the fence at the downhill end. A few inches lower, and the flight would have ended abruptly.

In a minute or two the aeroplane soared over the suburbs of St. John's, and Hawker, looking down, had the satisfaction of seeing the rival Martynside machine still on the ground. Seawards could be descried several great icebergs. Soon afterwards a lever was pulled, and the undercarriage, which had now done its work, went hurtling earthwards, while the aeroplane, relieved of its weight and air-resistance, began to climb quickly, and soon passed out of the sight of the many watchers.

The flight had now fairly begun. Almost immediately after leaving land the aeroplane entered the thick fog stratum which for a good part of the year overhangs the Newfoundland Banks and is a serious menace to shipping. More fortunate than ships, however, the Sopwith soon climbed above the fog, stretching like a great white table on all sides, and completely cutting off a view of the sea. Over this stratum the aeroplane sped due east for four hours, by the end of which the navigator calculated its position to be 400 miles from St. John's and above the main steamship track.

Conditions now became worse. With the approach of night a storm arose. Rain squalls lashed the aeroplane and its brave crew. Ominous clouds gathered in the path to be followed, and the wind blew briskly from the north. This was disappointing, as a side wind made it necessary to fly a bit sideways, head to wind, with loss of forward speed. But so long as the machine remained aloft, with plenty of space between it and the water, there was no cause for serious alarm.

When they were about five hours "out," Hawker noticed that the thermometer connected with the radiator showed abnormally high readings. Now, if everything is in order, the temperature of the cooling water should remain more or less constant, well below boiling point. This unexpected rise, as indicating something to be amiss with the circulation, was a legitimate reason for uneasiness; for while the aeroplane was in flight nothing could be done to remedy the trouble. The reader may bear it in mind that, though the air is very cold at great elevations, its pressure is also low, and the boiling point of water correspondingly so. Thus, at a height of 10,000 feet the latter is 193° F. as against 212° F. at sea level. For the water to boil would be absolutely fatal, since the loss of water as steam would eventually cause the engine to become too hot to continue working.

As the aeroplane advanced through the night the temperature of the water rose gradually to 170° F., at which it remained stationary for a time. Observations made with the help of the stars showed a southwards drift of 150 miles out of the course laid down, and the aeroplane had to be headed north-east to recover its proper line. By diving seawards quickly and repeatedly, Hawker endeavoured to clear away the obstruction in the radiator, and for a time with success; so that, though the airmen were worried, they did not doubt being able to reach their destination. To reduce heating, the engine was throttled down to "cruising" speed, and height limited to 12,000 feet.

But presently another storm, and another great bank of thick clouds, reaching skyward 15,000 feet, loomed ahead. To avoid the clouds Hawker tried to get above them, with the result that the radiator boiled furiously, throwing out steam that immediately became ice. Something else must be done; so the aeroplane was headed seawards to an elevation of 6,000 feet, where the darkness became thicker than ever. The aeroplane dropped still lower, with engine throttled down, till only 1,000 feet above the water. To Hawker's dismay, when he opened the throttle the engine failed to respond. All seemed lost, but within a few feet of the ocean the welcome roar began again, and the situation was saved. But it had been a narrow escape!

By now (5 a. m.) the dawn was beginning to show, greatly to the delight of the two men, for with daylight came greater safety. So far as could be ascertained by observation, some 950 miles had been covered, at an average speed of about 85 miles an hour; and the greater part of the journey lay behind them. But the radiator trouble had now reached a stage at which it became evident that a descent into the Atlantic was but a matter of time. It remained only to locate a ship, if possible, before the plunge occurred. The chance was a feeble one, for even on the main routes ships are very far apart; and unless the aeroplane were actually sighted by a ship while still in the air and able to make its presence known by the roar of the engines, the likelihood of being picked up was very small indeed.

CONQUERING THE AIR

To get the right dramatic effect, let us now leave the airmen and switch our attention elsewhere.

The fact of the start from Newfoundland was known all the world over within a few hours, and people opened their papers next morning expecting that some news of the aeroplane's progress would be recorded. Not a word. As the day wore on, and the time by which a landing should have been made in Ireland had passed, anxiety began to be felt. During the evening a false report of the aeroplane having fallen in the sea close to the Irish coast was contradicted. When day after day elapsed without bringing any reason for thinking the contrary, the public, which on both sides of the Atlantic was deeply interested in the plucky attempt, definitely gave up Hawker and his navigator as lost somewhere in the vast expanse of the Atlantic. On May 24 Mrs. Hawker received a telegram of sympathy from the King.

At 10.55 a. m. on the next day, a Sunday, two coastguards at Lloyds' signal station on the Butt of Lewis observed a small steamer standing in to signal. Up fluttered the flags giving her name—the *Mary* of Copenhagen; followed by another hoist signifying "Communicate by Wire." Then came four hoists indicating "Saved hands," and five more which spelled out "Sopwith Aeroplane." So excited were the coastguardsmen by news which they knew would electrify the country, that the *Mary* was almost out of signalling range before they thought of making certainty sure. Then flags fluttered up on their mast asking "Is it Hawker?" Back came the answering signal "Yes!"

Without the loss of a moment the news was started over the telegraph wires to Lloyds in London, where it arrived within the hour.

Now let us put back the clock six days. Finding that a

descent was inevitable, Hawker zigzagged about for over two hours, hunting for a ship. The wind tossed the aeroplane and lashed the Atlantic into big waves, extremely uninviting to behold. Rain and fog made it very difficult to see anything, but at last Hawker spied a vessel. After flying round this till it was certain that the men aboard had seen them, the airmen flew ahead of the *Mary* a mile or two and allowed the Sopwith to take the water. The waves smashed the top planes, and broke over the machine, but did not sink it. The airmen detached their boat, and waited for the *Mary* to come up. With much difficulty she launched a boat, which eventually got alongside and took off Hawker and Mackenzie-Grieve, but absolutely nothing else.

When picked up at 8 a. m. on May 19, they were 1,050 miles from Newfoundland. The master of the *Mary*, Captain Duhn, told them that his vessel was not equipped with wireless, so he could not inform their friends of their rescue; but that probably they would fall in with a ship carrying wireless. This, however, they did not do, and the first news of their escape from drowning reached the world in the manner described.

At the time of their descent half of the petrol supply remained in the tanks, and they were on their course. But for the radiator trouble, they would probably have reached Ireland. That a few detached fragments of solder should have brought so splendid a venture to nothing was the hardest of hard luck. On the other hand, that at the critical moment the crippled aeroplane should have fallen in with a ship amid the waste of waters was a piece of extraordinarily good fortune. But for the providential fact of the small Danish ship being in latitude 50° 20′, longitude 29° 30′, that Monday morning, it is a thousand chances to one that the Atlantic would have added two more to the names of its countless victims.

CONQUERING THE AIR

So completely had the public abandoned all hope of the airmen being picked up that the news of their rescue thrilled the country. In London it seemed as if everybody were a personal friend of the recovered airmen, so gladly were the tidings received. Total strangers shouted the news to one another across the street or shook hands in congratulation; in crowded cafés there were cheers and joyous demonstrations; church bells rang; preachers referred to the event from the pulpit; official quarters were besieged by inquiries after further news. Altogether, London gave itself up to rejoicing, and spent what has been described as one of the cheeriest days since the Armistice. And nowhere was it more heartfelt than at Surbiton, Harry Hawker's home, which blossomed out into flags, while people flocked to congratulate the airman's wife, who had never lost hope that her husband would be restored to her. Among other congratulations were telegrams from the King and from Queen Alexandra.

About 4 p. m. the rescued airmen were transferred from the *Mary* to a destroyer sent out to meet them from Scapa Flow, and later in the evening were received aboard H.M.S. *Revenge*, Admiral Fremantle's flagship. The next day, Monday, May 26, a destroyer landed them at Thurso, the northern terminus of the Highland Railway. Here began a veritable triumphal progress such as probably has fallen to the lot of but few men. Wherever the train stopped on its long journey to London, people crowded the platforms to catch sight of the airmen, or, if lucky enough, to shake them by the hand. Address after address of welcome was read by the representatives of local authorities, pipers blew their hardest, cheers shook the smoke-begrimed roofs of the stations. Even the dwellers in lonely cottages along the route waved greetings as the train passed. At Perth, which was reached at 5 a. m. the earliness of the

PLATE VI

H.M.S. *Furious*, naval aircraft carrier. She has a very large and quite unobstructed deck, from which aeroplanes rise, and on which they can alight. The "funnel" is horizontal, and discharges below the deck at the stern. [*Photo, Central News.*

hour did not prevent a crowd of thousands awaiting the arrival of the train. Edinburgh, Newcastle, Darlington, York, Grantham (where Mrs. Hawker joined the train) carried on the welcome, which culminated when at last, on Tuesday, the train entered King's Cross Station, where an enormous crowd had gathered. A force of some 300 Australian soldiers simply fell upon Hawker and his companion and shouldered them to the former's big car, which, not content with towing, they began to carry. To save his car from destruction, Hawker crawled over the heads of the crowd on to a police officer's horse, and this brought him to the Royal Aero Club in Clifford Street. The crowds outside the building eventually became so dense that the two airmen had to make use of a sidedoor and the services of some mounted police, in order to get away to their homes.

On the following day the two airmen went to Buckingham Palace, where the King bestowed on them, in recognition of their gallantry, the Royal Air Force Cross, a decoration which the strict letter of the law reserved for members of the R. A. F. Any technical difficulties standing in the way of its presentation to the two airmen were, we are told, removed at His Majesty's express request.

Two days later, at a luncheon given in their honour, a "scrap of paper" in the form of a cheque for £5,000, was handed to Hawker and Mackenzie-Grieve by General Seely on behalf of the *Daily Mail*,—a very generous consolation prize.

The flight had failed, but under conditions that rendered failure even more dramatic than success. It may well be doubted whether a safe arrival in Ireland would have been followed by demonstrations half as impressive as those which welcomed Harry Hawker and his companion back, as it were, from the dead.

Only one incident remains to be recorded. On Friday, May 23, the American steamer *Lake Charlotteville* sighted a strange object in mid Atlantic. This proved to be the Sopwith aeroplane, with only its tail and the rear part of the body projecting from the water. The machine was hoisted aboard by winches, and lashed to the deck; and search was made for the crew, whose rescue of course was not yet known of. During the voyage to Falmouth rough weather added to the damage which the machine had suffered before it was picked up, and by the time it reached England it little resembled the fine construction which had risen from the aerodrome in Newfoundland. Its recovery nevertheless gave great satisfaction to everyone concerned. The undercarriage dropped near St. John's was, it may be added, found and placed in a museum.

CHAPTER 13

THE FIRST CROSSING OF THE ATLANTIC BY AIR

EARLY in 1919 the United States Navy Department put in hand preparations for attempting the crossing of the Atlantic Ocean by flying boats. Nothing was to be left to chance; and, if organisation could ensure success, the attempt would be successful.

The route selected was from Trepassey Bay, in Newfoundland, to the Azores, and thence to Lisbon. To round off the enterprise, the actual ending of the flight would be at Plymouth, from which port, 300 years earlier, the Pilgrim Fathers had sailed in the *Mayflower*. The flight would thus fall into three main parts: Newfoundland to the Azores; the Azores to Lisbon; Lisbon to England; a total distance of 3,130 miles, of which the first "hop" would account for nearly 1,400 miles. Any idea of a non-stop flight from the New World to the Old was definitely ruled out. For one thing, the fuel capacity of the machines selected for the work was not equal to a distance approaching 3,000 miles.

The three flying-boats chosen were of the NC (Navy-Curtiss) class, and were numbered respectively NC1, NC3, NC4. A fourth ship (NC2) had to be withdrawn.

These NC's were biplanes, with a span of 126 feet, a length of 68 feet 3½ inches, and an overall height of 24½ feet. The hull of the boat body measured 44½ by 10 by 7½ feet, and was divided by bulkheads into six quite separate compartments.

CONQUERING THE AIR

The bow compartment contained the navigator's cockpit. Immediately behind it came that in which two pilots sat side by side, with duplicate controls, so that the duty of piloting might be instantly transferred from the one man to the other. The next two chambers housed the fuel and oil tanks; and in the stern was the wireless operator's cabin. When fully loaded, and with its crew aboard, an NC scaled $12\frac{1}{2}$ tons.

So weighty a craft needed a great deal of power to drive it along at a high speed. Accordingly four 400-h.p. "Liberty" engines were provided; two "tandem" over the hull, turning a tractor and a pusher air-screw; one to port; and one to starboard; the two last each revolving a tractor screw. Three engines sufficed to maintain flight; while the great size of the hull fitted the machine for riding out rough weather on the water, if necessity demanded.

To guide the flying-boats and render them assistance in case of trouble, American destroyers were stationed at regular intervals of about 60 miles along the route between Newfoundland and the Azores; while British warships did similar duty between the Azores and Lisbon. As the machines carried high-power wireless installations, it would be easy for their crews to keep in touch with the ships and receive reports of the weather and atmospheric conditions ahead of them.

The three craft left Rockaway, on Long Island, New York, on May 8, for Halifax. NC4 had engine trouble and had to put in at Chatham, New Brunswick, for repairs. NC1 and NC3 reached Halifax safely the same day, and two days later flew to Trepassey Bay, the "jumping-off" point. Here the NC4 rejoined them on May 15, and the next day they started together on the great adventure, at 10.05 p. m., Greenwich time.

Lieut.-Commander A. C. Read, in charge of the NC4, relates that at first the ships flew over icebergs, with the wind astern and smooth water below. This craft and the NC3 kept more or less together for an hour or so, when the NC4 drew ahead so much that at the first mark ship she circled round to give the other time to catch up. In the course of the next hour the NC4 got ahead again, and finally lost sight of the lights on her consort. The NC1 had fallen astern early in the flight. So that after the first two hours the NC4 proceeded as if alone.

The darkness of the night was presently relieved by the rising moon: and as visibility improved the air became so "bumpy" that the elevation was increased from 800 to 1,800 feet above the water. Any sense of isolation was prevented by the string of destroyers, which in turn sent up star shells, visible many miles away, and used their searchlights to guide the airmen. Some of the warships were in their correct positions, others some miles off the line, so that the course had to be changed frequently as the NC4 picked its way from one ship to another.

At 12.41 a. m. the NC4 passed destroyer No. 4, her speed having so far averaged 90 knots. Five hours later the dawn came, and the worst part of the voyage might be considered over. The engines were running well, and the wireless apparatus aboard picked up messages transmitted from over 1,300 miles away. Information received reported the NC3 to be astern, and the NC1 behind her.

A merchant ship came in sight at 6.55 a. m., and at 8 o'clock the NC4 ran through some light wisps of fog, suggesting possible trouble ahead. By 9.45 a. m. the fog was so thick that the pilot lost all sense of direction, and the plane began to get out of hand a bit until the sudden reappearance of the sun made it possible to put things right again. The boat was now raised to 3,400 feet, and flew between the fog and the clouds, occasionally altering course and altitude to dodge both. Inquiries by wireless brought in reports of low-lying fog, very thick; then of the fog thinning. At 11.27 a. m. the observer caught a glimpse through a rift in the fog of what looked like surf, and a couple of minutes afterwards rocks were sighted at the southern end of Flores Island, the most westerly of the Azores group—"the most welcome sight we had ever seen." Owing to the fog the NC4 had strayed 45 miles from its course, as a north-west wind had been blowing since their last observation.

The flying boat dropped almost to the shore, rounded a point, and presently picked up destroyer No. 22, the first to be sighted since No. 16. As plenty of petrol remained in the tanks, Commander Read decided to make for Ponta Delgada, in St. Michael, the largest island. The fog closed down, however, and this made a landing at Horta, in Fayal, advisable. The flying boat alighted in that port at 1.23 p. m., on May 17, having covered 1,380 miles in 15 hours 17 minutes of flying time at an average speed of 81.7 knots.

The NC1 and NC3 had both fared badly. NC1 lost her bearings in the fog and alighted 200 miles west of the Azores. Her crew was picked up; and the flying boat was taken in tow; but after 80 miles of towing had to be abandoned. NC3, under Commander Towers, had more remarkable experiences. Owing to failure of the lights on the instrument board, the pilot had to fly above the clouds to take observations by the stars. After failing to pick up several of the mark boats, Commander Towers decided to alight for observations, as fuel was running short. Too late, he discovered the sea to be very rough. The NC3 struck the water heavily, and received injuries which prevented her rising again. A gale blew up, and the flying boat was called upon to give an exhibition of her seaworthy qualities. She rode the gale out with the loss of her port wing float, and in this crippled condition "taxied" over the water 205 miles to Ponta Delgada, which she reached on May 19, losing her starboard float as she entered the harbour. It was a fine piece of seamanship; but it did not prevent NC3 from having to retire from the expedition.

After a rest of 3 days, Commander Read flew from Horta to Ponta Delgada, where a week was spent in preparations for the second long "hop"—from the Azores to Lisbon. This was made successfully on May 27, the 800 miles being covered, thanks to a stern wind, in 9 hours 25 minutes. Fourteen mark boats were out, so that the pilots had no difficulty in finding their way. A warm welcome awaited the NC4 at Lisbon, the first point in the Old World to be reached by air from the New. May 27, 1919, is a very important date in the history of aeronautics.

On May 30 the NC4 left Lisbon for Ferrol, 340 miles away, *en route* to England. A leak in one of the engines brought the machine down to the water for adjustments, after which she proceeded on her way and reached the Spanish port safely. Next day the great flying boat set out on her last jump, of 420 miles, to Plymouth. She headed across the Bay of Biscay, climbing to a height of 1,500 feet. Only two destroyers were sighted, and on all sides a mist blotted out the horizon. Near Brest fog and rain made things rather unpleasant, and after passing the Ushant Lightship it was necessary to come down almost on to the sea to see the water. But before the English coast was approached the air cleared, and presently a dark smudge visible far ahead told the crew that their goal was in sight. Shortly before 2 p. m. Commander Read was able to distinguish clearly the shores of Devon and Cornwall, and soon afterwards he passed over the great breakwater at the entrance to Plymouth Sound, amid a storm of cheers from the crowds lining the shore, and the shrieking of the sirens and whistles of the many ships in the harbour. A few hundred yards astern of the NC4 came three British seaplanes which had gone out to escort the American airmen.

The NC4 circled the harbour, and, with engines stopped, glided down on to the water close to the Barbican. The great flight was at an end.

CHAPTER 14

A MAGNIFICENT SUCCESS

THE Atlantic had now been crossed for the first time by heavier-than-air machines. But the achievement of the American airmen in their flying boat still left the *Daily Mail* prize to be won by a direct dash across the ocean.

While Hawker waited to start from Newfoundland, a third entrant for the prize was on its way by ship from England: a Vickers-Vimy standard bombing aeroplane, modified to render it more suitable for carrying through a transatlantic flight. The military fittings had been removed, and the capacity of the petrol tanks increased from 516 to 865 gallons, sufficient for a range of 2,440 miles, or 30 per cent in excess of the minimum distance to be flown. The machine was equipped with two 350-h.p. Rolls-Royce "Eagle" engines, either of which would suffice to maintain flight when half the petrol had been consumed.

As pilot was chosen Capt. John Alcock, D. S. C., and as navigator Lieut. A. Whitten Brown, R.A.F.,—the latter being of American parentage. The war records of both these airmen indicated them as an excellent pair for undertaking the flight.

The aeroplane and crew reached St. John's at midnight on Saturday, May 24, 1919. On the 26th. the machine was unloaded and removed to the cricket field at Quidi Vidi, selected as the aerodrome. The large hangar to house it not having arrived, the parts were assembled in the open, protected from the winds only by temporary screens. For some days operations had to be suspended on account of bad weather. On June 9 a trial flight was made and, but for some trouble with the wireless installation, everything seemed to be in good order. A second trial on June 12 proved quite satisfactory, so the aeroplane was then filled up ready for the start. Bearing the cause of Mr. Hawker's failure in mind, Capt. Alcock determined to leave nothing to chance. Every drop of water used in the machine was filtered, then boiled, and passed through a strainer into the tanks: while the petrol received equally thorough treatment. By the evening of June 13 everything was ready for an early start on the morning of the following day. A strong wind, blowing obliquely across the aerodrome, upset these plans, however; and the day was well advanced before a shift of the wind to the west, and favourable weather reports—coupled, it is said, with a rumour that a rival Handley-Page machine was about to start from Harbour Grace—decided Alcock to get away without further loss of time. After a final meal had been taken under the aeroplane wings, the engines were started for the last time, and as soon as they had warmed up, Captain Alcock gave the signal to remove the chocks under the wheels. The engines were now opened out full, and at 4.28 p. m. (Greenwich time) the machine began to move into the wind, on a surface running slightly uphill and not in very good condition. For a few moments it looked as if the heavily-laden Vimy (it weighed 13,500 lbs.) would not clear the obstructions at the end of the aerodrome, but fears were allayed when it "zoomed" over a fence and began to climb steadily. To the spectators it appeared as if the machine were in trouble when a hill suddenly concealed it. A few minutes later it was seen again, with its tail now well up and travelling at high speed, helped by half a gale blowing astern. Taking the same course over St. John's as that followed a few weeks earlier by

Hawker's Sopwith, it steered south-south-east over the ice floes near the coast and soon disappeared from sight.

The stern wind was of great assistance, as it added some 30 miles an hour to the cruising speed of 90 miles an hour: and in this respect Alcock and Brown had a great advantage over Hawker and Mackenzie-Grieve. As regards visibility they were, if anything worse off. Almost as soon as they cleared the land they ran into the fog stratum overlying the Banks, and climbing above this were shut in between it and clouds. Except for a very occasional glimpse, both sea and sky were entirely blocked out during the first seven hours of flight; and only on four occasions during the whole voyage could Brown take an observation.

As night approached and the light failed conditions became worse. The clouds and fog thickened, and eventually enveloped the aeroplane so thoroughly that all sense of direction was lost. The speed indicator, which by a sudden increase in the reading informs the pilot when his machine is diving, had ceased to function, and a "spin" which began at an elevation of about 4,000 feet carried the aeroplane down very close to the water, the sight of which enabled Alcock to get the Vimy under control again. Had the fog been thicker, the spin would probably have ended disastrously.

The propeller operating the wireless transmitting outfit had broken off very early in the journey, and as the receiving apparatus was badly "jammed" by signals not intended for the airmen, no assistance in finding their way came in from outside. The great need was therefore to get above the clouds, where the moon and stars would give valuable help. As they rose to a height of 7,000 feet, the moon showed itself two or three times, but not long enough for any readings to be obtained. The dawn found the Vimy still forcing its way through great banks of clouds too high to be surmounted. For five or six hours more conditions remained very unpleasant. Sleet and snow choked the radiator shutters, obscured the petrol gauge, and kept the speed indicator out of commission. A momentary peep over the edge of the cockpit, by exposing the face to the sleet, proved a very painful experiment.

The Vimy was pushed up steadily till it reached 11,000 feet, but without eluding the clouds. The navigator at last managed to fix the position, which, to their great satisfaction, was not far from the Irish coast. The airmen then decided to descend much lower in the hope of obtaining better visibility; but clear air was not met with until the aeroplane almost reached the water. Flying low, they were presently gladdened by the sight of the two small islands of Eeshal and Turbot, though the mainland lay hidden behind low clouds and drifting rain until they were actually over it. Ten minutes later the masts of Clifden wireless station suddenly appeared. Round these they circled, firing off Vérey coloured lights, but without receiving any reply. What was more disappointing, no suitable landing place could be seen in the neighbourhood, until, after some hunting, they spotted what looked like a very suitable green field. We may imagine the feelings of relief with which the Vimy was directed towards this and the completion of the journey. Alas! The "field" turned out to be a treacherous bog, into which the wheels sank, causing the aeroplane to turn over and bury its nose in it, damaging itself but, fortunately, neither pilot nor navigator.

The journey ended at 8.40 a. m. on Sunday, June 15, approximately sixteen hours after the start. The engines, which ran faultlessly throughout, had, with the help of the wind, sent the aeroplane along at an average rate of 118 miles an hour—

the highest speed that had yet been maintained during a journey of equal length.

Proud, indeed, must Alcock and Brown have felt as, stiffened with cold, and half deafened by the continuous roar of the engines—one of which had shed its exhaust pipe—they climbed out of the good craft that had brought them safely from the New World to the Old. A few crowded hours of glorious, if anxious, life lay behind them, success was with them, and a great reward in front of them.

Hardly had they landed when the operators at the Marconi station hurried up, supposing them to be the crew of an aeroplane sent out to watch for the airmen. On the true state of things becoming known, congratulations and cheers were heard on all sides and little time was lost in telegraphing the glad news to England.

At first some incredulity was shown, for the rapidity with which the flight had been accomplished seemed almost beyond belief. All doubts, however, soon gave way to universal expressions of pleasure that a feat of such magnitude had been achieved.

It hardly need be said that a great welcome awaited the victors on their way to, and after their arrival in, London; though not quite so overwhelming, perhaps, as that accorded to Hawker and Grieve, for the circumstances were less dramatic. The heroes of the day at least received, in the form of handshaking, cheers, and congratulations, all that the heart of man could desire, before they were free to make for their own homes. At a luncheon given in the airmen's honour, Mr. Winston Churchill, Secretary of State for War, crystallised into words what, in a more or less vague form, a great many people were thinking.

"In 1492 Christopher Columbus sailed across the Atlantic

and discovered America. I cannot help feeling that this afternoon we are to some extent in contact with that event, and that when we welcome our guests, the heroes of today, who have come back from the other side, come to us from America in something less than 16 hours—we are in the presence of another event of something like the same order as that stupendous event which revealed to Europe and Asia the boundless glories and possibilities of the new world across the Atlantic ocean. How different were those two voyages in all except two conditions—the peril and the pluck: otherwise the difference presents the most violent contrast that could be imagined. In the case of Columbus it occupied 90 days to traverse that immense expanse of waters, and our guests today have come back across the ocean in less than 16 hours; but into those 16 hours were crammed the concentrated perils which required the same great human qualities as were exhibited in that long earlier voyage of ancient times.

"It is more than 400 years since Columbus discovered America, it is only ten since Blériot flew the English Channel. . . . Think of the broad Atlantic, that terrible waste of desolate waters, tossing in tumult in repeated and almost ceaseless storms, and shrouded with an unbroken canopy of mist. Across this waste, and through this obscurity, two human beings, hurtling through the air, piercing the cloud and darkness, finding their unerring path in spite of every difficulty to their exact objective across those hundreds of miles, arriving almost on schedule time, and at every moment in this voyage liable to destruction from a drop of water in the carburettor, or a spot of oil on their plugs, or a tiny grain of dirt in their feed pipe, or from any of the other hundred and one indirect causes which in the present state of aeronautics might drag an aeroplane to its fate.

A MAGNIFICENT SUCCESS

"When one considers all these factors I really do not know what we should admire the most in our guests—their audacity, their determination, their skill, their science, their Vimy-Vickers aeroplane, their Rolls-Royce engines, or their good fortune. All these were necessary, and all of them contributed to their achievement, and to the event which brought us all together here this afternoon, to cheer the victors of the first non-stop Atlantic flight."

Before closing his speech Mr. Churchill announced that His Majesty had assented to the immediate award of the Knight-Commandership of the Order of the British Empire to both Captain Alcock and Lieutenant Brown.

The Vickers aeroplane, which had done its work so splendidly, was extricated from the bog, and sent to London. The makers presented it to the Nation as an object of historical interest, and it may now be seen in the Science Museum, South Kensington.

At the end of the flight the petrol remaining in the tanks was estimated as sufficient for another 800 miles travel. If the landing had been on hard ground it would therefore have been perfectly feasible for the airmen to reach London by air,—as indeed probably would have been done but for the accident. The aeroplane as a whole was found to be in excellent order, and the engines in remarkably good condition. These had each turned 1,600,000 times during the flight, and every one of the twenty-four pistons had travelled up and down in its cylinder a distance of over 360 miles, giving a total piston travel of 8,640 miles, or just one-third of a circuit of the globe!

This flight may frankly be regarded as a "stunt" performance, wherein it differed from the thoroughly organised preceding flight of the American NC4, and the subsequent voyage of the R34 airship. It has never yet been duplicated, and may not be for years to come. But as a demonstration of what could be done in the air it had a great effect in rousing the whole world to the possibilities of aviation, and so expediting the organisation of the civil aviation traffic of today.

CHAPTER 15

TO NEW YORK AND BACK BY AIRSHIP

THE double crossing of the Atlantic in the early days of July, 1919, by an airship may well rank in history with the first crossing of the same ocean just a century earlier by a steamship, the *Savannah*. The "herring pond" had already been traversed the same year by a seaplane and an aeroplane, feats entailing even greater risks than those of an airship's voyage. The voyage to be described was a deliberate and highly organised experiment designed to gather valuable information regarding atmospheric conditions over the Atlantic and to blaze the trail for a regular trans-ocean airship service. To quote the *Times*, it was to Sir John Alcock's flight as the running of a Great Northern express to Dick Turpin's ride to York.

The airship chosen for the trip was the "rigid" R34, which then shared with her sister, the R33, the distinction of being the largest British airship. She was completed in 1918, just after the end of the war. Her length was 645 feet, her maximum diameter 78¾ feet, and the united capacity of her 18 gas-bags about 2,000,000 cubic feet. When fully inflated with hydrogen gas, the airship had a useful "lift" of 30 tons, which could be distributed among the crew, the fuel for the engines, stores, water, cargo, and ballast.

Below the body of the airship were five enclosed cars or gondolas; two near the bows, one behind the other; two amidships, one on either side; and a central one further astern. The most forward car was reserved exclusively for navigation purposes and corresponded to the "bridge" of a ship. The other four housed between them five petrol engines developing 270 horsepower each. With all the engines running at once, the R34 could attain a speed of over 60 miles an hour in still air. As a precaution in case of the forward car being damaged, the rearmost car contained a duplicate set of control gears, so that, if necessary, the whole work of navigation could be conducted from it. The ship was equipped with electric lighting throughout, a telephone and voice-tube installation, and a long-range wireless apparatus.

A great girder running from end to end of the framework, at the bottom, inside the outer covering, served both as a stiffening keel and a corridor giving communication between one part of the airship and another. It also acted as crew's quarters, hammocks being slung along the sides, and in it were located the tanks for petrol and water ballast. As the R34 had been designed for military purposes, the living accommodation was not, of course, such as would be needed on an aerial passenger liner.

After completion the airship underwent an endurance test lasting 19 hours, during which she flew from the banks of the Clyde down over Ireland and back over the west coast of England. On being "passed" and handed over to the Admiralty, R34 made a notable long-distance flight along the German coast and over the Baltic. She left the shed at East Fortune (near Edinburgh) on the evening of June 17, and alighted there 56 hours later, after covering 2,400 miles. This performance justified preparations being made for the even longer voyage, which was to begin on July 2, as the weather records of the North Atlantic showed that atmospheric conditions were likely to be most favourable about that date.

TO NEW YORK AND BACK BY AIRSHIP

July 1, 1919, saw all the stores, which, including 4,900 gallons of petrol, weighed over 23 tons, aboard the R34 and the last finishing touches being given to the structure and engines, and her crew of 32 men anxiously awaiting the hour of departure. In command was Major G. H. Scott, A.F.C., and associated with him, as representing the Air Ministry, Brigadier-General E. M. Maitland, C.M.G., D.S.O., the senior officer of the British airship fleet, whose "log" of the double journey is one of the most interesting documents relating to aerial travel.

At midnight between the 1st. and 2nd. of July officers and crew sat down to their last meal on land, near the gigantic shed looming up gaunt and sheer from the country on the southern bank of the Firth of Forth. A bitter wind was blowing when, at 1.30 a. m. parties of men and girls in blue and khaki began to gather in the shed and group themselves round the guide ropes. The order being given, they took hold, and the last members of the crew went aboard. After a few final moments spent in adjusting and loosening the moorings came the command, "Walk her out," and the huge bulk of the airship slowly moved, bow first, into the open air. When quite free of the shed, the R34 was turned completely round, to face the wind. A bugle sounded, and the ropes were released. Bells rang out signals on board, and the engines began to throb as the airship rose slowly. Amid a burst of cheering from those left behind the voyage began, at 1.48 a. m.

"R34 slowly arose from the hands of the landing party and was completely swallowed up in low-lying clouds at a height of 100 feet. When flying at night, possibly on account of the darkness, there is always a feeling of loneliness immediately after leaving the ground: and this was on this occasion accentuated by the faint cheers of the landing party coming upwards through the mist long after all signs of the earth had disappeared.

"The airship rose rapidly to 1,500 feet, at which height she emerged from the low-lying clouds and headed straight up the Firth of Forth towards Edinburgh. A few minutes after 2 o'clock the lights of Rosyth showed through a break in the clouds, thus proving brilliantly that correct allowance had been made for the force and direction of the wind, which was blowing 20 miles an hour from the east. It should be borne in mind that, when an airship sets out for a long-distance voyage carrying the maximum allowance of petrol, she can only rise to a limited height at the outset without throwing some of it overboard as ballast, and that, as the airship proceeds on her voyage, she can, if so desired, gradually increase her height as the petrol is consumed by the engine." Thus General Maitland in his log.

The next few hours were among the most anxious of the flight, since the airship had to be kept as low as possible and yet avoid the high ground between Edinburgh and the Atlantic. The mountains to the north of the route created strong local wind currents, which tossed the airship somewhat as she passed over the mouth of the Clyde. The North Coast of Ireland soon appeared, and quickly faded away as the R34 headed out over the Atlantic.

By 7 a. m. the airship was enveloped in dense fog—low-lying clouds—through openings in which fleeting glimpses of the sea were obtained occasionally. Presently, at a height of 1,500 feet, the airship emerged, and found herself in a clear space, with another stratum of cloud some thousands of feet overhead. A large part of the journey appears to have been made through or above clouds, so that very little was seen of the ocean below.

TO NEW YORK AND BACK BY AIRSHIP

But, though travelling in a veil of mist, the R34 was not by any means out of touch with the world. Her wireless apparatus kept her in communication with the battle cruisers *Tiger* and *Renown* which had been stationed in mid-Atlantic to assist with weather reports and general observations. In addition the airship was in communication with East Fortune, Clifden (Ireland), the Azores and Newfoundland, so that there was no sense of isolation such as has assailed many navigators and explorers.

For the first two days things were uneventful, and time passed quickly enough, every man being kept busy by his allotted duties when standing his watch. General Maitland tells us that life in the keel of a large rigid airship is by no means unpleasant, there being very little noise and vibration except directly over the engines, no strong draughts, and, except in the early hours of dawn, no chilliness. The keel being 600 feet long, and journeys along it frequent, one got plenty of exercise; while those officers who had to climb the ladder leading to the observation platform on top of the airship could not complain of the lack of fairly heavy muscular exertion. When the time came for "turning in," considerable care was needed, since the walls of the keel were but thin fabric, and had anyone tumbled from his hammock he would probably have found himself a few moments later in the Atlantic.

To quote the closing entry of the first day:

"9 p. m.—The setting sun gradually disappears below the lower cloud horizon, throwing a wonderful pink glow on the white clouds in every direction. Air speed, 44 knots. Speed made good (owing to following wind) 55 miles per hour. All through this first night in the Atlantic the ordinary airship routine, navigating, steering, elevating, and also maintaining the engines in smooth running order, goes on watch and watch as in the daytime. The night is very dark. The airship, however, is lighted throughout. The radium paint used on the instruments is so luminous that in most cases the lighting installation is unnecessary."

The next afternoon a crack developed in the water jacket of the starboard amidships engine. This was disconcerting, as any interference with cooling might have put the engine out of commission. The engineer was able, however, to set things right with the help of a piece of copper sheeting and the ship's supply of chewing-gum, after the last had been reduced to the correct plasticity by his own jaws and those of his two assistants.

On the morning of the 4th. large icebergs were sighted, and early in the afternoon land was sighted to starboard. This turned out to be the coast-line of Newfoundland. The crossing from land to land had occupied just 59 hours. The weather had now cleared, but a contrary wind had sprung up of such strength that on the morning of the 5th. progress, with all five engines running, was hardly appreciable. Major Scott therefore turned inland to avoid the worst of it, and the airship was soon floating over the endless forests of Newfoundland, the resinous scent from which was welcome to the nostrils of the brave crew.

With the engines using over 40 gallons of petrol every hour, the slowness of progress became a serious matter. By midday of July 5, when New York was still 500 miles distant, it had become doubtful whether that city could be reached. A signal was sent to the United States authorities at Washington and Boston asking for the services of a destroyer to tow the airship for part of the way to conserve petrol, if necessary. During the afternoon the R34 struck a violent thunderstorm, and all engines were needed to carry the airship out of it.

TO NEW YORK AND BACK BY AIRSHIP

Fortunately only the edge of the storm was encountered, and the R34 got off lightly, though her occupants experienced much discomfort and anxiety. Later in the day another storm made it necessary to change course to escape it, though every extra mile meant a further drain on the precious supply of petrol. After that, however, things improved, and the American coast came in sight at 4 a. m. on July 6. A couple of hours later they passed the lovely island of Martha's Vineyard. It was now evident that they could not safely attempt to reach New York, as the petrol was almost exhausted, and that they must make direct to the landing place at Mineola, on Long Island, some miles east of the city.

It need hardly be said that the voyage of the R34 had aroused immense interest in the United States. Considerable disappointment was caused by her not being able to arrive on Independence Day (July 4), which she might conceivably have done had the winds been favourable instead of adverse. Even before she came in sight people were flocking towards the aerodrome. At 8.55 a. m. (United States time) the news that the giant airship was overhead brought everyone into the streets to watch her circling overhead. Presently a shout went up as a small object was seen to fall from the rear gondola. This was Major J. Pritchard, who had jumped out in a parachute to give landing instructions. The R34 presently released ballast from the stern to lower her nose and came slowly earthwards. When about 300 feet up, she dropped an anchor, which was at once seized upon by the strong landing party in attendance, and at 9.54 a. m. (1.54 p. m. Greenwich time) the R34 ended her journey, while the band played "God Save the King," and the spectators stood bareheaded.

The voyage had taken 108 hours 12 minutes, at an average speed of 33¼ miles an hour, and so closely had things been run that sufficient petrol for but 40 minutes more travel remained in the tanks.

The ship was absolutely none the worse for her journey, and had suffered no damage when landing. She looked as spick and span as when she left England. The crew, in spite of what they had recently gone through, also made a very good impression as they landed in their smart, clean uniforms. They were at once carried off to a local hotel and given the best of good times.

It soon leaked out that the R34 had brought with her one person who had no business to be aboard: a young rigger, whom at the last moment it had been decided to leave behind to save weight. Determined to see America, he managed to get into the R34 just before the start and hide himself between two of the gas-bags. Here he was discovered when the airship had travelled 60 miles, in a feverish condition. After a day in a hammock he was set to work, and whatever may have been the ultimate consequences he at least had the satisfaction of seeing the land where, as he put it, "they pay a man £20,000 to get into the ring for three rounds."

What might have been a serious disaster occurred on July 7. The airship, now well filled with gas, and fully exposed to a fairly strong wind, became almost unmanageable. The landing party detailed to look after her were lifted off their feet and had to send an urgent call for help. The mooring ring in the ship's nose tore out, leaving her anchored only by the rear car. Some of the crew climbed through this and managed to drop a rope by means of which her nose was hauled down again. Fortunately, no serious damage had been done, and to prevent such a happening being repeated 300 men watched the airship continually during the rest of her stay.

The wind continued to rise and the weather reports became

less and less assuring. A rapid fall of the barometer portended a gale, and if this caught the R34 at her moorings a catastrophe might result. It had been intended to leave Mineola at dawn on the 10th., but at 9 p. m. on the 9th. bugles were blown to summon the crew. Strenuous efforts were made to get the bags properly filled with hydrogen, a sufficiency of which had not yet been pumped into them.

"Meanwhile the wind continued to rise. By half-past ten there were 400 soldiers hanging on to the taut mooring ropes, while the great airship swayed and strained above them. There was no doubt about their ability to hold her, but what brought wrinkles to the commander's brow was the possibility that the mooring rings might tear away from the girders under the terrible strain. And all the time the hour drew nearer when the expected storm might burst and sweep the airship away. Gusts came rushing across the wide grass plain: overhead a thickening scud drove across the sky, at times blotting out the moon.

"The scene on the ground was weird and thrilling. Overhead the enormous bulk of the envelope swayed, shining silver and blue in the light of six powerful searchlights. Round the forward gondola crowded men of the landing crew, whose duty it was to keep the car from dashing against the ground. Backwards and forwards passed the silhouettes of the white-hatted sailors like figures on a cinema screen. Behind, the hiss of escaping hydrogen filled the air, so that the men had to shout to make each other heard. From under the bows of the airship came the hoarse voice of the officer in charge of the ground crews bellowing through a great megaphone, 'Tail right,' and 'Keep her up,' as the wind swayed the airship from side to side. Like the spokes of a wheel, four lines of dark figures lay back on the mooring ropes, grunting and straining like teams in a tug-of-war.

CONQUERING THE AIR

"Under the envelope Major Scott stood talking with General Charlton, the two figures, one short and stocky, the other tall and bulky, standing out in the white glare of the electric lights, while hundreds of men watched their quiet talk and admired the composure of the man just about to start on a 3,000-mile journey through the air with as much unconcern as if departing on the deck of some safe liner.

"In some respects the atmosphere of the R34's departure much resembled that of the departure of an ocean liner. All around were naval uniforms, the hissing of gas rushing from cylinders into hose pipes was an exact imitation of escaping steam, and the picture was completed by the engineers in their shirt-sleeves leaning out of the windows with that air with which stokers lean on their elbows at the side of a ship about to sail. The air was full of farewell messages; in every direction people were shaking hands with other people and indulging in other usual farewell manifestations.

"But there was a tinge of excitement and apprehensions in the air which has attended the departure of no other ship of any sort since men left shore to cross the Atlantic for the first time in history. Though there is little likelihood of a repetition of the perilous adventures which filled the outward journey, and though the crew regarded the worst as over when they came to earth here on Sunday last, it was impossible not to be thrilled by the thought that here were 30 men calmly preparing to launch themselves into the air and travel over the sea in an almost unknown element for a greater distance than men have ever been before." [1]

The R34 cast off her moorings at midnight in a wind blowing at 30 miles an hour from the south-west, and headed into it to carry out a promise to cruise over New York before turn-

[1] The *Times*.

ing homeward. The great city with its myriads of electric lights and great electrical sky signs offered a wonderful spectacle to the observers in the airship. Searchlights sweeping upwards presently "spotted" the R34 and gave thousands of New Yorkers the last—and in many cases first—sight of the strange craft that had come across the ocean on a literally flying visit.

Shortly after 1 a. m. on July 10 the R34 put about for England.

The Return Voyage

With a good strong breeze astern the airship sped along like a horse that has its head turned for home and its manger. The speed for some time was estimated at 74 miles an hour, sufficient to carry her beyond the reach of the threatened storm. By 9.15 a. m. 430 miles had been covered, and the mails sorted. These included parcels and letters for H. M. the King, the Foreign Office, the Admiralty, and the Postmaster General, besides a large number of newspapers for the editor of the *Times*.

With one of the engines stopped, to give it a rest, the good ship still bowled along at an average speed of 60 miles an hour. In the afternoon of the 10th. a five-masted ship under full sail was sighted, provoking mental contrasts between the old style of ship and the new. The 11th. opened rather inauspiciously with the complete breakdown of one of the engines in the rear car, owing to the shearing of bolts and breakage of the crankcase. This accident and a wireless report announcing bad weather in the south of England decided the Commander to give up his original intention of making for London, and to head for East Fortune instead. Before the close of the day the airship entered rain-clouds, and an unsuccessful attempt was made to get above them.

CONQUERING THE AIR

Let us now take a peep into General Maitland's log relating to July 12:

"8 p. m.—Supper, and a very good one too. We are well equipped with little luxuries on this return voyage, having learnt a thing or two on the outward journey about what is necessary and what is not.

"8.30 p. m.—Still pouring with rain. Height 4,000 feet. The wind whistles round the forward car. Very dark, and no visibility. Scott reduces height to 3,000 feet, and an extraordinary sight suddenly presents itself beneath us. Thousands and thousands of little clouds like tiny white puff-balls packed closely together, with blue sea just visible in between them, form a layer of cloud between us and the sea.

"12 midnight.—Still pouring with rain. Dropped flare: drift estimated as 10 degrees to southward. As we lay in our hammocks we listened to the rain beating pitilessly on the outer cover of our trusty ship of the air, and our feelings, despite the weather, are those of complete confidence and security."

A head wind reduced the speed to 28 knots on the 12th, but the weather had cleared up, giving the crew an extraordinarily wide view of the Atlantic, in which no sign of a ship could be discovered till 5.30 p. m., when two trawlers came in sight,—mere specks on the vast expanse of water. Two hours later land was seen about 10 miles away, and the wireless masts at Clifden could be made out with field-glasses, also two little islands off the Irish coast, undoubtedly the same as those which had told Alcock and Brown that they were at the end of their memorable flight.

At 8 p. m. the Irish coast-line was crossed, 61 hours 33 minutes after leaving the American coast. The airship passed over the mountains of Mayo, amid a magnificent cloud panorama, through gaps in which appeared lakes, harbours, islands, and green fields, the last an especially pleasing sight. Presently came the first welcome home, in the shape of an aeroplane which flew round the airship in greeting, and soon afterwards a message was received from the Air Ministry ordering the airship to land at Pulham, in Norfolk. Accordingly course was altered south, and during the night the R34 crossed the Isle of Man and passed over Liverpool, Derby and Nottingham. At 5 a. m. a message of congratulation came in from His Majesty the King; and at 6.20 a. m. on July 13 the R34 landed at Pulham, 3 days 3 hours and 3 minutes after the holding-down ropes had been released on Long Island.

CHAPTER 16

FROM LONDON TO AUSTRALIA BY AIR

IT is interesting to speculate what the population of Australia would be today were that continent as close to the British Isles as is, say, Canada; if a voyage to it occupied only as many days as it actually requires weeks. One can hardly doubt that the figures would need to be trebled, while in the case of New Zealand the multiplication would probably be even greater still.

The British Empire derives advantages from its units being so widely scattered in different climes. Within its bounds almost every conceivable necessity of life can be provided, and not only does the sun never set on it, but summer always reigns in one part or the other, so that, taken as a whole, the Empire is never without its harvests.

On the other hand distance is distance, and half the circuit of the globe has been a serious obstacle in the way of peopling the great countries "down under." In the days of the sailing ship, when a voyage to or from Australia was a matter of many months, people very naturally hesitated to try their fortune in so distant a country, so difficult to reach or return from, so isolated from the Mother Country.

The Suez Canal and the steam-engine between them brought the two countries much closer together in time, reducing months of travel to weeks; and the submarine cable and wireless telegraphy have practically annihilated distance as regards the transmission of news, messages and ideas. But so far as persons and material things are concerned the steamship remains the sole means of practical transport, and the speed of this transport is strictly limited by considerations of economy. Every knot added to the speed means a disproportionate increase in the amount of fuel burned, and there is no likelihood for many years of the present liner speeds being improved, for the simple reason that people generally would not be prepared to pay the heavy additions to freights and fares which the shipping companies would have to make.

To cut down existing times by half or even two-thirds is obviously impossible on the water. But in the air it can, and will, be done. The airship and aeroplane will presently provide a means by which passengers, mails, valuable documents, and articles of high value relatively to their weight and bulk may be hurried through the air from the British Isles to the Antipodes in a fortnight, or even less.

In 1919 the Australian Commonwealth Government offered a prize of £10,000 for the first flight by Australians from the Mother Country to the Dominion in an aeroplane constructed from parts made entirely in the British Empire. The flight must be completed in 720 consecutive hours—that is, within 720 hours of the start—and be made before the end of the year.

The prize was well worth winning, but not too large considering the great risks that would have to be run during the trip of 10,000 miles. As far as Calcutta there was a chain of aerodromes in France and Italy, at Cairo, Damascus, Basra, Karachi, Delhi and Allahabad; and the route had been traversed before. Beyond Calcutta possible landing places were few and far between, and excepting at Batavia, in Java, there was no good aerodrome available, and the flight would be of a strictly pioneering type.

It so happened that shortly after the war Brigadier-General

CONQUERING THE AIR

A. E. Borton, C.M.G., D.S.O., A.F.C., had flown from Cairo to India, and thence with a ship visited Burma, the Federated Malay States, Siam, Borneo and the Dutch East Indies. His object was to survey a possible air-route to Australia and make the necessary arrangements as regards landing places, and the supply of fuel, so that he might return to India and complete the journey to Australia by air. Unfortunately, the aeroplane used had in his absence been commandeered for service against the Afghans and been destroyed in a storm. The project therefore fell through.

General Borton had been accompanied by a young Australian airman, Capt. Ross Smith, M.C., D.F.C., A.F.C., who had served with distinction during the war with No. 1 Squadron, Australian Flying Corps, in Palestine; and by two Australian air-mechanics, Sergeant J. M. Bennett and Sergeant W. H. Shiers.

On hearing of the Australian Commonwealth Government's offer, Captain Smith was very naturally keen to compete for the prize. A brother, Lieut. Keith M. Smith, R.A.F., was awaiting demobilization in England, and he would be available to complete the crew of four needed for a long journey in a large and powerful aeroplane.

The great difficulty was how to get back to England in time. But this happily was solved by General Borton being recalled to London to report on the route. Through his good services Messrs. Vickers, Ltd., were induced to supply for the flight a Vickers-Vimy two-engined machine of the same type as that used by Capt. Alcock on his transatlantic journey. This aeroplane was not definitely entered until October, so that a great deal of necessary preparatory work and organisation had to be done in a short time—the selecting of "spares" and supplies, the collection of maps and all possible information about the least known parts of the route, arranging for supplies of petrol being delivered at stopping-places, and corresponding by cable with the Governor-General of the Dutch East Indies on the subject of preparing special aerodromes in order to break up the 1,750-mile stretch between Batavia and Port Darwin into four comparatively short sections. The help given by the Governor-General was an important contribution to the success of the enterprise. Though Alcock's machine had covered an even greater distance in one bound, and its fellow might be capable of doing the same, the risks of failure would obviously be considerably greater in the case of a machine that would already have put several thousands of miles behind it without a chance of a thorough overhaul. The provision of aerodromes at Bima, in the island of Sumbawa, and at Atamboea, in Timor, made it unnecessary to carry at any stage more petrol than would be required for a 1,000-mile stretch under adverse conditions. This in turn meant smaller and lighter tanks, and easier conditions for the engines.

A few words about the aeroplane chosen for the flight. It was a biplane with main planes 67 feet long and 10½ feet wide, set 10 feet apart. The upper plane stood 15¼ feet above the ground. From nose to tail the G-EAOU—to give it the official lettering painted on wings and body—measured 42 feet 8 inches. Its weight empty was three tons. The twin engines, disposed to right and left of the body, were 350-h.p. Rolls-Royce Mark 111. On these, perhaps more than on anything else except the pilot's skill and nerve, depended the fate of the expedition, for, with suitable alighting points so widely separated, a compulsory landing through engine trouble could hardly fail to be disastrous. Running at full speed they were capable of sending the aeroplane ahead at 100 miles an hour, but in view of the great distance to be accomplished it was decided in advance to "nurse" them by keeping the speed well below the maximum. This policy was evidently appreciated, for during the flight the engines behaved faultlessly, revolving the propellers many millions of times without the least sign of faltering.

In addition to itself and a crew of four men the aeroplane had to carry over 500 gallons of petrol, 40 gallons of oil, water, tools, kit, and "spares." The selection of the last required a great deal of thought and care, for while, on the one hand, dead weight had to be cut down to a minimum, the absence of some quite trifling spare part might be fatal. In the end the total weight was found to be considerably greater than the permissible limit, and to get things right the crew had to sacrifice their kits, retaining only the clothes they wore. A wireless set was ruled out as not justifying its weight; but room was found for emergency rations of food, sufficient to last a week should a landing have to be made where other food would be unobtainable.

On November 11 the fog, which had prevailed for several days, lifted, and, everything being ready, the Vickers-Vimy was flown from the works at Weybridge to the Hounslow aerodrome, the official starting-point. The next day five parts of the machine were marked and sealed, for it was a condition of the competition that only one machine might be used by one crew, and that it must have three of five sealed parts intact at the end of the journey.

At 8 a. m. the great biplane rose into the air, *en route* for Australia, despite the very unfavourable weather reports sent by the Air Ministry, and climbed above the mist which for many miles blotted out entirely the country below, until, suddenly, Folkestone and the white waves of the Channel—for a stiff wind was blowing—appeared in an opening, and the sun shone out encouragingly. In France the bad weather prophesied revealed itself, for the aeroplane entered a cloud of half sleet, half snow, blinding and bitterly cold. The elevator was at once put up. The Vimy rose steadily in a large spiral, and at a height of 9,000 feet emerged into bright sunshine, above the storm and amid the most wonderful cloud scenery. Of the earth nothing could be seen, and the compass had to be relied upon to steer a course for Lyons, the first landing-place.

The inexperienced person may envy the aviator riding the air above the clouds. But when the cold renders goggles useless by coating them with frozen breath so that his eyes are exposed to an icy gale of 80 miles or more an hour, and his limbs are so numb with cold that he can hardly operate the controls, the airman has even better reason for envying people warmly housed on firm ground. On this occasion the cold was so intense that even the sandwiches were frozen hard. Fortunately, a funnel-like opening in the clouds was encountered, and down this the Vimy spiralled into clear air below. The small French town of Roanne was quickly identified, so that it became easy to lay a course for Lyons, 40 miles further on, where the aeroplane landed safely, and so ended the first, and what was afterwards regarded as the worst, stage of the whole journey.

The next morning saw the aeroplane heading for Marseilles and the Riviera, and skirting the Maritime Alps, which presented a magnificent scene of cloud and rocky peaks. When the Mediterranean came in sight a course was set eastwards over Cannes, Monte Carlo and San Remo, and then across the waters of the Gulf of Genoa for Spezia. Here a strong head wind was met with, which reduced speed so considerably that it became evident that the short November day would not give time for arrival before dark at Rome, the next landing spot on the schedule. Accordingly, the Vimy was brought down into the Pisa aerodrome, which proved to be in a very sodden and sticky condition. The next day, the 14th., was too wet for flying to be possible, as the machine became bogged directly it began to move. November 15 opened equally badly, and the first attempt to get away was unsuccessful, the wheels sinking deeply into the mud. The aeroplane had to be dug out and hauled into a fresh position before anything more could be done. When the throttle was opened out again, the Vimy rolled slowly forward, sinking in and threatening to stand on her head. One of the mechanics threw himself on to the tail and kept her down while she gathered speed and at last rose from the ground, when he was hauled aboard by his companion. It was a lucky get-away, as the rain lasted for a week and longer and would undoubtedly have held the airmen prisoners.

The journey to Rome was uneventful, if somewhat unpleasant, owing to a boisterous head wind, but the view of the ancient city lit up by the evening sun made amends for any discomfort.

The next day's flight took the party over Naples and past Vesuvius—hidden by clouds—and then due east across the Appenines, between valley bottoms below and clouds above. The view was a very lovely one, but the rough nature of the country made the air very "bumpy," and flying consequently uncomfortable, until the mountains had been passed and the aeroplane was turned towards the next halting place—Taranto, which had recently played an important part as a big seaport in the Eastern campaign. Here a warm welcome was given the party by officers of the Royal Air Force still stationed at what was one of the main aerodromes on the London-Cairo route.

The afternoon was spent in going over the aeroplane and tuning it up for the next stage to Suda Bay on the north side of Crete. Of the intervening 520 miles by far the greater part would be over the Mediterranean, so that no risks whatever could be taken as regards careful preparation. On the morning of the 17th. we may picture the aeroplane crossing the heel of Italy and the open sea to Corfu, and then following the historic coast of Greece. Low-lying rain-clouds made it necessary to fly low. The pelting rain caused great discomfort and rendered steering so difficult that on one occasion the pilot was almost surprised by a cliff which suddenly loomed out of the mist. But for a well executed right-angle turn the Vimy would have been crashed on the rocky side of some obscure island, and the flight brought to a sudden and disastrous conclusion. It was a close shave.

Bad weather conditions lasted until the aeroplane reached the extreme southern point of Greece. The rain beat down pitilessly, soaking clothes and half-blinding the vision. But during the flight across open water the clouds dispersed, and the voyagers had a splendid view of the great island for which they were making, with its backbone of mountains hidden at the base in mist while its peaks towered into bright sunshine. After circling above the town of Canea, the great biplane came to rest in the Suda aerodrome, where, as at Taranto, a British welcome was given the crew.

The next day opened with heavy rain, which threatened to render the aerodrome a quagmire, so Capt. Smith lost no time in getting away. A difficult task awaited him, as he had to pick a way as best he could over the mountain range which extends from end to end of the island and throws up peaks to elevations of over 8,000 feet. In order to avoid these peaks, which were hidden in cloud, either the Vimy must be taken to a great height, or a way be found under the clouds through a pass. The latter course proved possible, but only by a small margin, as the clouds came down quite close to the saddle over which the aeroplane flew. After that all was plain sailing across the 250 miles of sea separating Crete from the North African coast, though, with cloud above and a featureless waste of waters below, travelling became very monotonous, the only sign of life discovered being two small ships, one towing the other. After three hours or so the African shore came in sight, sterile and sandy, and apparently as devoid of life as the sea itself; but, since it promised a safer landing than the Mediterranean in case of accident, it was welcomed by the crew. Steering over the port of Sollum, they turned eastward and followed the coast, making direct for Cairo. Presently in the distance could be seen the mighty forms of the Pyramids, and other familiar landmarks; and 7½ hours after leaving Suda the Vimy settled in the Heliopolis aerodrome, with 650 miles to her credit for the day's non-stop run.

The first main stage of the journey was now safely completed, to the great relief of the party, as the weather conditions had on the whole been extremely trying, and might easily have caused serious delay. In seven days they had covered nearly 2,500 miles, out of a total of 11,060 between London and Port Darwin, and so had maintained the necessary average. The next stage of 4,150 miles, from Cairo to Calcutta, had already been flown by three of the party, and being largely over plains and sea did not promise great difficulty.

At Cairo it was learned that the French aviator, M. Poulet, who in October had left Paris with a companion in a Caudron biplane intending, if possible, to be the first man to fly from

FROM LONDON TO AUSTRALIA BY AIR

Europe to Australia, had reached India. He was technically not in the race, but if he got to Port Darwin ahead of the Australian party, the latter would lose the prestige associated with carrying through a difficult undertaking for the first time. Capt. Smith and his crew were therefore naturally anxious to overhaul Poulet, who now had some thousands of miles start, —and a stern chase is proverbially a long one.

This consideration enabled them to repel the temptation to take a day off among their many friends at Cairo and to get a good rest before resuming the journey. As at Hounslow, the weather report was discouraging, but early next morning they started off for Damascus. After 50 miles along the Ismailia Canal, at a height which revealed a fine panorama of the Nile Delta, they crossed the battlefield of Tel-el-Kebir and the Suez Canal, through which a liner bound for the same destination as themselves was passing. Then over the great war-depot of Kantara, the base of supplies for the Palestine campaign, and out into the Sinai desert, in which the only signs of man's activity were the railway and pipeline to Gaza. A journey which occupied the Children of Israel forty years was turned off by the Vickers machine in as many minutes, and soon familiar land-marks in Palestine were picked up and left behind in succession—Gaza, with its trenches, Medjdel, Ramleh, the Holy City, the Dead Sea. Turning his craft northwards along the Jordan Valley, Capt. Smith was actually flying far below sea level, for the southern or Dead Sea end of the valley is 1,300 feet below the surface of the Mediterranean, and a height of only 500 feet was maintained above the valley bottom.

As the aeroplane reached the Sea of Galilee the weather, which had been miserably wet and cold for some time past, cleared up, bringing into sight the distant snow-clad tops of Mount Hermon and the Anti-Libanus. On and on, over a dreary and uninspiring landscape, until a streak of green amid the sands announced that they were not far from one of the oldest and most famous of the world's cities, Damascus. Here, in the aerodrome, many old friends greeted the airmen, who, after following out the usual daily and laborious routine of filling tanks with oil and petrol, and examining engines and controls, retired for a comfortable night's rest, anticipating good conditions for the morrow's flight.

Great was their disappointment to find rain falling heavily in the morning, and no signs of a break. They followed their usual wise policy of getting away while the ground still permitted, and after a very wet take-off, amid a shower of mixed water and mud, lay a course for Bagdad. Passing over what was once the noble city of Palmyra, they picked up the Euphrates, which guided them towards their destination. A stiff head wind now reduced speed so much that it would be impossible to reach Bagdad before dark—the sun was already setting—so a descent was made at Ramadie, 40 miles further north, the site of a famous engagement of the Mesopotamian campaign, and still the headquarters of an Indian cavalry regiment. Here, during the night, a strong wind rose, blowing in such a direction that there was great danger of the Vimy being lifted by the tail and turned over—which would have meant her practical destruction. The airmen and a large force of soldiers managed to seize her in time and turn her head to wind. Then the ailerons on the wings broke their control wires and flapped about so violently that it was hard work to tie them down before they were badly injured. Next day, however, the gale proved a friend, for it was blowing in the right direction and sent the aeroplane hurtling over the Mesopotamian plains at a greater speed than had yet been attained. Swiftly it travelled over old Bagdad—which had been dropped out of the schedule as a landing-place, thanks to petrol supplies being available at Ramadie—and over the scenes of much hard fighting a few years earlier, notably Ctesiphon and Kut el Amara, where General Townsend and his gallant men kept the Turks at bay for five long months. Three hours' flight brought the party to Basra, the old Bussorah, at the head of the Persian Gulf, whither all war supplies were brought from the Allied Countries while the fighting lasted. In the aerodrome outside the town a descent was made, and advantage was taken of the Royal Air Force depot there to devote a whole day to overhauling and adjusting the engines.

With daylight on November 23 the Vickers-Vimy rose *en route* for Bandar Abbas, 630 miles south, at the entrance to the Gulf. For once, in a way, the flying conditions were ideal, —a following wind, bright sunshine, and an unhindered view. Below, a wonderful panorama displayed itself. On the right stretched the green, warm waters of the Gulf; on the left, the plateau, seamed with deep gulleys and dry watercourses, which borders the Gulf on its eastern side. A cruel, inhospitable country for a disabled aeroplane, in which it was impossible to locate a single spot where a landing might be made safely. The engines, however, gave no cause for anxiety, but ran like the proverbial sewing-machine; yet the pilot drew a sigh of relief when at length he had his machine safely on the ground at Bandar Abbas; where the Persian Governor, the British Consul, and a large gathering of natives welcomed this strange visitant from far-away England.

The next "jump," from Bandar Abbas to Karachi—730 miles away—was the longest of the whole voyage. For many miles the course followed the barren and inhospitable shores of southern Persia and Baluchistan, along which, two thousand years and more before, Alexander's admiral, Nearchus, had led his fleet from the mouth of the Indus to the Persian Gulf. A hundred miles short of his destination Capt. Smith left the land and took a straight line over the sea to the aerodrome at Karachi, reached only 8½ hours after the start. The party now learned the welcome news that their rival, Poulet, was but one day ahead of them, at Delhi; so that they had a very good chance of overtaking him.

A start was made early the next morning for the old Indian capital, more than 700 miles eastwards. As the sun rose they entered the desert of Sind, over which they flew for three hours. Then desert gave way to a vast tract of fertile irrigated land, green with a greenness such as they had not seen since leaving Europe. The air now became very bumpy, and the Vimy was tossed about like a small ship in a gale. But a safe landing was made at Delhi, and the brave four had completed one-half of their long voyage. The elusive Poulet had meanwhile been active, and was still one stage ahead, at Allahabad. As nearly 2,100 miles had been covered in the three days,—the 21st., 22d., and 23rd.,—and everybody felt the strain, a "day off" was devoted to the machine and to sight-seeing. On the 25th. the great Central Plains, in which the most memorable object was the exquisite Taj Mahal, near Agra, were crossed to Allahabad. Poulet moved on the same day from this town to Calcutta.

The next day saw the Vimy in the capital of Bengal, where its arrival caused an interest almost embarrassing in its intensity. Once more it was learned that Poulet still kept his lead, for he had started that morning for Akyab in Burma. The second main section of the journey was now completed. Six thousand five hundred miles had been covered, and four thousand five hundred still remained to be flown.

The third, and final, main stage opened with an incident

which might easily have been a disaster. As the aeroplane rose from the racecourse and headed for some high trees which had to be surmounted, a couple of hawks flew into the propellers, with the most unfortunate results to themselves. It might be thought that a heavy wooden propeller, driven by a powerful engine, had little to fear from a small bird. But the shock between a propeller rotating at a speed of some miles a minute and even so light an object as a carelessly thrown cigarette-end has been known to make the propeller fly into pieces. The moments immediately following the collision were therefore exceedingly anxious ones for the occupants of the aeroplane. Had either propeller gone, the machine would have crashed into the trees and all been over. As it was, in the endeavour to avoid other hawks, the pilot almost struck the trees. However, all's well that ends well, and the aeroplane was soon winging its way over the combination of forests, swamps, and streams, collectively known as the Sunderbunds, the delta of the Ganges. This tract, a couple of hundred miles wide, offered no possibility of making a safe forced landing, so that everyone was glad when it had been put astern and the Burmese coast was reached at Chittagong. At that port the course was changed southwards to Akyab. To the great joy of the crew a small aeroplane was discerned in the aerodrome for which they were making—Poulet's Caudron. The French airman, a sportsman through and through, was the first to greet the Australians when they landed. Henceforward it would be a neck-and-neck race, a circumstance which increased the great interest being taken by the world generally in the progress of the Vimy.

On November 30 Poulet got away first for Rangoon, and the Australians did not take the air until he had an hour's start.   Excitement ran high in Rangoon, where an aeroplane had never yet been seen, at any rate not at close quarters.

After following the coast for 100 miles or so Capt. Smith turned his craft eastwards, crossing a low mountain range to pick up the great river Irrawady, which would guide them southwards to Prome.   From that point the railway was followed southwards to the capital, where a huge and cheering crowd awaited the airmen.   Poulet had not arrived yet, but an hour later his machine joined the Vickers-Vimy, to the great delight of the spectators, who had flocked in from far and near to witness the event.

The start next morning from the restricted area of the racecourse proved exciting, as the undercarriage of the aeroplane actually brushed the tops of the trees.   Poulet, who was to have left at the same time, experienced engine trouble, and the intention of flying with him to Bangkok, the next halt, had to be abandoned.   After crossing the head of the Gulf of Martaban to Moulmein, Capt. Smith set a south-easterly course, over the mountainous country which separates Siam from Burma.   The tops of the range were hidden in cloud, and as some peaks were known to rise 6,000 or 7,000 feet above sea level, the only safe course was to climb right above them. At a height of 11,000 feet the aeroplane was still in cloud and flying blindly except for the indications given by the compass and the instruments showing height and tilt.   It is notoriously difficult to keep a machine on a level keel or on a course when all sense of direction is lost; and flying now became dangerous. At one time the aeroplane was almost out of control and heading downwards at great speed towards the peaks lurking somewhere in the mist, but a cool head saved the situation.   In the hope that they might have passed the highest ground, the aeroplane was allowed to glide down to an elevation of about 7,000 feet, at which height the position became decidedly stimulating. Eyes were strained in the lookout for danger. Presently something dark loomed ahead. Was it a peak? In a flash the aeroplane was "flattened out" to avoid it. The cause of alarm proved to be country below seen through a hole in the clouds. The danger zone therefore had apparently been passed. Gliding still lower, at a height of 4,000 feet the aeroplane suddenly emerged from the clouds into clear air, to the great relief of everyone aboard. Below, an endless forest stretched to the horizon, covering country not yet explored. An hour later this gave way to the wide stretches of cultivated land bordering the Mekong River, and once over this it was plain sailing down to the Muang aerodrome, some miles north of the capital. Thus ended one of the most trying, and possibly the most dangerous, of the flights made up to date.

The next lap on the schedule was from Bangkok to Singapore, a distance of between 900 and 1,000 miles. But on being informed that there was a Siamese aerodrome at Singora, on the neck of the Malay Peninsula, and about halfway between the two cities, Capt. Smith decided to use this and break the journey. The trip to Singora included a very unpleasant experience of tropical rain, which soaked and almost blinded the pilots. On one occasion the machine very narrowly escaped being crashed against one of the rocky headlands of the coast along which they steered. The aerodrome when reached was seen to be half under water, and, what was far worse, thickly studded with tree-stumps! But it afforded the only possible landing, and there was nothing to do but take the very heavy risk of being smashed up. By a miracle the wheels avoided the stumps, and only suffered the loss of its tail skid, which was replaced, after many difficulties had been overcome by the ingenious mechanics.

CONQUERING THE AIR

During the night a gale, accompanied by heavy rain, compelled the unfortunate airmen to remain with the machine and prevent her getting adrift. By the morning they were soaked to the skin, but as their kits had been left behind at Hounslow, they had to let their clothes dry on them. A force of 200 convicts cleared away the stumps while a supply of petrol was being brought up from Penang—none was available at the aerodrome itself.

On the morning of December 4, after a very wet start through water which nearly turned the Vimy over, the Australians got clear of the aerodrome, crossed the rubber plantations of British Malaya, and made a safe landing in the small race-course at Singapore. This was difficult to alight on, and even more difficult to leave, for rain had made it heavy, and it was surrounded by trees and houses, on which the Vimy nearly came to grief when she started off for Java. Avoiding a heavy thunderstorm, Capt. Smith followed the eastern coast to Sumatra, so densely wooded that a landing on it was impossible, for 200 miles, crossing the Equator on the way. Beyond Banka the Vimy headed straight for Batavia over the open sea, dotted with numberless palm-clad islands, which afforded one of the most beautiful sights of the journey. Nine hours after leaving Singapore a descent was made in the aerodrome at Kalidjati, not far from Batavia.

The next alighting point, Surabaya, near the eastern end of the island, provided one of the most harassing incidents of the voyage. The aerodrome had been made on reclaimed land, and had a thin, hard crust on the top of soft mud. The great weight of the Vimy soon broke through this crust, and the machine was bogged. Much digging and hauling got her clear, only to sink in again. More digging and hauling, and the use of bamboo mats under the wheels, eventually brought the aeroplane on to the surface, but at the cost of two tires being punctured. The jacks used to raise the carriage to allow the punctures to be repaired sank into the ground more than once. At one time it really looked as if the journey was to end at Surabaya, with only 1,200 miles more to be flown to reach Australia. An exasperating situation indeed for men who had suffered and striven so much! But necessity is ever the mother of invention, and it occurred to Capt. Smith that, if sufficient bamboo mats were procurable, a roadway might be made over which the wheels would run without sinking in. Thanks to the services of a local official, a very large number of mats were procured—many of them the walls of native houses—and a double pathway formed 300 yards in length. By 9 o'clock next morning everything was ready for a start. Unfortunately, as the aeroplane ran over the matting the draught from the propellers displaced mats in the rear, and these fouled the tail, causing the Vimy to leave the track and bog itself.

With much labour it was dug out once more and brought back to the starting point. To prevent further trouble, the mats were then fastened together and pegged firmly to the ground. The second attempt proved successful, and to their great delight the airmen found themselves climbing skywards *en route* for Bima, in the island of Sambawa. All the way the scenery was as lovely as landing sites were conspicuous by their absence, and after a few hours of pleasant travelling the great machine arrived in the excellent aerodrome prepared for it.

On December 9, Atamboea, in Timor, was reached, and there remained only the very last lap of the journey, 450 miles across open sea to the Australian coast. But even the sea could be hardly less inhospitable to an aeroplane than the country traversed during the preceding week, and the travellers had the satisfaction of knowing that H. M. S. *Sydney*, which had won fame by sinking the German cruiser *Emden*, had been detailed to patrol the stretch of waters between Timor and the mainland.

With hope high in their breasts the gallant four mounted their trusty machine on December 10. As they rose from the aerodrome the carriage brushed the tops of some trees, and, but for the good luck that stood by them, the Vimy would have been brought to earth. How little often divides success from failure! Avoiding a chain of hills, they headed by compass straight for Port Darwin. Timor dropped behind and for two hours sea only was visible. Then a smudge of smoke appeared in the distance and the expected warship came in sight. This was very cheering. A downward swoop carried them close to the *Sydney* and within hearing range of the welcoming cheers that rose from her decks. Then in turn the warship faded from sight, and eyes were directed eagerly southwards, searching for the goal. Just before 2 p. m. a distant haze was seen on the horizon. Was it land? A few more minutes settled the doubt, for Bathurst Island lighthouse was identified. We may well envy the crew their feelings at that moment, for now, unless the very hardest of hard luck should intervene, the prize was definitely theirs. It would indeed have been a tragedy had anything now gone wrong. But the aeroplane behaved gallantly to the last, and at 3 p. m. the Vimy landed on Australian ground, 27 days 20 hours "out," and with 52 hours in hand.

Quickly the news flashed all over the world, and while the citizens of Port Darwin were still lionising their countrymen telegrams of congratulation began to pour in by the hundred.

Among them was one from His Majesty King George V. It ran as follows: "Delighted at your safe arrival. Your suc-

PLATE VII

Handley-Page-Napier twin-engine air liner preparing to start on a test trip.

[*Photo, London News Agency.*

The cabin of a Handley-Page-Napier air liner used on the London–Paris airway.

[*Photo, London News Agency.*

cess will bring Australia nearer to the Mother Country, and I warmly congratulate you and your crew."

In England the *Daily Mail* next day contained a leading article headed "Wonderful!" To quote its opening paragraph. "There can be only one opinion about the feat which Captain Ross Smith and his comrades have performed in flying the distance of nearly 11,000 miles from England to Australia—half round the world. It is beyond comparison the most wonderful flight yet achieved. What adds to its glory is that it has been carried through with magnificent skill and endurance in the teeth of hurricanes and manifold difficulties. We may well be proud of such gallant and resolute airmen and of such a brilliant designer as Mr. Royce, whose engines, as in the Atlantic crossing, have emerged triumphant from the severest test that could be imposed." This expressed public opinion fairly enough, though the writer might well have added a few words recognising the high quality of the work and materials put into the aeroplane itself by Messrs. Vickers, Ltd., which alone enabled it to withstand the buffetings and rough treatment that it encountered.

Though the aeroplane had reached its official destination immediately it alighted in Australia, the journey was by no means at an end, since the big centres of population—Sydney, Melbourne and Adelaide—demanded a sight of machine and crew. But more than three months elapsed before the remaining 3,500 miles—figures which make one realise the vastness of Australia—were completed, and the Smiths reached their native city in South Australia. The route taken was across Northern Territory, in which some delay was caused by the repair of one propeller, to Charleville, in Queensland. There a long stay was made to replace the propeller and give the engines a thorough overhaul. A tremendous welcome awaited the crew at Sydney, and again at Melbourne, where a cheque for £10,000 was presented by the Prime Minister, and the Vimy formally handed over to the Commonwealth Government on behalf of its makers. The last episode of all was a flight to Adelaide, where perhaps, the greatest height of enthusiasm was reached, for Capt. Smith and his brother were there literally at home.

In recognition of their exploit the brothers received the honour of knighthood; well earned, everyone will admit.

CHAPTER 17

FROM CAIRO TO THE CAPE BY AIR

A few days after the signature of the Armistice in November, 1918, three surveying parties were despatched into the heart of Africa. Their duties were to locate positions, along a line roughly running from Khartoum to Bulawayo, suitable for aerodromes. In addition, the sites selected had to be cleared, and at many of them depots of petrol formed for the use of aircraft that might land there.

The work was extremely trying to the surveyors, owing to the tropical heat, the variable climate, insect pests and dangerous animals, to say nothing of the great difficulty encountered in getting from one point to another through trackless jungles and swamps, and the necessity for being on guard against the possible hostility of natives, whose help had to be relied upon for the manual work of clearing that had to be done.

The officers detailed by the Air Ministry to carry through the operations showed so much determination and vigour that, a year later, they had completed their task; and between Cairo and Cape Town there extended a chain of twenty-three aerodromes and nineteen emergency landing grounds. Taking the first in order from north to south, the list is as follows:

Heliopolis (near Cairo)	Wady Halfa
Assiut	Atbara
Assouan	Khartoum

CONQUERING THE AIR

Tabora	Livingstone
Abercorn (on L. Tanganyika)	Bulawayo
Broken Hill	Palapye
Jebelein	Pretoria
Eliri	Johannesburg
Mongalla	Bloemfontein
Jinja (on the Victoria Nyanza)	Victoria West
Kisumu	Cape Town
Mwanza	

As the route measured 5,206 miles from end to end, the average distance between possible landing places—including the emergency grounds—worked out at 124 miles.

The route having been opened, at great cost and labour, it remained to make some use of it, and that without undue delay, for tropical vegetation grows at a speed which can be realised only by experience, and some of the clearings would soon revert to jungle if left to themselves.

Britain's greatest newspaper, the *Times*, lost no time in organising a flight, and in this they received the assistance of the Air Ministry and of Messrs. Vickers, Ltd., who provided a twin-engined machine of the type which had already flown the Atlantic and travelled from England to Australia. The flight was not, however, to be a merely spectacular performance, carried out in the shortest possible time, but "a serious attempt to show whether Africa could be traversed easily and safely from end to end by proper aircraft in ordinary conditions, and a pioneer effort in exploration from the air."

As leader of the expedition was selected **Dr. P. Chalmers-Mitchell**, secretary of the Zoölogical Society, a gentleman of high scientific attainments; and as pilots Capt. S. Cockerell and Capt. F. C. Broome. Sergeant-major James Wyatt (mechanic) and Mr. C. Corby (rigger) completed the crew, all of them experts in their respective lines.

The journey promised to be full of interest and by no means devoid of risk and adventure. Apart from the prepared landing places there would be few spots in some sections of the route where a forced descent could be made without serious danger to the machine, if not to the lives of its occupants. To alight on the great expanses of *sudd* or tangled morasses of water-logged, decaying vegetation into which the Nile broadens out in its upper reaches would mean disaster. In Central Africa storms of tropical violence might be encountered, and should the aeroplane be caught in one of these while traversing the great forests or jungles its position might easily become precarious. In short, a successful voyage entailed keeping closely to the route, landing in suitable places, freedom from mechanical troubles, a constant supply of petrol, water and food, and preservation during the periods necessarily spent on the ground from marauders, whether two- or four-legged, and from the various diseases lurking in the Dark Continent.

The aeroplane left Brooklands, near Weybridge, on January 24, 1920, and after a very severe buffeting by adverse winds reached Heliopolis safely on February 1. Here Dr. Chalmers-Mitchell, who had proceeded overland and by sea, "joined up." Heliopolis it may mentioned, will in the future very probably become one of the world's great air-junctions; a point on which the air-traffic from Europe, Africa, Asia, and Australia will converge. Geographically it is well qualified to serve as the centre of air routes running to all points of the compass.

On February 6 the Vickers-Vimy rose from the spacious aerodrome amid the cheers of a large crowd, and the clicking of many cameras. After circling once or twice to gain height, the aeroplane sped southwards on its way to the Cape. In glorious weather and heat which rendered the air very bumpy the five adventurers followed the Nile as far as Luxor, where a descent had to be made on account of one of the engines overheating. A cylinder had sprung a leak and let out the cooling water,—a trouble which was to recur many times. An hour and a half's work put things right, and the flight continued that day to Assouan, where one of the greatest dams ever built by man stores the Nile water for delivery during the dry season. What a contrast between the aeroplane, the most recent of the great inventions of mankind, and the memorials of hoary antiquity, dating back to the dawn of history, over which it flew during the first day of the journey! From their lofty elevation the travellers saw to the westward the terrible Libyan desert, a vast expanse of great rolling sand dunes never yet traversed on foot by Europeans, a cruel, waterless, foodless, uninhabited waste; and east of the Nile the scarcely more hospitable stretches of sand and rocks, that in ancient times supplied Egypt with quarried stone.

At Assouan a halt of a day was devoted to necessary adjustments of the engines; and early on February 8, after a night spent under the wings of the aeroplane, the party left for Khartoum, now following the Nile, now taking short cuts across the bends of the river. A fresh leak that developed brought the machine down into one of the emergency landing grounds, where an hour or two had to be expended on making things good. Then the flight continued by compass, straight for Khartoum, over wild deserts and the craters of extinct volcanoes. It is interesting to note that, thanks to the aeroplane, a discovery was thus made of a volcanic region hitherto unknown to geologists, though its existence had been suspected.

While passing over this forbidding region, where the heat was terrific, one of the engines sprang a leak, overheated, and struck work. The pilot at once headed for the Nile, keeping the other engine going, and managed to make a good landing a few miles from the river, in wild, but fairly level, surroundings. After a long delay and much walking a native was discovered and sent for water, which presently arrived on camel-back. The engine having been staunched and filled up, the aeroplane rose again, and made Khartoum as dusk was falling, after covering 618 miles during that day.

February 9 was spent on attending to the engines, and cleaning out the body of the machine, which had accumulated a great deal of dust—resembled a dust-bin, to use the pilot's words.

The following day the expedition left Khartoum; intending to fly before nightfall to Mongalla, on the upper reaches of the White Nile. To attain that northern outpost of the Sudan, it would be necessary to cross large areas of the *sudd* swamps and, in general, country in which assistance would be less easily found than in that already traversed. A flight of 208 miles with a following wind brought them safely in 2 hours to Jebelein, on the Nile, where they landed to fill the petrol tanks and stop a slight leak. Leaving again about 11 a. m., they were soon compelled by magneto trouble to make a forced landing in a dry swamp, among long, dead grass. Repairs occupied the rest of the day, and the night had to be passed in the open. The bitter cold and the presence of elephants and prowling beasts, including leopards, made things very uncomfortable for the travellers during the hours of darkness. On the following day the aeroplane managed to start, but so bad a leak at once developed that the pilots decided to return to Jebelein for repairs, as it was too risky to attempt a crossing of the *sudd* area before the engines had been put in better condition.

CONQUERING THE AIR

At Jebelein three days were devoted to doing everything possible to the engines, the leakiness of which had now so got on everybody's nerves that the question of abandoning any attempt to proceed further south was seriously discussed. Eventually the party decided to push ahead, trusting to luck and the efficiency of an improvised apparatus for pumping water from an extra tank into the radiators to make up loss by leakage.

On February 14 the Vickers-Vimy left Jebelein for Mongalla, 538 miles away to the southward, and on the further side of the formidable *sudd* swamp. Dr. Chalmers-Mitchell admits that they took a heavy risk in essaying the flight after experiencing so much trouble with the water jackets. Instead of making for Eliri, on the south-west, the next scheduled landing place, the pilot took the direct route to Mongalla, though this involved crossing a greater breadth of swamp. The smoke from bush fires now proved a serious obstacle, for it obscured the ground and made it impossible to pick up landmarks. The Nile, their best guide, had disappeared in the swamps, and the heat was so terrific that the engines ran short of water in spite of the reserve supply delivered by the pumping apparatus. A descent became inevitable. Captain Cockerell searched for a landing ground and finally spotted a burnt patch in the midst of dense jungle, on which a safe landing was effected. Unfortunately, no water could be found. While the party were hunting for it, Mr. Corby, who had been left on guard, found himself surrounded by natives armed with bows and arrows. They proved friendly, however, and accepted a cigarette apiece; but the smoking of these made them violently sick, fortunately without affecting their friendliness.

Water had to be found somehow, so a flight was taken in search of it. A second descent was made on a burnt patch near a creek, which did not meet requirements. After much difficulty the aeroplane was got into the air again, and brought down in a dry swamp near the Nile, infested with mosquitoes, centipedes, and crocodiles, and nauseatingly "smelly." The natives again proved friendly, and one of them was despatched on foot to Mongalla for petrol. The men spent a miserable night on the plane, to dodge crocodiles, and next morning, as no petrol had arrived, Dr. Chalmers-Mitchell and Captain Broome started on a six-hour tramp through bush and swamp, guided by a native, who brought them safely to Mongalla, absolutely exhausted by the terrible equatorial heat. Meanwhile, Captain Worsley, D.S.O., had received at Mongalla the note despatched overnight and taken 50 gallons of petrol to the aeroplane by canoe. Captain Cockerell succeeded in getting the Vickers-Vimy off the terrible bumpy ground, and in ten minutes covered the distance which had given his two companions several hours of painful tramping.

Five nights were passed at Mongalla, since the engines had to undergo as thorough an overhaul as could be given them in the existing conditions, which included almost insupportable heat, such as might be expected near the Equator. The high temperature made the petrol practically boil in the tanks, causing great wastage, which could be reduced only by filling-up after sundown and starting early in the morning.

The first attempt to get away for Kisumu on February 20 failed, owing to trouble with the radiator shutters, the wires for opening which had become slack with the heat. The shutters were locked open, and at the second trial the aeroplane started off successfully. For a time no trouble occurred. Then overheating made its appearance in a new form—a burned-out inlet valve. This compelled a descent on to the emergency ground at Nimule, which was in bad condition and punctured a tire at the moment of landing. The collapse of the tire caused the machine to swing round and break the spring on the tail skid. A new valve was fitted and the spring repaired before night came on, when a good camp-fire had to be maintained to keep off the lions, whose roaring greatly disturbed the campers.

An attempt to get away the following afternoon proved futile, as the air was so rarefied by the heat as to make it impossible to gain height. After 20 minutes of circling round, the pilot brought the aeroplane down again on the landing ground. The next day a start was effected at dawn, and for once a run was made without any kind of mishap. Crossing the Victoria Nile at Murchison Falls, the expedition reached Jinja, on the north shore of the Victoria Nyanza, where a good, if somewhat small, aerodrome was found. No leaks had shown themselves, and it looked as if this particular trouble had been overcome. At the start for Kisumu next morning, however, the magnetos proved refractory, and a day had to be spent in the aerodrome putting them right. Everyone would have been greatly disheartened by the lengthening chapter of accidents but for the news that new engines were lying at Kisumu.

That place, at which the Uganda Railway terminates on the Victoria Nyanza, was reached early on February 24. The first inquiry the pilots made on arrival was for the new engines. Alas! these had been salvaged from a wrecked ship after being under salt water for three months, and were quite useless. Nothing remained to be done except give the old engines a thorough overhaul and scrap every item of kit that could possibly be spared, so as to lighten the aeroplane for the coming stages of flying at high altitudes. On the 26th. the travellers fought their way against a strong head wind to Mwanza, at the southern end of the lake, where the petrol tanks were filled up, before continuing the flight to Tabora, in Tanganyika Territory, which they reached safely the same evening.

February 27 ended the expedition. Just after the aeroplane had left the ground, one of the engines failed; and a descent had to be made into the bush among great ant-hills. These tore off one of the wheels, and so damaged the aeroplane that it had to be condemned as unfit for further use. The disaster caused great disappointment to all concerned, though the pilots at any rate were quite prepared to make another attempt on a fresh machine. Dr. Chalmers-Mitchell took the railway from Tabora to Dar-es-Salaam on the coast, whence he returned to England by sea; while Captains Cockerell and Broome sailed from the same port for Cape Town, where they handed to Viscount Buxton a letter from the King.

The failure of the expedition was not due to any lack of skill on the part of the pilots; nor to any defects in the aeroplane, which never gave the slightest trouble. The cooling arrangements of the engine, and the magnetos must be blamed for the unfortunate end of the expedition. And in fairness to these it should be stated that the immense heat subjected them to conditions not specially provided for, as they doubtless would have been had experience gathered from similar flights been available. Engines of the same kind had successfully driven an aeroplane across the Atlantic and from London to Australia; but, whereas those flights had been made at high altitudes, where the air is always cool, that over Africa followed comparatively low levels.

The actual flying time taken between Cairo and Tabora totalled only 36½ hours for the 2,700 miles covered, so that the speed averaged 75 miles an hour. The body of the aeroplane remained at Tabora, to end its life as a pavilion for a sporting club. The engines were sent back to England for examination.

It must not be thought that the expedition was a failure, any more than any other pioneering attempt which does not achieve its object. Very valuable information, calculated to make easier the way for future aerial navigation, was gathered. The very difficulties encountered proved the need for rapid communication such as aircraft only can provide in a country of forest, jungle, and swamp, with widely separated centres of civilisation, which in many cases are extraordinarily isolated.

The wildness of the country traversed between Khartoum and Tabora was shown by the abundant animal life. As the aeroplane sped along, the travellers often caught sight of elephants, rhinoceroses, giraffes, hippopotami, buffalo and many kinds of buck. The first four species took comparatively little notice of the great, noisy bird passing overhead, but the buffalo and deer fled panic-stricken. In years to come they will probably learn to regard flying-machines with the indifference displayed by flocks and herds in this country.

In view of the termination of the *Times* flight at Tabora, the heading of this chapter may appear misleading. But the whole of the story has not yet been told, for where one party failed another succeeded.

On February 4, two South African airmen, Lt.-Col. Pierre van Ryneveld and Flight Lieut. Brand, left Brooklands in a Vickers-Vimy, bound for the Cape by the route already taken by the Chalmers-Mitchell Expedition. The "Silver Queen," as their aeroplane was named, encountered dreadful weather while crossing the Mediterranean at night. Clouds obscured the stars and the wind blew from the southwards with a velocity of 50 miles an hour. The pilots missed Crete altogether and reached the African coast an hour and a half behind schedule time, in a completely exhausted condition, after battling with the elements for eleven hours. When landing at Sollum the tail skid received damage, but this was made good with parts taken from a Ford car.

The "Silver Queen" left Cairo in darkness on February 10, the pilots' desire being to reach Khartoum—1,044 miles away—in an uninterrupted flight. More than half the distance had been covered when the same trouble overtook the "Silver Queen" that had dogged its predecessor. The water leaked from a radiator, compelling a forced descent, made in darkness among boulders. The aeroplane itself was wrecked, but the pilots and engines escaped uninjured. This mishap occurred at Korosko, on the Nile, the scene of one of Sir A. Conan Doyle's most stirring stories. Lt.-Col. van Ryneveld and his companion returned to Cairo with the engines, which were installed in a similar aeroplane, "Silver Queen II."

A second start was made from the Heliopolis aerodrome on February 22. The next evening the South Africans reached Khartoum, where some time had to be devoted to stopping the leaks apparently inseparable from African air-travel. On the 26th. "Silver Queen II" arrived at Mwanza, and three days later passed over Tabora, overtaking the *Times* machine, which had crashed there on the 27th. Had a landing been made, the stranded airmen and Dr. Chalmers-Mitchell would have been picked up and taken on towards the Cape.

All went well with Col. van Ryneveld's effort as far as Bulawayo, where "Silver Queen II" crashed while leaving the aerodrome, after having covered 3,880 miles in 13 days.

But the plucky pilots were not to be robbed of a triumph. A new aeroplane—a De Havilland 9—was sent up from Cape Town, and on March 20 they completed their journey, on the very suitably named "Voortrekker" (Pioneer). Including the

11-day wait at Bulawayo, the flight had occupied just 4 weeks. The two South African Dutchmen were accorded a great reception in acknowledgment of their endurance and courage, and the Union Government voted them a sum of £5,000 as a reward for their achievement.

It is an interesting fact that Africa had been traversed lengthwise for the first time only 20 years earlier, and then from south to north, by a young Oxford undergraduate, E. S. Grogan, during a long vacation.

The route taken by the South African airmen was retraced some years later by Mr. Alan J. Cobham, the hero of many a long distance flight. His most remarkable exploit had been a journey with Air Vice-Marshall Sir W. Sefton Brancker, K.C.B., A.F.C., from London to Rangoon and back, a distance of 17,000 miles. The aeroplane used on that occasion, a de Havilland 50, had been built in 1923 and already had done much hard work with its 240-h.p. Armstrong-Siddeley "Puma" engine. The trip began on November 20, 1924, and terminated on March 19, 1925, the actual flying time being 220 hours.

Soon after his return Mr. Cobham was commissioned by Imperial Airways, Limited, to survey a route from Cairo to the Cape, and ascertain what would be useful intermediate air-routes from Cairo to Central Africa and from the Cape northwards. The task was a much more difficult one than the Rangoon expedition, as the aerodromes prepared for the 1919 flights had become overgrown and needed a great deal of attention.

It took four months of preparatory work, including the organisation of supplies of petrol, oil and spares along the route, to put things in order for the attempt.

The pilot selected for the journey another de Havilland machine of the same type. In view of the fact that the aeroplane would have to take-off in rarefied air from aerodromes thousands of feet above sea level, a 385-h.p. "Jaguar" engine was substituted for the less powerful "Puma." The "Jaguar," like the other, is of the radial air-cooled variety; and the flight would establish among other things the fitness of such a type for use in tropical regions where the more complicated water-cooled engines had given much trouble.

Mr. Cobham, a mechanic, and a photographer armed with cinematographic apparatus left Stag Lane Aerodrome, Edgeware, on November 16, 1925. As the object of the expedition involved a considerable amount of photography and reporting of topographical and other details, no attempt at a quick flight southwards was made. The aeroplane flew steadily from place to place without encountering any of the serious mishaps that had overtaken the machines of the pioneers, and eventually reached Cape Town on February 17, 1926, after having been only 94 hours in the air while turning off 8,500 miles. Mr. Cobham had the satisfaction of breaking a record, as the first man to fly from London to Cape Town in the same machine, using the original engine.

After a short stay at Cape Town, Mr. Cobham set off on the homeward flight, which, as his main purpose had been fulfilled, was to be "against time." The de Havilland left Cape Town on February 26, early in the morning and reached Kimberley the same day. On the 27th. the party alighted at Bulawayo, after dodging many tropical rainstorms, one of which broke just as the aeroplane touched ground, soaking the crew to the skin before they could get to shelter. At one point during this day's journey the interesting spectacle of 20 lions trotting along in single file was witnessed by the travellers.

Apart from heavy rainstorms no particular difficulties were met with until the confines of the Sudan had been reached.

CONQUERING THE AIR

Here the heat became almost unendurable, and even at an elevation of 7,000 feet it was 90° F. in the shade. Near the ground the thermometer ran up to 160° in the sun. Ordinarily, quick motion through the air has a cooling effect, but in this case the only wise course was to keep as much under shelter of the screens as possible. Putting one's head over the side exposed the face to what might have been the blast from a furnace.

After leaving Khartoum the aeroplane ran into a sandstorm, which persisted to a height of 12,000 feet. At that height visibility was limited to a few yards, except in a downwards direction, and the Nile afforded the only means of steering a course. Beyond Atbara what had been taken to be the great river proved to be nothing more than a shadow. Mr. Cobham therefore descended to reconnoitre, and picked up a deep dry watercourse, by following which he eventually reached the Nile. To make the short cut across the great bend of the river between Abu Hamed and Wady Halfa it was necessary to fly very low and steer entirely by the railway track and telegraph posts for a distance of over 200 miles. From Wady Halfa to Assouan the river, which, thanks to some abatement of the dust storm, could now be seen clearly, showed the way. On the following day 480 miles were covered in 4¾ hours, and Mr. Cobham and his companions landed on March 7 on the Heliopolis aerodrome, near Cairo. The northward journey of 5,500 miles had occupied only 9½ days, and it was the first to be made in this direction across the length of Africa.

A 60-mile-per-hour north-westerly gale held up progress a day at Cairo. On the 9th. Mr. Cobham flew to Sollum, where a broken tail skid lost him another day. This was, however, a blessing in disguise, as a gale had been raging on the Mediterranean which might have had serious results had he faced it.

FROM CAIRO TO THE CAPE BY AIR

The 11th. saw the de Havilland at Athens. The next day Mr. Cobham crossed Greece and the Adriatic Sea to Taranto in Italy, and then flew over the Appenines to Pisa. Leaving this place early on the 13th., he took a straight line to Lyons over the Alps at a height of 12,000 feet, getting a magnificent panorama of the mountains. At Lyons the tanks were filled up and a course was laid direct for Paris and London. The arrival of the famous airman was awaited at the Croydon air port by a huge crowd. Before he came in sight a large number of aeroplanes rose and went to meet him and accompany him to the landing place. The flight finished at 4.20 p. m., and had then taken less than 15 days from Cape Town. The mail steamer *Windsor Castle* left that port at the same time as the aeroplane; but though it travelled day and night continuously, and had 3,000 fewer miles to go, it did not reach England till two days after the aeroplane, which had alighted 26 times *en route* and spent the larger part of the 15 days on the ground.

In the evening Mr. Cobham was received by the King, to whom he handed a letter from the Governor-General of South Africa, the first letter to be brought by air to England from the southern part of the Dark Continent.

The expedition was a triumph for the pilot, the aeroplane and the engine. The last never faltered in the most intense heat, when air "cooling" seemed almost impossible; and it appeared also not to resent having its induction pipes invaded by dust in large quantities when sandstorms were encountered.

CHAPTER 18

It is only in accordance with the natural fitness of things that the first continent to be crossed in a single flight should have been the United States, the birth-place of the practical aeroplane. In no country could such a flight have greater significance, for the United States are divided geographically by great mountain ranges and deserts into two naturally rich and fertile regions one of which is washed by the Atlantic, the other by the Pacific Ocean. The continent was not crossed by white men till centuries after its first settlement by British pioneers. In fact, not until 1805 did explorers find a way through the mountains from the east to the Pacific coast.

The discovery of gold in California in 1848 led thousands of people to face the terrible hardships and dangers of a transcontinental journey in the four-wheeled "prairie schooner." Many of them left their bones in the waterless alkali deserts and in the folds of the hardly less forbidding mountains. But the lure of gold brought wave after wave of immigrants into California, and when they found how good a country this was, apart from its mineral wealth, the future of the Pacific Slope was assured.

At first it took six months to reach San Francisco by land from the Missouri. The provision of roads cut down the time considerably, but California remained more or less isolated until political considerations brought about the construction of the Union Pacific Railway, followed in due course by the laying down of various other transcontinental tracks. The two oceans were now, in terms of time of travel, only four or five days apart; and intercommunication between East and West developed apace. The opening of the Panama Canal in 1915 brought the two coasts many thousands of miles nearer each other by water and the coming of the aeroplane promised an important third method of transport, with possibilities of placing San Francisco within a day's journey of New York. The transport of mails, money and documents across the States at a much higher speed than that of the fastest trains would confer advantages of which the business centres of America were well aware.

It was only natural that, in a country of great distances, with a large and energetic population of high mechanical attainments, the aeroplane should be exploited on an extensive scale. The crossing of the Atlantic by air in one bound turned the thoughts of American airmen to pitting their endurance and machines against the 3,000 or so miles separating the eastern and western shores of their country. The task was at least as dangerous as that of flying the ocean; for, though landings might be made safely at several points, in many districts a forced descent would be more dangerous than on to the waves of the Atlantic. What chance of surviving would a pilot have if he rammed a peak of the Rockies by night, or were driven by engine failure to alight in one of the deep canyons which intersect the high ground?

We may begin the story of how the deed was done by introducing our readers to Lieutenants John A. Macready and Oakley G. Kelly, of the U. S. Army Air Service, who are the heroes of this chapter. Lieutenant Macready, a graduate of Leland Stanford University, and a well-known amateur boxer, started earning his living as a miner, cattleman and lawyer.

CONQUERING THE AIR

During the war he entered the aviation section of the U. S. Signal Corps, and in due course became a very capable military airman. His professional duties associated him with a worthy comrade, Lieutenant Kelly, to whom belongs the credit of suggesting a transcontinental non-stop flight, and doing a great deal of the necessary preliminary work, upon which in a very large degree depended the success or failure of the attempt. A suitable aeroplane, also the petrol and oil that would be used by its engine, had to be chosen and tested carefully. The selection of a course demanded the closest study of the geography and physical features of the United States. Special maps must be prepared; and close contact established with the Weather Bureau, so that a start should be made when there was a fair prospect of favourable weather. The United States are so vast that, without the aid of the telegraph and wireless, the picking of a suitable day would be sheer guesswork.

The machine eventually chosen was a Transport T2, a monoplane of Fokker type, driven by a single 420-h.p. Liberty engine. It could carry 557 gallons of petrol in tanks inside the wings, and another 180 gallons in a large tank in the fuselage. This quantity was estimated to suffice for the transcontinental flight, with a fair margin to spare, assuming the winds not to be adverse. We may note in passing that 737 gallons of petrol take up a good deal of room—120 cubic feet—and weigh about $2\frac{1}{4}$ tons. The aeroplane could just get off the ground if its total weight,—including fuel, pilots, spares, etc.,—did not exceed 10,850 pounds.

As the prevailing winds in the United States blow from west to east, the two airmen decided to start from the Pacific coast and fly eastwards. There was one serious drawback. The highest mountains would be encountered comparatively early in the flight, when the petrol load had not been reduced sufficiently to make high flying possible, so that it would be necessary to traverse them through passes, with a good chance of hitting the peaks if fog or clouds hid the course.

On October 4, 1922, the airmen started for Long Island, 2,700 miles away, from Rockwell Field, San Diego, just north of the Mexican border, with their machine so heavily laden that it ran a mile along the ground before it got clear. After circling round twice to gain height, a course was laid due north for Temecula Pass, 50 miles distant. The aeroplane rose very slowly but steadily, and cleared the pass. Near San Jacinto it ran into thick fog, through which nothing was visible 50 feet off. To attempt to find a way through the mountains under such conditions was more than even the bravest of airmen would consider for a moment, so the machine was turned about. Instead of landing on reaching San Diego, the Lieutenants decided to convert the cross-country flight into an endurance test. This would furnish valuable information about the consumption of water, oil and petrol, and give them a chance of finding out their own capacities for "sticking it." Incidentally, there was the possibility of lowering the duration record of 27 hours odd; and the certainty of escaping any chaffing over so speedy a return after much farewell handshaking and back-slapping.

When over Rockwell Field the airmen dropped a message telling of their intentions, and then, taking six-hour spells of piloting, they circled the aerodrome for the rest of that day, the night following, and the next day until dusk, when for safety's sake they landed while the ground was still visible. They had been in the air continuously for 35 hours 18 minutes, and had broken the duration record by more than eight hours. Unfortunately, the record was not accepted by the International Association, owing to some formality not having been observed. The two pilots at least had the satisfaction of knowing after this feat that both the aeroplane and they could last out a journey which was not expected to take nearly so long; and they had gained some very useful experience in regard to the working routine of a very long stay aloft.

A month passed by before weather and other conditions warranted a second attempt. At San Diego everything looked lovely, but on the further side of the Rockies the winds were unkind. On the night of November 2, favourable weather reports came in, and the two airmen hurriedly prepared for the second start, which they made next morning as soon as it was light enough to see.

Using their previous experience, this time they flew several miles out to sea to gain height, before heading for the mountains. They were thus able to get through the Temecula Pass easily, and cross the higher mountains beyond as far as Banning, in California, where the aeroplane had attained a height of 2,400 feet. Then across the Salton Sea, a body of very salt water which, like the Dead Sea, is below sea level.

After this the aeroplane sped for 400 miles over the barren lands through which the great Colorado River has cut deep canyons. As Tucson was approached the ground began to rise into the spurs of the Rockies so rapidly that at times the climbing powers of the machine hardly sufficed to clear the summits. In this broken country the atmosphere was much disturbed by currents which tossed the aeroplane up and down hundreds of feet, so that there were several rather anxious moments and the pilot's muscles became tired with controlling his large and heavy craft. At Deming, New Mexico, the elevation reached 5,200 feet, and much higher ground lay ahead.

On, on, over the extensive salt marshes and great lava beds of New Mexico, studded with the craters of extinct volcanoes, into which aviators now peered for the first time. The passage of the great bird caused a stir among the Indian inhabitants of this strange country, and no doubt was long discussed in their cave dwellings. The aeroplane was now climbing as fast as the decrease of its petrol load permitted, but not sufficiently fast to clear the highest ground that had to be traversed near Ticelote. After all but hitting a mountain, the pilot turned round and flew several miles in the wrong direction, until it was reckoned safe to try again. Still not enough height, so a second detour, lasting 40 minutes, was made, and at the third trial the T2 passed the summit with about 30 feet to spare.

The most dangerous part of the journey was now done, and ahead lay the great prairies of Oklahoma and Kansas. But difficulties were by no means over, for night fell, clouds formed, and a strong side wind rose. Rain set in, and all round were thunderstorms with bright lightning flashes which lit up the landscape below. Keeping very low to avoid the clouds, the pilot managed to dodge the worst storms; and many an isolated rancher must have been startled when a great monster roared out of the darkness over the roofs and flashed out of ken, pouring flames from its exhaust pipes. On the whole the airmen were lucky, as the storms they met were the fringes of a violent tornado, which did great damage in the countries traversed by it.

For a while a railway proved a useful guide, but in Texas this was left and a course steered by compass for the junction of the Missouri with the Mississippi. The strong side wind made it difficult to keep to the correct line, but shortly before dawn the lights of St. Louis were sighted, showing the reckoning to be correct. The pilots welcomed the daylight after over twelve hours of darkness which, as one of them admits, had been very trying to his nerves.

CONQUERING THE AIR

Considerably more than half the distance to be flown now lay behind, and the aeroplane, relieved of a good part of the original load, was flying easily. But ill fortune presently supervened, in the shape of cracked cylinder jackets, from which the cooling water began to escape in such quantities that a descent must be made. The "resting" pilot poured everything liquid available into the radiator—water, coffee, and even soup! At Indianapolis the engine was evidently at its last gasp, and became so hot that it "seized" just as the T2 glided on to the landing ground.

Both pilots, in disgust at this stroke of bad luck, vowed themselves finished with transcontinental flights—but after a few days' rest began to scheme another attempt, this in the reserve direction—from east to west. They would then not encounter very high ground until the aeroplane was in a condition for flying high, after using up the bulk of its petrol. If only they could take advantage of one of the winds which occasionally blows from east to west, they would have a much greater chance of success than they had enjoyed during the previous attempts.

But the desired winds would not set in until April, and to help fill in the time they removed to Dayton and made renewed attacks on the duration record, which an enterprising French airman had just raised to 34 hours. Three times during the winter they tried, and three times they failed. But on April 17 and 18 they stayed in the air just over 36 hours, so beating not only the Frenchman, but their own feat of the previous October. By a very interesting coincidence, the ground from which they started was the very one over which the brothers Wright had made their earliest flights; and Orville Wright himself acted as official observer. He must have felt much as George Stephenson would feel were he able to watch the passage of a huge present-day express locomotive. Only twenty years separated the earliest few-minute flights of his crude biplane from the day-and-a-half performance of the great monoplane on which he had to keep an official eye! So rapidly has aviation advanced.

The engine of the "plane" having been changed, the pilots flew to Mitchel Field, on Long Island, and made ready for their long flight back to California. After a few days of waiting, the wind conditions became favourable. The aeroplane was accordingly transferred to the more spacious aerodrome at Roosevelt Field for its tanks to be filled.

At 12.36 p. m. on May 2, 1923, the aeroplane, after two unsuccessful attempts, rose from the ground and with difficulty cleared the hangars and some telegraph wires, so heavily laden was it. Very, very slowly it gained height as it passed over Coney Island and Pennsylvania. Quite early in the journey the ignition apparatus developed a fault, and would have brought the aeroplane down sooner or later had Lieutenant Kelly not been able to make a very delicate adjustment while the machine was in flight.

As night fell the airmen were over Dayton, well ahead of schedule time, but with clouds massing and a long night in front of them. The fact that they were flying westwards, and therefore away from the sun, would increase the period of darkness from $12\frac{1}{2}$ to $13\frac{1}{2}$ hours, since in $12\frac{1}{2}$ hours they would cover one twenty-fourth of the earth's circumference, or thereabouts. Flying in total darkness is very trying unless there be some light visible to give the pilot a point to steer by. Failing this, he must depend entirely upon the instruments on the dashboard of his cockpit to tell him whether he is flying level, or even right way up; and the instruments are but a very poor substitute for the natural sense of balance derived through the eyes. Darkness also makes it difficult to estimate the drift, caused by cross winds, which may carry the pilot far out of his course. And when darkness is accompanied by rain, mist, or fog, conditions are further aggravated.

The moon rose as the aeroplane neared Terre Haute, but thick clouds overhead blocked its light out completely. The pilot suddenly noticed flickers on the propeller, which at first he thought to be caused by his companion examining the machinery with his flashlamp. But the light gradually strengthened and soon resolved itself into a powerful beam appearing periodically on the left, sweeping the sky towards the right, and then disappearing. This was the great revolving searchlight at Belleville, 70 or 80 miles ahead, emitting a beam of 450,000,000 candle power, to guide the airmen. As the aeroplane passed overhead the beam was turned on to it, as a sign of greeting. The T2 then sped into the darkness again, amid a thin drizzle, and with but very occasional lights to show where the earth was.

During their long flights together Lieutenants Macready and Kelly relieved each other every six hours. The active pilot occupied a small cockpit in the nose of the machine abreast of the engine. Ten feet further aft was a duplicate control, to be used only in emergencies, as from it the pilot had a very limited view through a door in the covered-in fuselage. When the end of a spell came, the pilot signalled to the "relief" to take the helm, by shaking his wheel vigorously. An exchange had to be made quickly by the one sliding out of his seat and the other sliding into it. The periods "off" could not be spent in sleep, as the relief pilot had to attend to a number of details, such as checking consumption of petrol and oil, examining the engine, making any small repairs needed, and taking food, in the shape of sandwiches, broth, and coffee,—the two last carried in half-gallon thermos flasks. So that both pilots had to go without any sleep at all, while they were in the air.

Soon after midnight the aeroplane emerged from under clouds into bright moonlight, very welcome to the airmen, as they could now see the fences subdividing the "sections" of land underneath them. A section is a square mile, and its boundaries invariably run due north and south and due east and west, so that they give valuable help in deciding direction and drift. For several hours the course lay over the Kansas and Oklahoma prairies, showing pale in the moonlight and sprinkled here and there with the lights of towns or settlements.

As sunrise approached, the fields of Oklahoma gave way to the curiously eroded country of New Mexico, and below them the airmen recognised Tucumcari, the very place which they had wished to reach at dawn. In fact, they had delayed the start an hour or two to prevent any possibility of encountering the difficult country further west during the period of darkness. Beyond Santa Rosa the course lay over the barren volcanic country through which the muddy Rio Grande winds its way south-eastwards, to St. John's, in Arizona. The ground now rose so fast that the aeroplane could hardly keep above it, though the altimeter (height indicator) registered 10,000 feet. At last the pilot had to recognise that the course mapped out over the mountains must be abandoned, and a hunt for a practicable opening through them began. For miles the aeroplane skimmed close to the top of a great forest until a pass came in sight which looked promising. But instead of leading into the expected cultivated valley, it opened into a series of canyons of very uninviting aspect, and so narrow as hardly to give room for turning about. It became necessary to take a chance and fly west by compass. The T2 at last reached easier country to fly over, though very bad to land on—the sandy and rocky wastes of Arizona. Presently the Colorado River came in sight, and fell behind. Then followed the wide Imperial Valley, refreshingly green to the eye with its cultivated fields.

Only one more range now remained to be crossed, and this the T2 managed easily enough. On the further side the pilot descried San Diego, the end of the journey; and none too soon, for the two men were now both so thoroughly worn out as to be unable even to feel any excitement at having all but completed their difficult task. Anxious to reach ground as quickly as possible, they dived down from 8,000 feet and passed just over the roofs of the houses, which, to their surprise, were black with people on the watch for them. One of the onlookers, on the top of one of the city's skyscrapers, became so excited that he took off his coat to wave it, and finally, in an excess of enthusiasm, flung it down into the street.

The T2 landed in Rockwell Field at 11.26 a. m. on May 3, having travelled about 2,700 miles in 26 hours 50 minutes, at an average speed of about 100 miles an hour. Lest the reader should imagine that a mistake has been made in the time—for the aeroplane left Long Island at 12.36 p. m., the previous day —he must remember that the "local" time of San Diego is far behind that of New York, owing to the difference in longitude.

Soon after their arrival the two airmen began to receive telegrams of congratulation sent by Americans of all ranks, from the President downwards. One of them asked the acceptance of £1,000 won by a gentleman who had betted to that extent on their success.

FIRST NON-STOP FLIGHT ACROSS AMERICA

Across the United States in One Day.

About a year after the performance of the feat just described Lieutenant Russell L. Maughan, of the United States Air Service, crossed the continent from Long Island to San Francisco in one day, between dawn and dusk. On June 23, 1924, he left Mitchel Field at 3 a. m. (Eastern Standard Time), and 21 hours 48 minutes later he landed in Crissy Field, San Francisco. The flight differed, however, in one important respect from that of Macready and Kelly, as it was divided into six sections, intermediate descents being made at Dayton, St. Joseph (Missouri), North Platte (Nebraska), Cheyenne, and Salduro (Utah), for refuelling. The machine used was a Curtiss Pursuit aeroplane. Lieutenant Maughan had to wait an hour at Dayton for a repair to the starting handle; and of the total "elapsed" time only 17 hours 52 minutes were actually spent in the air, so that the average speed for the 2700 miles exceeded 150 miles an hour—an easy record for a flight of such length. It is difficult to compare this feat with that of the other two airmen, for the machine, having to carry only sufficient fuel for a "hop" of 600 miles, was not heavily laden; and the pilot had periodical rests. On the other hand, he was at the helm during the whole time of flight, having no companion to relieve him, and had to stand the racket of much higher speed.

They were both of them great achievements, and we may leave the matter at that.

CHAPTER 19

AIRCRAFT IN THE POLAR REGIONS

THE enormous difficulties that explorers of the polar regions have to overcome, not only as regards finding a way over ice-packs, across open "leads," up glaciers and over snow plateaux, but in the constant struggle against cold and starvation, render this form of exploration the most arduous that human beings can undertake. They must rely entirely on themselves; if things go wrong, there is very little chance of finding help in a region ordinarily quite untenanted by mankind.

The idea of exploring those inhospitable tracts by air was first considered many years ago. The possibility of floating swiftly in a few hours through distances which on foot would demand as many weeks, or even months, of strenuous toil and hardship to traverse, and at a height giving a much wider view than could be obtained in any other way, certainly possessed great attractions. Risks indeed there would be, but they hardly could be greater than those which had claimed so many victims from among explorers using the orthodox methods.

Not until the late 'nineties of last century, however, was any use made of balloons in attempts to reach a Pole. In 1895 a Swede, Auguste Saloman Andrée by name, chief engineer to the Swedish Patent Office, laid before the Academy of Sciences at Stockholm a scheme for making a dash to the as yet unattained North Pole in a balloon specially constructed and equipped for the purpose. Coming as the scheme did from one who had proved himself a daring aeronaut, and had had some experience of the polar regions, it received serious consideration, and, what was even more important, sufficient financial backing to enable it to be put to the test. The King of Sweden headed a subscription list, and his lead soon brought in the necessary funds.

Thus encouraged, Andrée toured Europe to collect any scientific information which would assist him. He also went thoroughly into the subject of manufacturing balloons, since the envelope of the one used for his expedition must be the very best obtainable. Eventually, Chinese silk was selected as the material, and M. H. Lachambre, of Paris, as the maker of a balloon designed to hold about 160,000 cubic feet of hydrogen gas. The thickness of the envelope was greater at the top, where the gas pressure would be highest, than at the bottom; a very special varnish was used; and, to prevent any possibility of chafing, the cords of the network covering the envelope were woven, instead of being knotted, together at points where they crossed.

The car took the form of a basketwork cylinder having a sloping bottom which, if it struck the ground, would slide along without revolving. In the sides were windows, and from the top hung a large number of cords with buckles at the ends, to which the multitudinous articles carried could be attached, such as compasses and other scientific instruments, cooking utensils, provisions, guns, ammunition, and so on. The equipment included sledges and a very cleverly constructed and light collapsible boat.

In order to reduce wastage of gas and ballast, and to render the balloon steerable within certain limits, three drag ropes, weighing about five hundredweight each, were provided. Each rope consisted of several sections joined end to end by catches that could be detached by turning a crank in the balloon.

Things were so arranged that the sections would fall off successively, beginning at the bottom. The drag ropes, by causing the balloon to travel slower than the wind, would give the wind a purchase on a sail put out on the side opposite to that towards which the course was to be deflected.

When completed, the balloon, probably the most carefully made and elaborately equipped ever put together, was exhibited in the Champ de Mars, in Paris, before being despatched to Gothenburg in Sweden. There it was embarked in the ship *Virgo*, along with the parts of an octagonal open-topped shed inside which it would be inflated, and the apparatus needed for inflating it. Towards the end of June, 1896, M. Andrée and eight companions—two of whom were to accompany him in the balloon—reached Dansk Gatt, a strait between Dane's Island and Amsterdam Island, to the north-west of Spitzbergen. Here the cargo was landed, and after much hard labour the balloon shed rose on the shores of the straits. The inflation of the envelope followed, and after that came the putting in place of the many items of cargo.

Andrée's plan was to await a south wind, which, he hoped, would blow him to the Pole. From the Pole he might be carried either to Alaska or into Siberia. He calculated that the balloon ought to keep aloft for a month—here he was probably over-optimistic—but, should a descent have to be made on to the ice, the sledges and other equipment were available for travel over it, and, since the stock of provisions was large, he thought his friends need feel no anxiety if he were missing for a year.

The wind, unfortunately for Andrée's plans, persisted in blowing from the north, and as the early and long northern winter was approaching, on August 17 the leader, to his bitter

A corner of one of the freight houses at Croydon Air Port, showing goods ready for transport by air to Cologne. [*Photo, Sport and General.*

Some of the buildings at Croydon Air Port. The central tower is the Control Tower, with platform all round for the look-out man. [*Photo, Sport and General.*

disappointment, had to order the deflation of the balloon, which was packed up and taken back to Gothenburg.

In May of the next year the expedition returned to Dansk Gatt, where the shed was found to have weathered the winter storms so well that a little work put it in good order. For the second time the balloon was inflated and equipped; and once again the expedition awaited a favourable wind. At last it came. On Sunday, July 11, Andrée and two companions, Strindberg and Fraenkel, entered the car, the word was given to cut the holding ropes, and the balloon rose majestically from inside the protecting shed. Weighted down by the drag-ropes, it was swept by a high wind across the water. The ropes caught on some rocks, giving the apparatus for detaching sections a chance of proving itself. This it did, and the balloon, maintained automatically at a constant height by the ropes, travelled fast northwards, crossed a ridge, and was lost to sight.

What happened to the three brave aeronauts will probably never be known. Eleven days after the start a pigeon shot by some fishermen was found to be carrying a despatch from Andrée dated July 13: and a week later a buoy was picked up carrying a message dated the day of the departure. Another buoy, found floating off Iceland in May, 1898, contained a despatch also dated July 11, 1897, dropped two degrees north of Spitzbergen.

Since then no trace whatever of the ill-fated expedition has come to light, though from time to time vague rumours, worthy of little credence, have drifted in from Siberia and northern Canada. Andrée may have been the first to reach the North Pole: in any case he deserves a tribute of admiration for his brave attempt to do so.

Ten years after this sad failure the American, Walter Wellman, made preparations, near the spot selected by Andrée, for seeking the Pole in an airship having a gas capacity of over a quarter of a million cubic feet, and driven by an 80-h.p. motor. Further description here is unnecessary, as it closely resembled the one used by the same aeronaut in that attempt to cross the Atlantic which forms the subject of an earlier chapter. Bad weather, the wreck of his balloon shed, and Peary's success in reaching the Pole, combined to make Wellman abandon his project.

The next intrusion of aircraft into polar regions dates as recently as 1923, when Mr. Hammer, the Dutch-American airman, took a seaplane to Spitzbergen, and, from his base at Green Harbour, conducted several successful flights over the northern part of the Island.

In 1924 the Oxford University Arctic Expedition, headed by Mr. F. G. Binney, made considerable use of an Avro seaplane to take aerial photographs of some 70 miles of the coastline of North-east Land, which lies eastwards of Spitzbergen. The machine had an air-cooled engine, and an enclosed cabin for the use of the observer. It carried a sledge—built into the rear part of the body—a wireless equipment, a tent, sleeping bags, ice axes, and rations for two men for two months, to afford a fair chance of escape overland in case of a forced landing. On one occasion the engine gave out, owing to the breakage of a piston, and Mr. Binney and his pilot had to alight some distance from the base. A strong current swept the seaplane out to sea, despite desperate efforts to bring it to shore with paddles improvised from ice axes and pieces of a box lid. Finding their efforts useless, the two men threw out a sea anchor, retired to the cabin, and hoped for the best. Their greatest trouble was thirst, as they had nothing drinkable aboard but a small flask of brandy and a bottle of concentrated lime-juice. After drifting for six hours they entered very rough water, where the seaplane was tossed about like a cork and waves broke over the upper wings. As a last resort the pipe connecting the fuel tank with the engine was cut, so that the escaping petrol might lessen the force of the waves. All hopes of rescue had been given up when three Norwegians sighted the derelict and very pluckily put out to its rescue in a small motor boat which, after nearly being swamped, took the seaplane in tow and brought it back into safety. Thanks to its stout construction, the machine had not suffered very serious damage, and after being repaired it enabled a large number of aerial photographs to be taken. When the Expedition started back for England, the Avro had to be left to the mercies of the Arctic winter.

A very interesting aerial adventure in the Arctic regions occurred in May and June, 1925, when Captain Roald Amundsen, the Norwegian conqueror of the South Pole, and five companions, tried to reach the North Pole in two flying boats.

Headquarters were made at King's Bay, Spitzbergen, where there is a large settlement—the most northerly in the world—associated with the working of extensive coal mines. King's Bay is only 700 miles from the Pole, and easily accessible. The machines selected had each two 360-h.p. Rolls-Royce engines, and a boat body divided into five watertight compartments by cross bulkheads with communicating hatchways. The foremost was the navigator's cabin; then came the pilot's compartment, with two seats and duplicate controls; then the tank compartment; then one used as mess and storeroom; and finally a long, tapering, and unoccupied compartment at the tail end. When fully loaded each flying boat weighed about six tons. For the benefit of the uninitiated reader it may be pointed out that a flying boat differs from a seaplane, such as the Avro referred to above, in that it has no separate floats, the body being made boat-shape and resting directly on the water. It is, in fact, a covered-in boat, connected with a superstructure which includes the planes, struts, engines, etc.

On the afternoon of May 21, the two machines, distinguished as N24 and N25, were ready to start. In N24 were Messrs. Ellsworth, Dietrichsen, and Omdahl; in N25, Captain Amundsen, his pilot Rüser-Larsen, and Mr. Feucht, a mechanic.

At 5 p. m. the N25 took the air, followed closely by the N24. A low-lying fog bank forced the machines to a height of 3,000 feet, at which, for a couple of hours or so, only occasional glimpses could be caught of ice below through openings in the mist. In latitude 82° N. the fog ceased, and a gleaming world of unending ice was seen stretching in all directions to the horizon. Not a single spot presented itself whereon a safe landing could possibly be made, but this did not cause anxiety, as the engines were running perfectly. At the same time the inhospitable character of the ice-fields showed that the risks of the enterprise were greater than had been anticipated. The wind now blew freshly from the north-east, reducing speed considerably. But the two flying boats kept on steadily northwards, within easy sight of one another.

At 1 a. m. on May 22, when the flight had lasted just nine hours, his mechanic told Amundsen that half the petrol had been consumed. If they were to turn back they must do so now, but in order to find their exact position a landing must be made, as ordinary methods of observation could not be followed in the air so close to the Pole. The N25 accordingly dropped to 300 feet and cruised about searching for a possible landing place. One of the engines now began to backfire and show signs of stopping altogether. This made a descent unavoidable, since one engine could not keep the machine in the air. Fortunately, at the critical moment the N25 happened to be passing over an ice lane, covered with new ice, with high walls on either side—a kind of level *cul-de-sac*.

Into this Rüser-Larsen headed the N25, and by good luck the flying boat came to rest undamaged, just short of the end of the lane, with its nose up against the high ice. Soon afterwards the lane closed up behind the N25, and it was now fairly trapped in a hollow between much higher floes which might at any moment close in and crush it. The position was thus a very critical one. To get the machine into the air again appeared impossible. Whether the N24 also had landed, and, if so, where, was unknown.

Observations taken during the night, gave the position of the landing as 87 deg., 43 min., 2 sec., North Latitude, and 10 deg., 19 min., 5 sec., West Longitude. They were therefore only 140 miles from the Pole, and in nine hours had got nearer to it than any other explorer save Peary, who had actually reached it in 1909.

The N25 soon became frozen in, resisting all efforts to move it. So Amundsen decided that the only course open was to make on foot for Cape Columbia, to the north-east of Greenland, and over 400 miles away. The prospect cannot have been a very pleasing one, as the party had no dogs, and with the polar pack thawing and breaking up in the summer heat travelling conditions would be at their very worst.

After a fruitless search for N24, the three men made another effort to free the flying boat, and manœuvre it up a slope on to the floes, whence they might possibly be able to launch it. The engine trouble had been traced to a leaky induction pipe, easily put right. While they were endeavouring to cut away the ice, a Norwegian flag was seen waving in the distance, and presently the crew of the N24 came into sight, on the further side of a "lead" covered with new ice. Their flying boat had been landed not far away, but had sprung a leak which would have sunk it had not the crew managed to haul it up on to the ice. While trying to join Amundsen's party two of the other men went through the ice and would undoubtedly have been drowned but for the life-saving waistcoats bought just before leaving Norway.

All six now set to work on clearing N25, and with the engines running full out, and five of the party pushing their hardest, the flying boat was got on to a floe. An examination of N24 decided Amundsen to abandon it and endeavour to take the whole party home in the sister machine. They therefore stripped N24 of petrol and stores and devoted their whole attention to doing what they could with N25. Difficulty after difficulty had to be faced and conquered, and as every day reduced the limited food supply, it became evident that, if they did not succeed by a certain date, the idea of flying back to Spitzbergen must be abandoned while sufficient food for a land trip still remained.

An attempt to start from the floe on to which the N25 had been moved proved a failure, for the ice gave way under the heavy load. During the following night, while the craft was still in the water, the man on watch shouted "Turn out! Turn out!" The ice was moving and threatening to crush the boat to pieces. Some hacked for dear life, to relieve the pressure, while others carried stores and equipment ashore to prevent them too being lost. Eventually the danger passed for the time being.

The next ten days or so were spent in making track after track across the floes along which to get the flying boat moving. Hollows had to be filled up with broken ice and snow trampled hard and rough stretches levelled off: very exhausting work for men whose food had to be sternly rationed. Five tracks in succession were rendered useless by the ice moving, and the N25 suffered some serious injuries from the same cause. At last June 15 was fixed as the day on which, if they failed to get into the air, they would start on foot for Cape Columbia.

The sixth track fared like the other five; but at the seventh attempt better fortune favoured them. A surface 12 yards wide and 600 yards long was cleared of snow, to expose the ice beneath. But before this was compacted sufficiently hard for the purpose the men had to do three days' hard trampling.

On June 14 the engines were started up, but the flying boat refused to rise. Everything that possibly could be spared having been thrown overboard, the pilot tried again. Another failure, the track was too bad; and there was no facing wind to help.

They reached the day of fateful decision, June 15. It was a case of "now or never" as regards getting home through the air. The next few hours would decide whether they should see Spitzbergen again that day or have to face months of painful and dangerous travel over the ice.

With June 15 came fortunately a fall in temperature to harden the ice, and a breeze blowing in the right direction. Feeling more hopeful than they had been before, the six men took their seats. The great machine began to glide forward, gathered speed, jumped a small dip in the ice on to another floe, and at last the gallant six enjoyed the inexpressible delight of being in the air again. It is a fine tribute to the engines that the men now considered themselves as good as at home.

This confidence justified itself. The flying boat soon rose above a fog stratum to a height of 3,000 feet, and swung somewhat away from the outward course, to survey new country.

CONQUERING THE AIR

While the men munched biscuits and chocolate to their hearts'
content, free from all need for rationing, the good N25 headed
for North Cape in Spitzbergen. At last the mountains of that
country came in sight, also the waters of Hinlopen Strait,
lashed into white-topped waves by a stiff breeze. A trouble
which, had it developed a bit sooner, might have had disastrous
effects, now threatened a difficult ending to the flight. The
ailerons, or flaps at the rear edge of the main planes, used for
maintaining sideways balance, began to work more and more
stiffly, and finally jammed. The pilot was therefore compelled
to alight on the sea. The flying boat had a very rough time
in the waves, but the pilot managed to "taxi" it safely to land
on the west side of North Cape. With infinite relief the men
felt their feet on hard ground again, even though the ground
was some distance from their destination. Any anxiety as to
being able to reach King's Bay was, however, soon set at rest
by the reappearance of a small sealing ship. Getting aboard
their flying boat again, they hurried out to meet it, and once
on its deck they considered their adventure to be at an end.

All things considered, they came out of it very well. In a
region of ice hummocks and rough floes they were remarkably
fortunate in striking a spot on which to descend without wreck-
ing the machines. Again, it was a piece of good luck that
at the eleventh hour, or more correctly at one minute to twelve,
they succeeded in rising from the ice. They certainly deserved
to get away after their plucky and exhausting fight, waged
against long odds for more than three weeks.

Captain Amundsen announced soon after his return to civilisation that an airship had been purchased from the Italian
Government wherewith to fly from Spitzbergen to Alaska.
After his recent experiences he felt that an airship, with its
more leisurely and controllable gait, and its ability to remain

aloft for long periods, was more suitable than a heavier-than-air machine for carrying out an Arctic survey.

The *Norge*, as the dirigible was named after Amundsen's native land, Norway, belonged to the semi-rigid class, of which it was a notable example, having a gas capacity of 670,000 cubic feet. Three 250-h.p. motors gave it a maximum velocity of 62 miles an hour; and at cruising speed it could travel 5,000 miles without refuelling. In preparation for the voyage, the roomy cabins originally provided were removed to reduce weight and allow of carrying extra fuel and the special outfit required. This included a wireless equipment for direction-finding and keeping in touch with ships and land stations at distances up to 1,000 miles.

The airship, with a crew of nineteen, under the command of Col. I. N. G. Nobile, left Rome on April 10, 1926, and the next day reached Pulham, in Norfolk, having covered the 1,400 miles in thirty hours. Leaving Pulham on April 13, it made for Oslo, in Norway, where it arrived the following evening. On the 15th. it flew from Oslo to Gatchina, near Leningrad, and there remained weather-bound for the rest of the month.

The temporary shed erected in Spitzbergen was reached without any misadventure, and on May 11 the *Norge* started for the Pole and Alaska. It passed over the Pole at 3.30 a.m. on May 12. Here the elevation of flight was reduced to 600 feet for a careful survey, but nothing could be seen except thin ice and open water. Nor was any land sighted between the Pole and Point Barrow, in Alaska.

Amundsen's intention was to end the voyage at Nome, but the airship encountered dense fogs and heavy snowstorms, which upset his plans. The fog froze on the rigging, forming icicles, some of which, as they fell, were caught by the propellers and hurled like bullets through the envelope. The crew were kept busily at work patching the leaks. Eventually the search for Nome had to be abandoned, and the commander decided to descend at Teller, 75 miles northwest of Nome. The whole of the local Eskimo population assisted in mooring the ship under the direction of a member of the crew who had dropped with a parachute to superintend operations.

In the 71 hours elapsed since leaving Spitzbergen the *Norge* had covered nearly 3,400 miles. During the whole of the time the crew had been on duty, or at least awake, since the intense cold made sleep impossible. The voyage, however, had been a complete success, proving conclusively that no polar continent existed, and showing the possibility of travelling from Europe to the Orient by way of the North Pole—a short cut as compared with routes in warmer latitudes.

In the meantime, another intrepid flier had passed over this region, so long the goal of explorers both by land and air. On May 9, 1926, at 12.50 a.m., Lieut.-Commander Richard E. Byrd of the United States Navy, with his pilot Floyd G. Bennett, in the airplane *Josephine Ford*, sighted the Pole. These fliers left the town of Kings Bay, Spitzbergen, early the morning of May 9, in a Fokker plane driven by three powerful motors. Byrd's own description of the flight (quoted here by courtesy of the *New York Times*, in which it first appeared) follows:

"It was long past midnight, Greenwich time, when we left, and that was well, for should the sky be clear we would have excellent positions for the sun all the way to the Pole, with a higher sun as we went along.

"As I looked around from our slowly increasing altitude, it gradually came home to me with full force that, after all our trials, we were finally on our way and would go for the Pole as long as the motors lasted—and they were of the best.

AIRCRAFT IN THE POLAR REGIONS

"In case we should come down on the ice we were prepared as well as it had been possible for us to prepare to cope with the elements and fight our way back.

"I had given a great deal of attention to this, and we had on the plane with us, first, a short-wave radio with hand dynamo for sending in case we were forced down; second, the best hand-made sled for man hauling supplies over the snow; third, two and a half months' food, consisting mainly of pemmican, chocolate, pilot bread, tea, malted milk, powdered chocolate, butter, sugar and cream cheese (this food had been carefully worked out to give the greatest possible number of calories); fourth, a rubber boat for getting across leads in the ice; fifth, extra fur clothes and shoes; sixth, a rifle and pistol and ammunition; seventh, a Primus gasoline stove; eighth, a light waterproof tent; ninth, hunting knives, ice knives and axes; tenth, a complete medical kit with surgical instruments; eleventh, smoke bombs.

"We soon reached Cape Mitre, 20 miles from Kings Bay, flying around a thousand feet and climbing in spite of the heavy load. Just as Amundsen and Ellsworth had done last year, we headed north for Amsterdam Island. Would we also have an experience like theirs? Would we finally get back from the polar world? Must we look for a miracle to get us back to our base?

"Twenty-six miles from Cape Mitre we passed Haakon Peninsula, which is a high, jagged peak about the height our plane was flying, 2,000 feet. A line drawn from this peak tangent to Amsterdam Island's westernmost point lies in the true north direction, and I determined to take full advantage of this fact to line up the plane on the true north, and get the error or variation of the compass from the north, which is generally large and uncertain in the Arctic regions and causes navigation of the air in the Arctic to be far more difficult and uncertain than in most other parts of the world.

"In 5 or 6 minutes we came to Danes Island, where Andrée, thirty years ago, left for the Pole with two companions in a great free balloon. They were never heard of again. So, the only other two attempts to reach the Pole from Spitzbergen had met hard luck. Would ours be more fortunate? . . .

"To my great surprise, I saw the edge of the great polar ice pack only a few miles ahead, where I had expected it to begin fifty or a hundred miles further north. Then when we reached the edge of the ice pack I got another surprise. There were a very few small, broken pieces of ice at the edge of the solid pack. That probably was because it was early May and before the edge of the ice pack could be broken up by the heat.

"From then on until the end of the flight, I spent the busiest hours of my life. I knew we must navigate with considerable accuracy or we never could get back again. I lined Bennett up with the mountain on Haakon Peninsula and the westernmost edge of Amsterdam Island.

"Our sun compass was on a trapdoor in the top of the navigation compartment of the machine, and to get at the compass I had to stand on a box and stick my head and shoulders out into the windstream at the rear edge of the great wing of the plane. The sun was toward the north and the wing hid the sun from us. I could use our other compass through one of the cabin windows of the pilot's cockpit.

"I had noticed coming up the coast that we had a wind from the right, and fearing that was setting us out of our course I opened the trapdoor in the bottom of the plane to get the amount we were drifting and the speed of the plane from our drift indicator by sighting with it on the snow. . . .

"On the average, I calculated the drift and speed once every three or four minutes and when I found any change in the drift made the corrections for the course on the sun compass and then checked Bennett on the new course. . . . I was astonished at the accuracy of his steering. Luck was with us. There was not a bump in the air, no upward and downward currents that tilt the plane and throw the compass spinning. The sun was bright and we had a wonderful view of the formidable ice pack. It was covered everywhere with snow and criss-crossed with pressure ridges like a crazy quilt. The constant movement of the polar ice pack causes ridges and opens leads of water, but we saw very few such leads that had not recently been frozen over, with the fresh snowless ice looking greenish against the white snow around them."

When about an hour from the Pole it looked as if disaster might overtake the plane, almost within touch of the goal. Byrd's story continues:

"I suddenly saw what I thought was a bad oil leak in the right-hand motor. I took the wheel and asked Bennett to give me his opinion of the seriousness of the leak. He jotted down that it was very bad and that he was afraid the motor would not last long. What should we do? It was one of the big moments. We decided to keep on for the Pole and decide what to do after reaching it. We would fly with that motor as long as it would run. We were about an hour from the coveted goal and every minute of the time we were taking unexplored regions off the map. It was tough to have the motor trouble here so near the Pole and so far from land, but we would go on. . . .

"At the end of the hour I took my calculations and found that we were at the Pole! We reached it at 9.04 a. m. Greenwich time, just about the hour we had hoped to get there.

"Bennett and I shook hands simply and I went back into the cabin, stood at attention, and saluted for Admiral Peary. The

Navy had reached the Pole again, the blessed old Navy!"

Byrd and Bennett did not land at the Pole, but after taking observations, returned to Spitzbergen, which they reached by mid-afternoon—sixteen hours after their departure, having flown some 1,600 miles. Here they were met by Amundsen and Ellsworth, waiting to start on their own great adventure. "These two great heroes," said Byrd, "had been down on that polar ice and had gone through great suffering. They knew what lay before and beneath us during that flight. They knew and forgot self and all personal ambitions and were moved as I have seldom seen men moved." Three days later they were themselves above the Pole.

CHAPTER 20

THE FIRST FLIGHT ROUND THE WORLD

THE honour of being the first to circumnavigate the globe by air was one for which the nations were certain to compete as soon as aeronautics had reached a stage of sufficient development, and other conditions permitted. The difficulties of emulating in another element the hero of Jules Verne's famous novel were of such a character as to tax not merely the pluck and endurance of the individual airmen but the organising powers of other men who would necessarily have to play an important part in any attempt likely to promise reasonable hopes of success.

The Atlantic and Pacific oceans presented the main obstacles. The first had been flown both in a single jump and by stages, including one very long span. The second could obviously not be crossed except in high latitudes, where severe cold and fog would be a serious obstacle for the greater part of the year.

Suffice it to say that in 1924, when the various great flights recorded earlier in this book were already matter of history and examples of what could be done by determined pilots and good machines, several nations had entered the field,—France, Italy, Portugal, Britain, Argentina and the United States. The efforts of all except the last failed. The United States expedition won through and added a thrilling achievement to the many with which American airmen must be credited.

The American officers who took over the management of the

proposed flight, went about their work in a characteristically thorough manner. They decided that the route to be chosen should be "prepared" as far as possible by the forming of depots of stores, spare parts, and tools at selected places; so that, wherever misfortune might overtake an aeroplane, there would be a good chance of repair or replacement being effected. The route was subdivided into seven sections, each of which was entrusted to an advance officer, made responsible for arranging all matters that could in any way assist the airmen: for example, the laying down of mooring buoys in harbours, and providing accommodation at landing points. It may safely be said that the hard work done by these officers contributed very greatly to the success of the expedition.

Another important matter to which serious and prolonged consideration had to be given was the selection of suitable aircraft. Eventually Mr. Donald Douglas, of Santa Monica, California, received a commission to design a machine which could be made suitable for flying over both land and water, by means of interchangeable wheeled undercarriages and pontoons. The design that received official sanction was a biplane of 50-foot span, which, when fully loaded and carrying its crew of two, would scale something over 4 tons. The standard 450-h.p., 12-cylinder, Liberty engine was to be fitted.

A sample Douglas Cruiser having been built, it underwent severe tests at Dayton, Ohio, as a land machine, and afterwards at Hampton, Virginia, as a seaplane. When certain modifications had been incorporated and the model passed as satisfactory, four machines were ordered for the flight, and built under the eyes of the four men selected to pilot them. They were Major Frederick L. Martin, and Lieutenants Lowell H. Smith, Erik H. Nelson, and Leigh Wade, all of them men of great experience and tried capacity.

THE FIRST FLIGHT ROUND THE WORLD

The route finally selected was to begin at Seattle, Washington, follow the west coast of Canada and Alaska, the Aleutian Islands, the peninsula of Kamchatka, and the Kurile Islands to Japan. Thence the fliers would travel by Shanghai, Annam, and Saigon to Burma and India, and then take the usual route to Europe and England. The Atlantic would be crossed from the Orkneys, via Iceland and Greenland to Labrador—the path traced by the Vikings to whom the first discovery of the New World is now credited—by stages not exceeding 600 miles in length; and the east coast of America be followed to Boston, whence the airmen would proceed overland to Seattle. The Americans chose the westward direction in preference to the most popular eastward, as it fell in better with the climatic conditions to be encountered. Thus, given good luck, the airmen would escape the worst of the Northern Pacific fogs, the China Sea typhoons, and the Indian monsoons, and be across the northern Atlantic before winter set in.

The four machines were named after large towns on the north, south, east, and west of the United States—Chicago, New Orleans, Boston and Seattle. Passing over the stage of preparation, we may transport ourselves to Lake Washington, a few miles from Seattle, where, in the early days of April, 1924, the four machines, fitted with pontoons for the stage which would end at Calcutta, awaited the word to start. The pairing of aeroplanes and crews was as follows:

Seattle:— Major Frederick J. Martin (in command)
Sergeant Alva Harvey
New Orleans:—Lieut. Erik H. Nelson
Lieut. John Harding
Boston:— Lieut. Leigh Wade
Lieut. Henry H. Ogden

CONQUERING THE AIR

Chicago:—   Lieut. Lowell H. Smith
                   Lieut. Leslie P. Arnold

On April 6, early in the morning, the *Seattle, New Orleans,* and *Chicago* rose from the water, followed, after some delay, by the *Boston,* which was overladen and could not rise till lightened. The squadron followed the Straits of Georgia, between Vancouver Island and the mainland, until clear of the island. A glance at a good map will show that this strait is at its northern end much occupied by a multitude of islands, and as the expedition, before reaching these, had run into fog, the pilots were compelled to fly very low and so had some narrow escapes from collision with rocks and ships' masts.

After leaving the shelter of Vancouver Island the aeroplanes kept as much as possible behind other islands, fighting headwinds, sleet, and snow until, at 5 p. m. they reached Prince Rupert, their first stopping place. As they took the water Major Martin, almost blinded by the snow, brought the *Seattle* down in a sideslip, which might easily have put that machine out of the race, but unfortunately did only repairable damage.

On August 10 the four 'planes headed for Sitka, 300 miles north. Their way along this dangerous coast was made the more hazardous by fog, which very nearly brought the *Boston* and *New Orleans* to grief. At Sitka they were held stormbound for a few days, and on the 13th. they continued their journey to Seward, passing along the seaward end of the wonderful Malaspina Glacier, which is constantly discharging vast masses of ice into the waters of the Pacific. As on the preceding stretches, the pilots had many anxious moments, being overtaken by one snowstorm after another, which made it almost impossible to steer a course. They simply had to take their chance of dashing into headlands as they followed what they could see of the coast-line. But in the end the brave eight arrived safely at Seward.

April 15 witnessed the first serious mishap that overtook the expedition, as it flew from Seward to Chignik, a salmon cannery station on the Alaskan peninsula which points like a pistol at Asia. The *Boston, New Orleans,* and *Chicago* reached their destination after much buffeting by snowstorms, but the *Seattle* was missing. To turn back and hunt for it was impossible, owing to lack of fuel.

Major Martin had been forced down by a fracture of the crankcase and consequent loss of lubricating oil. Fortunately he was able to find shelter behind a headland, and the next morning the destroyers sent to search located the *Seattle*. A new engine was ordered by wireless to be sent from Dutch Harbour, the depot on the Aleutian Islands, and meanwhile the other three pilots were instructed to push on to that place and there await their leader.

The *Boston, New Orleans,* and *Chicago* reached Dutch Harbour on April 19, after the usual battle with snow squalls and headwinds. As this was the last important base before Japan, new motors were installed on all three planes to lessen the risks of the Pacific crossing.

On April 25 Major Martin, having received and fitted the new engine, left his shelter in very bad weather for Chignik, at which place he arrived late in the afternoon.

On the succeeding three days flight was impossible, and the *Seattle*, riding at her moorings in by no means peaceful water, got coated with some hundreds of pounds of frozen spray. This had to be chipped off before she could rise.

On April 30 Major Martin received weather reports from Dutch Harbour good enough to warrant an attempt to catch up with his companions. Unfortunately, local snowstorms made visibility very bad, and while taking a short cut across a headland Martin lost his way. The aeroplane presently entered a fog, and in trying to climb out of this it collided with a steep mountain side and was wrecked beyond repair.

Major Martin and Sergeant Harvey were now definitely out of the race, and in a somewhat desperate predicament,—left stranded amid fog in unknown mountains of a practically uninhabited country. Their emergency rations would, even with care, last but a short time.

For two days and nights the fog held them prisoners in such shelter as the battered 'plane provided. It then thinned sufficiently to justify some exploration, and the two men set off in search of human habitations. After passing two ridges they nearly fell over a precipice which barred the path and forced them to turn back and try another way.

At the end of three days of wandering, during which they suffered greatly from cold, hunger, snow-blindness and want of sleep, the two men stumbled upon a cabin in which they found food and shelter. Here they stayed two days while a blizzard, which they fortunately had not encountered in the open, raged outside. On May 9 they reconnoitred and struck salt water, which turned out to be Moller Bay, and next day they reached a salmon cannery at Port Moller and so ended their adventures. Their disappearance from human ken for ten days had caused great anxiety, and wireless messages filled the ether over the North Pacific. On May 2 an official order reached Dutch Harbour, appointing Lieut. Lowell Smith commander and instructing him to push on to Japan as soon as possible. Accordingly, on the following day the *Chicago* and her two companions moved on to Atka, an island nearly 400 miles west of Dutch Harbour, where they remained weather-bound till May 9. On that day they reached Attu, the most westerly of

THE FIRST FLIGHT ROUND THE WORLD

the Aleutian Islands and the very last outpost of North America. While held up here by the weather the airmen received by wireless the very welcome news that Major Martin and Sergeant Harvey had reached safety.

The way to Japan included the Komansdorski group of islands, belonging to Russia, the eastern coast of Kamchatka, and the long string of islands—the Kuriles—which form a series of stepping stones between Kamchatka and the Flowery Kingdom. A difficulty in the way was that no permission had been obtained to land in Russian waters or territory. Consequently, when the planes reached Copper Island of the Komansdorski group on May 15 they had to alight outside the three-mile limit close to the U. S. ship *Eider,* where they lay while negotiating with the local representatives of the Soviet. Next morning a boat came off with a message to the effect that no landing would be permitted, but by this time everything was ready for the next "hop"—to Paramushiri in the Kuriles— and the airmen therefore got away without delay on a long flight of about 600 miles which would bring them definitely to the western side of the Pacific. Flying due west, they presently picked up Kamchatka, and, making a left-hand turn, followed the coast above a low fogbank from which projected a string of ice-topped mountains. As they neared their destination the fog increased in depth and, in conjunction with snow and rain, gave them a good deal of trouble. They reached Kashiwabara Bay, in Paramushiri, safely at 11.35 a. m., and so completed the first aerial crossing of the Pacific. Shortly after their arrival came in a wireless message of congratulation from the Secretary of War at Washington.

A great reception awaited the airmen at Tokio, reached on May 24, and they had their fill of official and other functions. In the intervals they changed the engines and pontoons, in readiness for crossing the sea to Shanghai. This great port on the Yang-tse-Kiang welcomed them on June 4, but embarrassed them with the number of junks and smaller vessels which crowded the water so thickly that taking-off was a matter of great difficulty and some danger. On June 7 the three planes flew south to Amoy, and on the next day reached Hongkong, passing through the edge of a typhoon on the way. After two days at the British port, they left for Haiphong, in northern Annam; and June 11 saw them heading for Tourane, 400 miles further down the coast. During this flight the *Chicago* got her turn of engine trouble—a cracked cylinder jacket which led to serious internal damage and a forced landing in a lagoon which, luckily for Lieuts. Smith and Arnold, was within gliding distance when the engine finally struck work. The other two planes alighted close by, and on learning what was wrong their pilots set off to Tourane for help. On reaching that place Lieut. Nelson and a Frenchman went in search of the lagoon by car while a new engine was being brought up from Saigon by destroyer. After a good deal of hunting the *Chicago* was located, and towed by native craft along waterways to Hué, the capital of the country. While Smith and his companion were dismantling the old engine, a new one was being hurried by sea and land to replace it, and on June 15 the *Chicago* joined the other two ships at Tourane.

The expedition had now entered regions already traversed by other airmen, so there is no need to describe in any detail their further progress until England was reached on July 16. Proceeding from Tourane to Saigon, Bangkok, Rangoon, and Akyab to Calcutta, the crews there changed the pontoons for wheeled undercarriages, which would be retained until pontoons were replaced for the Atlantic crossing. As the flight approached Karachi, the engine on the *New Orleans* began to disintegrate, and Lieut. Nelson, after a fine display of airmanship, only just managed to bring his machine to port. The engines of all three planes were changed at Karachi.

After leaving this place the airmen made good progress: to Bandar Abbas on July 7, to Bagdad on July 8, to Aleppo on July 9, and to Constantinople on July 10. After resting one day, they made Bucharest on the 12th., Vienna, on the 13th., Paris on the 14th. A "day off" was taken for official receptions and to see the sights; and the Americans then hopped across the Channel to Croydon Air Port, which was left the following day for Brough, near Hull, where the machines were thoroughly overhauled and the pontoons fitted. During the fortnight that this work occupied the airmen visited London. It need hardly be said that they were given there a welcome worthy of the occasion.

On July 30 the party flew to Kirkwall, in the Orkneys, which was to be the jumping-off place for Hornafjord, in Iceland. During the next two days fog delayed a start, but on the 2nd. the planes left Kirkwall. Only a few minutes out they ran into a fog bank, and while getting clear from this the *Boston* and *Chicago* lost the *New Orleans*, and, after circling round a bit, returned to Kirkwall to await news. A few hours later the *New Orleans* was reported passing over the Faroe Islands, and the same evening a wireless message announced that Lieuts. Nelson and Harding had won through to Hornafjord, after a narrow escape from crashing in a fog.

The next day the *Chicago* and *Boston* went in pursuit. This time the *Boston* was scheduled by fate for engine trouble, which overtook her south of the Faroes, when the oil pump ceased working and a descent became unavoidable. The sea was rougher than it looked and the *Boston* received some severe damage. The *Chicago* circled round, but was waved away, as Lieut. Wade realised that his greatest hope lay in the companion plane summoning help. The *Chicago* therefore made off at top speed, dropped a note on Suderö Island and another close to the U. S. destroyer *Billingsby*, picked up north of the Faroes. The warship wirelessed to the U. S. cruiser *Richmond*, which also steamed to the rescue. Before they reached the *Boston*, however, she had been taken in tow by a trawler. Attempts to bring the seaplane to the Faroes were rendered fruitless by the waves, and on the arrival of the *Richmond* tackle was lowered to lift the *Boston* on deck. At the critical moment the tackle broke, and the *Boston* fell back heavily into the sea. She was patched up and taken in tow again, but the wind rose and during the night the plane sank when only one more mile would have brought her to land.

The two surviving crews moved on August 5 from Hornafjord to Reykjavik, the capital of Iceland, where they were welcomed by 25,000 people, and found several American warships in harbour. In this up-to-date city they had to remain for sixteen days, awaiting news of the weather ahead and of the establishment of depots on the Greenland coast. The original programme had scheduled a flight of 500 miles in a N. W. direction which would bring them to the nearest point of Greenland. A second flight of about the same length would take them along the coast and round the southern end of Greenland to Ivigtut, on the western side, facing Labrador. But it was found impossible, on account of an unusual amount of ice that year, to establish the nearer depot, and finally it was decided to form one at Fredricksdal, just round the southern end. This new arrangement entailed making an 830-mile hop, in place of a 500-mile, across open water.

On August 17 there arrived at Reykjavik the Italian airman Locatelli, and three companions, in a great Dornier Wal monoplane flying boat, engaged on the same task as the Americans. An invitation to join with them in the flight to Greenland and make use of the assistance of the American warships strung out along the route was accepted gladly.

On August 21 at 6.55 a. m. the three machines took off from Reykjavik harbour. The Italian was much the fastest of the three, and after vainly endeavouring to keep in step it shot ahead and was lost to view. The two Douglas Cruisers held steadily on their way, flying conditions at first being very good. Five hundred miles out, however, they entered thick fog which, strange to say, became worse as the wind increased in strength. The murk drove the machines down close to the water, within reach of the many icebergs dotted about the sea within 100 miles of Greenland. As the pilots could see only about 50 yards ahead, the chances of avoiding an iceberg directly in their path were small, and on more than one occasion they had escapes of the kind that brings the heart into the mouth.

Flying by compass course, the planes reached Cape Farewell, and rounded it to follow the western coast to Fredricksdal. The fog here was right down to the water, and the men flying above it could see nothing of the country below. But just as they came to where Fredricksdal was expected to be, the fog parted, and through an opening they spied a Danish ship, sending out smoke signals to show them that they were at Fredricksdal. Descending through the rift, the *Chicago* alighted on the water and reached its destination at 5.30 p. m. after a very trying journey lasting eleven hours. The *New Orleans* had been separated by the fog, but she arrived not long after the *Chicago*, making use of the same opening in the clouds. Of Locatelli there was no news. The American warships were sent in search of the Dornier Wal, and after three days' hunting she was located by the *Richmond's* searchlights, with her crew safe and sound. Locatelli, encountering the fog and fearing collison with icebergs, had alighted with the intention of going on when the weather cleared. Unhappily, some damage was done to the engine as the great machine took the water, rendering it unable to rise again: and, a heavy sea getting up, the tail was badly injured. So that, after the crew and their personal belongings had been taken aboard the *Richmond* the monoplane was scuttled, so that it might not be a danger to shipping.

On August 24 the *Boston* and *Chicago* flew to Ivigtut, where new engines were installed for the jump across to Labrador: and on the 31st. they left for Icy Tickle in that country, 560 miles away. The weather was considerably "mixed" but on the whole better than during the 830-mile trip. The *Chicago* narrowly escaped falling out of the race just before reaching America again, for the fuel pumps both failed 200 miles out from Labrador, and the reserve "gravity" tank did not contain sufficient fuel to carry the machine that distance against the strong head wind which had risen. Fortunately for Smith and Arnold, a hand pump had been fitted to cope with such an emergency, and by pumping continuously for three hours Arnold kept the reserve tank filled from the main tank, and so saved himself and his pilot from the horrible disappointment of failure at so late a stage.

At 3.20 p. m. August 31, 1924, the two planes alighted at Icy Tickle and could claim to be in America again. The crews were met by a message from the President of the United States, congratulating them on their great feat—also by a large number of reporters, who had long been in this out-of-the-way spot awaiting their arrival.

The journey southward to Boston was made in four hops.

THE FIRST FLIGHT ROUND THE WORLD

The first took the airmen along the fog-bound coast of Labrador, through Belle Isle Strait and close to the north-western coast of Newfoundland to Hawkes Bay. The next day, September 3, Pictou, in Nova Scotia, was reached. Here they were joined by their old comrades, Lieuts. Wade and Ogden, and a new Cruiser, *Boston II*, which had been brought there so that these two should have the satisfaction of "being in at the finish." The Nova Scotians gave them a foretaste of what might be expected in the way of welcome on reaching the United States.

On September 5 the three Douglas Cruisers set off for Boston. Following the north coast of Nova Scotia westwards, they crossed at the narrowest point of the neck joining it to the mainland into the Bay of Fundy, and kept to the coast of New Brunswick. Opposite St. John's thick fog met them, and this finally made it advisable to alight at Casco Bay, just over the national boundary line, in Maine. The next day an escort of ten aeroplanes brought the three Cruisers to Boston.

The six airmen were now back in their native land, though with more than 4,000 miles to cover before the circuit of the globe would be completed. Hardships—of which they had undergone many—lay behind them, but strenuous times awaited them during their triumphal progress to New York, Washington, Dayton, Chicago, Muskogee, Dallas, El Paso, San Diego, Los Angeles, San Francisco, Eugene, and finally, Seattle. They found, somewhat to their surprise, that their countrymen had followed their doings with the greatest interest and were determined to give full vent to their pride in and appreciation of the successful outcome.

The very splendid feat of airmanship briefly sketched in this chapter, ended at 1.28 p. m. (Pacific time) on September 28, 1924. The *Chicago* and *New Orleans* had covered 26,345 miles in a total flying time of 15 days, 3 hours, 7 minutes, distributed among 175 calendar days. Had the aeroplanes been able to travel as continuously as Mr. Phileas Fogg, they would have had that energetic traveller handsomely beaten.

The world will be circumnavigated by air countless times in the future by aircraft in comparison with which the Douglas Cruisers would look very small and flimsy. But nobody will be able to rob the six Americans of the honour of having done in the air what the companions of Magellan did centuries earlier on the seas.

CHAPTER 21

FROM ITALY TO JAPAN AND BACK

As judged by distance covered, the most remarkable aerial journey to be noticed in this book is one made in 1925 by a young Neapolitan, the Marchese de Pinedo, who had served through the war as a pilot, and afterwards occupied a high post in the Italian Air Service.

This daring airman, accompanied by a mechanic, left Rome on April 21, in a Savoia "amphibian" flying boat, having a single 450-h.p. engine, a maximum speed of about 124 miles an hour, and a cruising range of between 900 and 1,000 miles.

From Rome he flew to Brindisi, and thence, south of Asia Minor and north of Palestine, to Bagdad. From that city he took the usual route to India, and by May 12 was in Calcutta. Then, turning south, he flew to Akyab, Rangoon, Penang and Singapore, and worked his way along the Dutch East Indies to Timor. On May 31 he crossed to Australia, landing at Broome (Western Australia). He next followed the Australian coast southwards to Melbourne, where he remained for more than a month preparing for a northward trip to Tokio. This began on July 16 with a flight to Sydney. He left Sydney for Brisbane on August 6, and reached Rockhampton, in Queensland, on August 7, Townsville on August 10. Three days later the Marchese was in Thursday Island, one of the Prince of Wales group, in Torres Straits. Crossing to Dutch New Guinea, he steered a N. W. course to Amboina in the Molucca Islands, and on to Menada, in the tip of the "tail" of

Celebes. By the end of August he reached Manila, where the "amphibian" underwent a thorough overhaul in the United States Naval Air Station at Corregidor.

From the Philippines the Italian airman crossed the water to Formosa, travelled along the coast, and jumped across to Shanghai, on the mainland of Asia; and from Shanghai, he reached Japan via Mokpo, in Korea. On September 26 he alighted at Kasumigaura naval air station, near Tokio, after having covered 20,000 miles since leaving Rome.

At Tokio the Savoia underwent a second overhaul and the engine was replaced by a new one sent out from Italy. Some of his admirers urged the Marchese to return to Europe by way of America, but as no arrangements could be made in time for patrolling the course, he wisely decided to follow out his original intention of regaining Rome by way of China and India.

The homeward trip was made without any serious incident, and before the end of the year the Italian airman was in his native country again, with the wonderful record of 35,000 miles flown to his credit.

CHAPTER 22

FROM SPAIN TO BUENOS AIRES

In 1492, on August 3, Columbus sailed from the Spanish port of Palos de Moguer with his little *Santa Maria*, and two other smaller vessels, on the memorable voyage which led to the discovery of the New World.

Skip 434 years, to January 22, 1926. On the waters of the harbour floats a great Dornier Wal flying boat the *Ne Plus Ultra*, about to start on an attempt to reach South America via the Canary and Cape Verde Islands. In command is Major Franco, of the Spanish Army, and his companions are Captain Ruiz de Alda, Lieutenant Duran, and a mechanic.

The first "jump" will be to the Canary Islands, 812 miles away; the second, 1060 miles, to the Cape Verde Islands, and the third, to Pernambuco, one of 1,777 miles. But the ultimate goal of the expedition is Buenos Aires, 6,259 miles away. In the previous year two Portuguese airmen, Commanders Cabral and Coutinho, had flown from Lisbon to Pernambuco via Las Palmas, St. Vincent, and St. Paul's Rocks. At the last place their Fairey seaplane was wrecked and they had to wait until a new machine reached them by ship. Consequently their flight occupied more than two months; but it blazed the way for future attempts.

The Spanish expedition had been well organised, and hopes for its success ran high. Great popular interest centred on the machine which was to speed as a messenger of goodwill from the mother country to the daughter countries which had separated a hundred years before, but still were bound to her by the ties of blood.

Throughout the night the flying boat had been guarded by the townsfolk, many of whom spent hours praying for its good fortune. At eight o'clock the ship rose swiftly from the water, encircled the monument reared to the memory of Columbus, and sped southwards. By 4 p. m. the flying boat had reached the Canary Islands. Following a wait of a few days the journey was resumed—on the 20th.—from Gando Bay, Grand Canary, after the flying boat had had its load reduced. As before, everything went well and by the evening of that day the *Ne Plus Ultra* was at the Cape Verde Islands, having put more than 1,000 miles behind it since the morning.

On the 30th. the airmen left the islands with the intention of reaching, if possible, the South American mainland, over 1,750 miles away, that same way. If they had succeeded they would have made the longest flight over water—that of Alcock and Brown in 1919 alone excepted.

Throughout the day wireless messages came in from various sources reporting the progress of the flight, which proved quite uneventful until, off the Fernando Noronha Islands, 300 miles from Pernambuco, the light failed and the Dornier Wal had to descend on to the sea. It was towed safely into harbour, and on the following day arrived at Pernambuco, where the airmen received a wonderful welcome from the populace, which, though of Portuguese origin, manifested the greatest enthusiasm over the Spanish airmen's achievement. It is worth mentioning that a good part of the journey from Fernando Noronha to Brazil was done on one engine only, as the other gave trouble.

The next "leg" of the trip—1,260 miles from Pernambuco to Rio de Janeiro—was turned off on February 4, the *Ne Plus Ultra* arriving at its destination at 8 p. m. On February 9

PLATE IX

A Marconi " All-purposes " 150-watt aircraft wireless set for telegraphy and telephony, fitted in the pilot's cockpit of an Imperial Airways passenger machine.

[*Photo, Marconi Wireless Telegraph Co., Ltd.*

the flying boat made a 1,200-mile flight to Monte Video, and next day reached Buenos Aires, shortly after noon. In honour of its arrival the city was dressed in flags and all business was suspended. A number of Argentine aircraft went out to meet the Spaniards, who circled several times over the city and then alighted in the port.

The delight exhibited naturally in Spain over the successful conclusion of the expedition equalled any yet witnessed in connection with aeronautical achievement. Prisoners in the gaols had reason to be grateful to the airmen, for they either were released then and there or had part of their sentences remitted. The King conferred the order of the Golden Key on the three officers; at Ferrol the crowd invaded Major Franco's home and filled it with flowers; while at the great Rio Tinto copper mines the workmen unanimously decided to "down tools" and to celebrate the occasion in a fitting manner. In the capital a monster demonstration paraded the streets, and squadrons of aeroplanes flying overhead scattered flowers and miniature flags broadcast to the crowds below.

The notable feature of this flight was the high average lengths of the sections into which it fell—812, 1,060, 1,450, 300, 1,260, 1,200 and 150 miles. No other aerial journey of equal length had included so many "long jumps."

CHAPTER 23

LIFEBELTS OF THE AIR

ORIGINALLY designed for spectacular descents from balloons, the parachute—which signifies "fall-breaker"—is now regarded as the aerial counterpart of the marine lifebelt, as a means of escape when the ship is foundering.

It is stated, but on somewhat doubtful authority, that one Fante Veranzio launched from a tower in the 18th. century the first parachute ever made—a crude rectangular piece of canvas attached to a frame. The celebrated aeronaut Blanchard is said to have used a parachute in 1777, before the invention of the balloon; but here again there is no certainty. We do know definitely, however, that in the years 1794-5 Blanchard experimented with animals, dropped in small parachutes from balloons; and tradition has it that he himself made a parachute descent and had one of his legs broken.

The credit of the first really successful parachute descent undoubtedly belongs to André Jacques Garnerin, a Frenchman. On October 22, 1797, he rose from the park of Monceau, Paris, on a parachute attached to a balloon, and when at a height of 2,000 feet cut the connecting cord. The balloon soared aloft and burst, while the parachute descended, swinging from side to side in a manner which alarmed the spectators, and made Garnerin himself very dizzy. He landed safely, however, and was able to mount a horse and ride back in triumph to the starting place, where a great reception awaited him. Garnerin certainly deserved the admiration of the multitude for a feat which demanded great pluck and daring. We know now that in calm weather the risk run by a parachutist is very small; but at that time to trust oneself to a contrivance which might or might not act, and, if it failed, would let its passenger fall to certain death, appeared about as hazardous an undertaking as could be imagined.

"Citizen Garnerin"—those were the days of the French Revolution—became famous in France, and beyond its borders. In 1802 he gave the British public its first sight of a parachute. in action. On September 21 he ascended from the Volunteer Parade, North Audley Street, and released his white canvas parachute when at a height given variously as 4,000 and 8,000 feet.

The basket attached to the parachute swung violently backwards and forwards, till it looked as if Garnerin would be flung out. Men shouted, and women screamed and fainted in alarm. The brave parachutist, giddy from his tossing, landed safely. He afterwards made many more descents; and his sister, not to be outdone by a mere man, became the first woman parachutist. She is said to have made over 40 descents.

The pendulum-like behaviour of a parachute is due to its endeavour to turn upside down. The French astronomer, Lalande, suggested cutting a central vent-hole, so that the air imprisoned under the hemispherical dome of the distended parachute should, by its escape, have a steadying effect. This suggestion was tested and found to be so practical that it has been adopted in all parachutes made since.

For 35 years after Garnerin's display nobody used a parachute in England. Then the ill-fated Cocking experimented with one of his own design, which collapsed in the air and caused his death. His parachute resembled an umbrella turned inside out; in other words, it was of cone shape with the point downwards. To prevent it collapsing upwards, it had a tubular metal rim; which necessitated its being always open. There is no doubt as to its stability, for a cone dropped point down has no tendency to turn over. Unfortunately, the rim proved unequal to its work, and crumpled up when the parachute was released. Cocking fell thousands of feet, and, though the material of the parachute broke his fall somewhat, he struck the ground so violently that he died soon afterwards. His parachute had the fatal defect of wanting to collapse, whereas the ordinary parachute naturally keeps open.

So far as is known, only one balloonist, prior to the Great War, used a parachute to save his life; and that was a Pole, Kuparento by name, who, in 1804, when his balloon burst in mid-air, flung himself out with a parachute and escaped unhurt. It may be added that on several occasions burst balloons have acted as parachutes, the lower part of the bag blowing upwards into the upper part, and so have compelled aeronauts to make involuntary parachute descents. The American, John Wise, actually did the balloon-parachute "stunt" deliberately as an entertainment, ripping his balloon when high above the ground.

The ordinary parachute, when laid out flat, has a diameter of about 28 feet, and when in its floating shape measures 22 or 23 feet across. It weighs from 25 lbs. to 80 lbs., and, as it has an area of about 350 square feet, it has to carry only about half a pound per square foot of surface when supporting a person weighing 11 stone. In still air its rate of descent with such a load is about 7 miles an hour, the speed at which one would strike the ground after a jump off a wall eight feet high. That is to say, the parachutist comes to earth without feeling anything like a severe shock. Cases have been known in which, owing no doubt to the action of an upward air current, descent was remarkably slow. An instance is on record of a lady parachutist who took nearly three-quarters of an hour to fall 6,000 feet,—so that her average speed was only about 1½ miles an hour. In fact, she was so long coming down that when she landed she found her husband busy packing up the balloon from which he had dropped her!

The practical utility of the parachute, and its claim to be the lifebelt of the air, may be regarded as having been very small indeed until the parachute was called upon to play a part in the grim business of war. The helplessness of the airman in a damaged aeroplane, or of an observer in an attacked military balloon, had, some years before the outbreak of the Great War, revived interest in the parachute. An American airman, named Berry, first performed (near St. Louis) the extremely plucky feat of throwing himself with a parachute off an aeroplane in flight. About a year later the French aviator, Pégoud, astonished Europe by a similar performance. Pégoud was the first man to "loop the loop" in an aeroplane and an interesting story is told in this connection. Pégoud used to go up alone, jump off, and leave the aeroplane to look after itself. It is said that on one occasion M. Blériot, while watching Pégoud's performance, noticed that the abandoned aeroplane turned head over heels several times on its way earthwards, and landed right way up. He suggested to Pégoud that what the aeroplane could do by itself it could also do under human control, and shortly afterwards Pégoud made his first exhibition of "looping the loop."

It is obvious that a parachute meant for emergency use by the occupant of an aeroplane or balloon cannot be suspended after the manner of an "exhibition" parachute. It must be compact, and easily got at by the user. During the war several types of parachutes were developed, all of which packed up into a small space, were attached to harness on the aeronaut's body, and were designed to open out automatically as soon as the user flung himself into the air.

Speaking generally, these "lifebelt" parachutes may be divided into two main classes. In the first the parachute is packed into a case which is attached by a cord to the balloon or aeroplane, and is dragged from its case when the aeronaut leaps. The second, or pack, class is not connected to the machine in any way, and the parachute is released by a smaller parachute, which opens and drags the case off it; or by the airman pulling a ripping-cord when he has fallen clear of the machine. Very few instances, not averaging one in a hundred, have been known of a parachute failing to open; and the cause of these few failures is known and has been remedied.

During the War a great number of kite-balloons were used by both sides for observation purposes; and these "Ruperts" became favourite objects of attack by raiding aeroplanes, from which the enemy fired incendiary bullets into the gas bags. The observer's only hope then lay in his parachute, which, in the great majority of cases, brought him safely to earth. Over 800 observers were saved by their parachutes.

The basket of a balloon lends itself so much better than does an aeroplane's cockpit to a leap into space that British airmen did not use the parachute during hostilities. In the last six months of the War German aviators adopted it, and out of the ten men who had to quit their aeroplanes in a hurry and trust to a parachute nine saved their lives. Nowadays the military airman is provided with a parachute as part of his standard equipment. It is either worn on the back or serves as a cushion.

We will now relate two instances in which the parachute proved a veritable lifebelt. During the Great War machines collapsed in the air from causes which were unknown at the time, and pilots were sent up in similar machines to put them through tests designed to prove whether certain kinds of strains were responsible. It need hardly be said that the carrying out of such tests called for the greatest courage; as the pilot ran a very good chance of being killed.

One of these test pilots was detailed to try out a particular kind of machine subject to mysterious failures. He rose some thousands of feet, and then dived at a terrific speed. The ailerons—wing flaps for controlling balance—began to quiver, and finally set up such violent vibrations that the main planes collapsed. Fortunately the pilot had a parachute with him, and at the critical moment he jumped clear. While his machine splintered itself into fragments in a headlong crash, he floated safely to earth.

The hero of the second adventure was Lieut. John A. Macready, whose great trans-American flight is described elsewhere. On June 19, 1914, he was making a night trip from Columbus to Dayton. As he approached his destination his engine stopped while he was about 3,000 feet above the ground. To descend in the dark on rough ground meant almost certain destruction. So Macready prepared for making the first parachute jump ever carried out at night.

"I loosened my safety belt and threw one leg over the side of the ship, keeping one hand on the control stick. Finally I crawled out on the wing and attempted to nose the ship up, so that I could leave without danger of having the parachute catch.

"I let go of the plane and let the wind blow me free. I decided to count two before I pulled the ripcord of the parachute, so as not to foul the plane. I don't know in what position I was when I left the ship, whether I was upside down or not. But I heard the parachute open with a snap and I knew I would land safely in some place."

The aeroplane struck the ground with a crash and at once took fire. The crowd which collected naturally thought that the airman was being burned to death underneath it. Imagine the relief and surprise when Macready appeared in its midst! He had landed safely on the edge of a 100-foot cliff, released himself, and walked up to see the end of his unfortunate machine, the fate of which he would have shared, but for his "life-belt."

As the reader may be curious as to the sensations experienced by a parachutist descending from an aeroplane, the following account has been reproduced by kind permission of *Airways*, from an article by Mlle. Justine Finet describing her first drop.

"When the altimeter showed 850 feet the lashings were untied to allow the parachute to drop a little way below the undercarriage and then, on a signal from the pilot, I left my seat and climbed very cautiously out on to the left wing.

"Clinging like grim death to the wing strut as the machine tore through the air at 80 miles an hour, I began to wonder why on earth I had ever been keen on making a parachute descent. From my insecure perch nearly 1,000 feet above the ground the idea did not seem nearly as attractive as before, and I was just debating as to whether I could safely regain my comfortable seat in the plane when I saw that the pilot was signalling to me to jump. It was now or never, so, closing my eyes, I stepped backwards into space.

"Down I went like a stone, the air whistling past me, and, though I could feel myself dropping, my mind felt a perfect blank. Then, with an almost imperceptible jerk, my headlong fall ceased, and, looking up, I saw the beautiful red-and-black silk parachute spread out above me.

"The aeroplane which I had just left was now circling round, and it seemed to be ever so high up, although my drop had only been about 60 feet before the parachute opened out. Looking beneath me, I saw that I was already halfway down, descending in almost a straight line owing to the stillness of the air. It was a wonderful sensation drifting gently down from the sky—like floating on a calm sea—and all my fears and nervousness had completely disappeared. The ground seemed to rise slowly up towards me, and I landed easily upon the grass of a large meadow where several cows were grazing peacefully."

The greatest risk that a parachutist has to run is that of landing when a descent is made in a strong wind. It may be compared to jumping from a motor-car or express train moving at high speed. And even if the ground be reached without injury, unless the parachute be released very promptly, the parachutist may be plucked up like a feather when the parachute, arrested by his landing, turns over and catches the wind. To obviate dragging, quick-release attachments are provided, which open in a moment and leave the parachute free to do what it likes.

And there is, again, the smaller risk of landing on a house, and falling off it, when the parachute will not have time or room for breaking the fall. But such risks are very preferable to the almost certain destruction awaiting the occupant of an aeroplane that has got out of control or taken fire. It may become the rule to provide every traveller in a commercial aeroplane with a parachute, if the difficulties at present in the way of several persons taking the air in very quick succession can be surmounted. It has even been suggested that passenger aeroplanes should have a body which the pilot could release as a whole, leaving it to the care of a parachute fastened to the top. The enormous size of an effective parachute is the obvious trouble here, though the idea is by no means unpractical.

The record parachute descent, as regards distance dropped, is probably that of Lieut. A. W. Stevens, of the U. S. Air Service. In June, 1922, he jumped from an aeroplane 24,200 feet (about 4½ miles) above the earth and arrived safely on the ground at McCook Field, Dayton.

CHAPTER 24

AIRCRAFT IN WAR

THE Great War which ended on November 11, 1918, was the first in which the whole of the mechanical resources of highly civilised nations were devoted to the grim business of slaughter. The motor vehicle, the armoured-car, the "tank," colossal guns on land; warships, both surface and submarine, of unprecedented size and speed, on the sea; and aircraft in the air:— all these represented the strenuous output of the chief combatants' workshops.

The two most notable of the engines of war were the submarine and the aeroplane. The first for a season caused the outcome of the conflict to tremble in the balance, and threatened Britain with the spectre of starvation. It failed, but only by a narrow margin.

Like the submarine, the aeroplane in 1914 had been very little used in actual fighting. In fact, but for its employment during the Balkan Wars of 1912, it may be said to have smelled no powder at all, though it had taken part in army manœuvres in several countries. When the war began there were in existence few, if any, "fighting" aeroplanes; that is, machines equipped with machine-guns and other apparatus enabling them to take an active part in battle or to fight one another. It had not yet been properly realised how efficient, as a means of offence, the aeroplane might be made. So in the early days of the War the pilot was essentially a scout, sent out to bring back information as to the enemy's movements.

CONQUERING THE AIR

Britain began the War with some 100 "assorted" machines of a good many makes, a large proportion of them having very doubtful value for the rough-and-tumble of campaigning. The French, Russians and Germans, with their much larger armies, had correspondingly larger aerial forces; and each nation could put 300 or more machines into the field. As judged by present-day standards, the aeroplanes mustered at the opening of Armageddon were very slow and clumsy, and lacked climbing power. Compared with their successors which saw the end of the War, they were as Thames barges to destroyers.

Nevertheless, they did very useful work as the eyes of the various armies. Badly equipped though the British squadrons were, they proved invaluable in the early days of the War, and the reports brought in by the airmen, at critical moments of the fighting, concerning the movements of the German troops had very far-reaching effects.

The mobility of the flying-machine asserted itself at once, and it soon became apparent that, if the War should be long drawn out, aircraft might prove to be the decisive factor. As if by way of compensation, whereas the greater part of the combatants were immobilised in trenches as never before in the history of warfare, one fighting branch enjoyed an unprecedented freedom. Aircraft saved the War from becoming absolutely stagnant and repulsive. A new type of fighting man came into being—the military airman. In many cases little more than a lad fresh from school, he soared aloft on his aerial steed and engaged in heroic combats with his "opposite number" among the enemy. On land every move—where movements were possible—was a matter of long preparation and massive attack, the practical results of which might be very small indeed. Aerial fighting, on the other hand, was largely an individual affair, one against one or a few at most; and a matter in which, as in games, much depended on the nerve, cleverness, and quickness of the fighter. One has to go back to the Homeric tales of fights between Greek and Trojan heroes for the counterpart on land of the aerial "dog fights" in which opposing airmen wheeled, swooped, and performed all kinds of gymnastics thousands of feet up in the air, while the entrenched armies below looked on. The "star" airmen earned world-wide renown, as they added success to success, and the tale of enemy aircraft shot down by them grew longer and longer. A halo of romance gathered round the names of such sturdy and resourceful fighters as Ball, McCudden, Rickenbacker, Richthofen, Immelmann and Guynemer.

Not that the military airman led a life of continuous excitement. On the contrary, stirring incidents were few and far between, and the ordinary routine entailed much drudgery and discomfort, besides a great deal of danger. Patrolling for hours on end over the enemy's line in bitter weather, with shells from anti-aircraft guns bursting all round, could hardly be regarded as a picnic.

At the beginning of the War the aeroplane was primarily a scout, as already noticed. If it carried any weapons of offence at all, they would be a revolver or rifle, with perhaps an odd bomb or two and a few bundles of darts. But neither side was long content to allow the opposing aeroplanes free passage over its own territory; so that aerial "scrapping" between the pilots became inevitable. This led to the equipment of all aeroplanes with machine-guns, which, by the rapidity of their fire, did a good deal to compensate for the difficulty of taking aim from a quickly-moving platform at an equally quickly-moving target.

As the War lengthened, specialising took place, and aeroplanes eventually fell into three main classes,—the fighting scout, the observation machine, and the bomber.

The fighting scout was a small one-man machine, powerfully engined, so that it could climb very rapidly and travel at speeds of up to 140 miles an hour, and very nimble in manœuverng. Some of the later scouts could dive with safety at a speed of 300 miles an hour—5 miles a minute. Two machine-guns were carried; a Vickers, fixed immediately in front of the pilot, and a Lewis, above and in front of him. The last could be slid down a curved frame to be reloaded. To aim his Vickers the pilot had to manœvre his machine till they pointed at the mark. When he considered that he was "on" the enemy, he pressed a button on the "joy stick," and the gun connected therewith promptly pumped out a stream of bullets at the rate of anything up to 1,000 a minute.

As tractor screws were used on most war aeroplanes, and all scouts were single-engined machines, special measures had to be taken to enable a gun to fire through a screw, otherwise the first drum of ammunition discharged would probably have cut off the propeller blades. The blades were therefore in the first instance protected by small pieces of very hard steel attached to them, which turned any bullets aside. Later on, synchronising gears were adopted, which ensured the bullets passing between the airscrew blades, by making the revolutions of the engine control the machine-gun. Wonderful as it may seem, bullets passed unobstructed along a path crossed by the blades 5,000 times or more per minute.

The duties of a scout were various, but all essentially offensive. One of the most important was to keep the air as free as possible from enemy machines, by chasing and attacking any that came in sight. A squadron of scouts would be sent out to patrol at a great height along a line miles behind the enemy's front trenches, ready to dive down on any hostile scout or other machine. When opposing squadrons met, things began to happen, and it was in the resulting scraps, often fought at such a height that the combatants were quite invisible, even in a clear sky, that the great airmen made their reputations.

Another of the important tasks allotted to the scout consisted of escorting the larger and slower observation and bombing machines and keeping enemy scouts at a respectful distance from them while they went about their business. A third activity, developed greatly in the last year of the War, was "ground strafing"; in other words, flying very low and attacking troops on the march or in billets, trenches, railway trains, road convoys, and so on. During the strenuous and disastrous days of the German break-through in March, 1918, this form of attack, carried out with the utmost gallantry by British airmen, did a great deal in slowing the Teuton advance. One can sympathise with the general desire to take cover evinced by troops when suddenly attacked by a swarm of scouts pouring bullets on their devoted heads, and flicking out of range almost before anyone had time to think of retaliation. The pilots, being within easy rifle shot, ran very heavy risks and, considering the size of the target offered by even a scout, it is remarkable how few of them were brought down while engaged in these close-quarters exploits.

The "aristocrats of the air," as the "scouts" have been aptly named, were detailed to attack night raiders, whether aeroplanes or airships; and to "put down" the enemy kite-balloons, by igniting them with incendiary bullets. In the closing months of the War the scout habitually carried a supply of bombs to drop on some prearranged object, or on anything suitable that might "happen along." Some of the long-distance bombing-raids on German airship sheds were carried out effectively by scouts, though as a rule special machines engaged in this kind of work.

The observation aeroplanes were usually two-seaters, carrying an observer as well as a pilot. The first operated a Lewis gun, mounted on a rotating frame giving a large field of fire, while the pilot had a Vickers fixed in front of him as on a "scout." These machines "spotted" for the artillery directing and correcting gunfire by means of coloured lights or, later, by wireless. They flew at a moderate height, well within reach of the anti-aircraft guns, and as they had, in many cases, to stick to a given line, the work was very trying and dangerous, even if the accompanying scouts managed to keep enemy aircraft out of the way. On reconnaissance flights the observer,—who really was a more important person than the pilot, though he did not get his fair share of the credit—took notes of any movements of troops, alterations in the enemy's trench system, new artillery positions, and so on. He was usually an older man than his companion, since his value as an observer depended on sufficient military knowledge to enable him to interpret correctly what he saw below him. It certainly required much more training to become a useful observer than to qualify as a skilled pilot.

Many observation aeroplanes carried special cameras with which to make a photographic record of a section of country. The aeroplane travelled to and fro at a constant height, in straight lines, and plates were exposed at such a rate that the resulting photographs overlapped a little. When stuck together with the edges matching like those of a wall paper pattern, a series of photographs yielded a map from which the experienced eye could decipher a mass of information such as even the best observer could not possibly have recorded in the

PLATE X

A bird's-eye view of part of London, taken from an aeroplane. In the centre is the Tower Bridge; while St. Paul's Cathedral is seen in the top left-hand corner.

[*Photo, Surrey Flying Services.*

same time. By comparing aerial maps taken at short intervals apart it was possible to discover many things that the enemy would gladly have kept hidden. During the last twelve months of the war nearly 265,000 photographs were taken by British machines behind the German lines on the Western Front alone.

This class of machine was designed for stability. There is an officially recorded case of one flying itself for more than a hundred miles after both pilot and observer had been killed, and landing undamaged behind the British lines!

The Bristol Fighter was intermediate between the scout and the observation classes. It had the speed of the first, though not quite its handiness, and carried an observer; and it possessed most of the virtues of both kinds of craft, so that it enjoyed a high reputation as a good all-round machine.

Aeroplanes designed for bombing had necessarily to be exceptionally powerful, in order to carry sufficient fuel for the long trips they had to make as well as an adequate supply of "eggs," i.e. bombs. The day bombers were fast two-seaters, able to fly at heights of anything up to four miles, where they would be more or less secure from observation and the attentions of enemy scouting machines. They shared with the reconnaissance machine the duty of taking photographs.

For bombing by night specially large machines, notably the Handley-Pages, proved most successful. They had two engines and, though not very speedy, could carry a great load, including up to a ton of bombs. A journey of 250 miles "out" and as many home was well within their capacity. Had the War lasted a little longer, some enormous machines, intended to reach Berlin with a two-ton load of huge bombs, would have been tested. These had a spread of 120 feet, and a flight endurance of 1,300 miles. They carried several machine-guns to enable them to beat off attacks from any quarter.

CONQUERING THE AIR

The activity of aircraft on all the fronts robbed the War of the greater part of its secrecy. During the daytime it was practically impossible to move troops, guns, or supplies, without immediate detection, and even changes made under cover of night were apt to be betrayed subsequently by sharp eyes peering from the skies and by aerial photography. "Camouflage" was gradually raised to an art. But even the most ingenious disguises for guns and other apparatus often failed to deceive. When a big "push" was in prospect an essential condition for its success was that for some time previously the air should be swept clear of enemy aircraft. And when the destined day arrived swarms of aeroplanes would cross the lines at dawn, some to attack hostile craft and keep them away at all costs; others to bomb strategic points far behind the enemy's trenches; others to search for danger spots; others to guide the fire of the artillery and collect information which would assist the headquarters staff in directing operations. The timely report of this or of that trench having been deserted, or of preparations being made for a counter-attack puts trump cards into the hands of the attacking force. A battle was not therefore, as formerly, confined to so many square miles of ground, but included the air to a height of three or four miles; and the outcome of the ground fighting depended very largely on the aerial fighting.

One of the most dramatic illustrations of the value of aircraft occurred during the closing scenes of the operations against the Turks in Palestine. When the final thrust against the enemy's lines was due, British aeroplanes sped far to the rear of the Turkish trenches and mercilessly bombed their aerodromes, effectively preventing any of their machines rising into the air. The Turks were thus deprived of their "eyes," whereas all their movements were as an open book to the British; and when at last they broke and fled they were pursued and hunted from above by British aeroplanes which, having the air all to themselves, could carry on their deadly work with impunity.

The development of aircraft was so much hastened by the stern necessities of war that those four momentous years saw as much improvement in performance and design as might have come about in two or three decades of peace. There was a bitter and never-ceasing struggle to produce something better than the other side could put into service. The addition of a few miles an hour to the speed, or of a hundred feet per minute to the climbing rate, became a matter of great importance. Engines had to be made more powerful and more reliable. Head resistance must be decreased by stream-lining every part exposed to the rush of air, and by enclosing the bodies of aeroplanes. Wings had to be given more efficient curves, and weight to be cut down while strength was increased. Every few months one side would bring out a new type that could outfly and outfight corresponding machines on the other; and in due course the "reply" to this would appear. Money was absolutely no object, and so long as the designer and manufacturer could deliver the goods, they were given practically a free hand.

And all the time the pilots increased their proficiency in proportion to the efficiency of their mounts. What before the war would have been regarded as hair-raising "stunts" became part of a pilot's everyday stock-in-trade—looping the loop, side-slipping, rolling, Immelmann turns, and all the rest of it. Acrobatics is the only word that fitly describes the movements of a fighting scout in action.

Britain entered the war with four squadrons fit for active service—or rather, able to be used in active service, for some of the machines were far from fit. At the Armistice she had 200 squadrons, averaging sixteen machines each, in the field. To these should be added a huge number ready for delivery or in reserve, to say nothing of the many hundreds devoted to training purposes. In the four and a quarter years the personnel of the British air service had grown from about 280 officers and 1,800 men to 30,000 officers and 290,000 of other ranks, including women and boys; a total about equal to that of all the forces employed in the Boer War.

Seaplanes and Flying Boats

In order that aircraft should be turned to account over the sea as well as over land, special types had to be developed. The ordinary aeroplane with wheeled undercarriage, rising from an aerodrome near the coast, could carry out reconnaissances within such a distance of land that, in case of engine failure, the crew would have a good chance of being rescued. But an aeroplane that took the water was in most cases permanently out of commission.

The seaplane, which may be described as a land machine provided with large floats in place of wheels,—it has been aptly described as a land machine wearing a pair of huge galoshes— can ride on the water while repairs are carried out, and afterwards rise again into the air. Unfortunately it is not very seaworthy in rough water, owing to a lack of stability; and is liable to upset when "landed." Nevertheless, seaplanes were used a great deal and very effectively by both sides during the War. The Germans employed large numbers of them to patrol the Baltic, the Heligoland Bight, and the coasts of Holland and Belgium. Seaplane stations were to be found at Wilhelmshaven, Nordeney, Heligoland, Borkum, Sylt, Kiel, Warnemünde and Rügen—the last three in the Baltic. Most of these machines were, but for their steel floats, similar to well-tried aeroplane types—such as the Albatross, Gotha, and Brandenburg. One of exceptional size found after the Armistice at Warnemünde, had a wing spread of about 150 feet and carried four engines. The German seaplanes kept to the eastern side of the North Sea, but their existence was a threat to the Grand Fleet at Scapa Flow, in the Orkneys, and Rosyth, in the Firth of Forth; as nobody knew but that a squadron might suddenly appear and drop torpedoes among the ships. For this kind of work the seaplane was suitable, since the torpedo could be carried conveniently between the floats.

The seaplane served the German well enough, as it had to operate mainly in home waters. The German warships stayed in port most of the time, and there were no German merchant ships on the sea. But German submarines kept very busy attacking Allied ships of all kinds far from land, so that the duties which fell to British marine flying craft had a much wider scope. Practically the whole of the North Sea must be kept under observation from the air. This involved long-distance patrols, and more weatherly craft than seaplanes.

Hence the development by the Admiralty of the flying boat, with mahogany hull having hydroplane steps on the bottom so that it should rise in the water as it gained speed and soon have sufficient velocity to leave the surface under the lift of the wings. The flying boat could stand a good deal of rough weather. In one case a craft of this kind rode out a 60-knot gale, and drifted 50 miles without injury.

A boat body suggests a great deal of resistance to the air. As a matter of fact flying boats give at least as good a performance as aeroplanes of equal weight, power and carrying capacity.

The flying boat is essentially a big machine, since its seaworthiness is largely dependent on its size. At the beginning of the War the chief difficulty in the way of designing such craft was the lack of powerful enough engines. The moving spirit in the improvement of the flying boat was Lt. Col. J. C. Porte, afterwards made a squadron commander in the Royal Naval Air Force. When war broke out he was in the United States, superintending the testing of a flying boat built by the Curtiss Company, of Hammondsport. He at once sailed for England and devoted himself to designing flying boats for the Admiralty, and organising a base for them at Felixstowe, on Harwich Harbour. Here, three great sheds, measuring 300 by 200 feet each, were built, with concrete runways in front sloping down to the water By means of wheeled cradles a flying boat could be quickly transferred from the sea to a shed or vice versa.

Thanks to the energy of Commander Porte, a dozen or so flying boats of a very practical kind were in service when the German submarine campaign opened in the early part of 1917. In order to reach the Channel, the scene of their chief depredations, the submarines usually traversed the North Sea to the Straits of Dover, travelling as much as possible on the surface to reserve their electric batteries and maintain a good speed, besides avoiding the British mines moored at a greater depth than a submarine drew when on the top. If a flying boat could catch a submarine afloat and drop its four 100-lb. or two 230-lb. bombs on or close to it, that submarine would probably not cause any more trouble.

It was decided to organise a regular system of submarine-hunting in an area of which the North Hinder lightship—moored exactly 52 miles from England, Holland and Belgium—was the centre. On the charts three circles, of 10, 20 and 30 miles radius respectively, were drawn from this centre, and the enclosed stretch divided into 24 portions, bearing distinctive numbers, by eight equidistant arms running outwards from the lightship. Lines joining the points where the arms cut the circles formed a gigantic spider's web. The parts were constantly patrolled by the flying boats, seaplanes, and airships, and in due time the charts were dotted with marks to show where submarines had been sighted or bombed, or located by wireless signal sent out by them. As time went on, the sectors in which the best hunting could be expected became known and received most attention.

During the summer months of 1917 the flying boat station at Felixstowe hummed with activity. Mechanics worked day and night continuously in shifts to keep the boats in service. To visualise what happened when things went as desired let us follow the actual fortunes of a certain two-boat patrol that left the harbour one July evening in good weather.

Each craft carried, besides its crew of two pilots, a wireless operator and an engineer, a full load of bombs, and sufficient fuel for a 7-hour trip. At the usual cruising speed of 60 knots and height of 1,000 feet above the sea, boats A and B put out to sea, flying abreast and a mile apart. When they were well inside the Spider's Web, the wireless operator on A reported that he had picked up wireless signals from a submarine, and shortly afterwards the pilot spotted one, a few miles ahead and moving on the surface in the same direction as the flying boats. Putting on full speed, he darted towards it, hoping that it would prove to be German. The wireless operator wound in his aerial, the engineer stood to his machine-guns, and the second pilot made the necessary preparations for releasing the two 230-lb. bombs. The submarine had not begun to dive when she was close enough to be seen to carry unmistakable signs of enemy origin. It was now too late for her to dive. A's first bomb struck her fairly on the stern and exploded, bringing her bows out of the water. B, following close behind, dropped two 100-pounders just ahead of the submarine, doing more damage. The U-boat, twisted and turned, and vainly tried to submerge. A got its second bomb home, this time ahead of the conning-tower, and in turn B dropped her remaining two. This brought the end. The U-boat suddenly stood on end, and then slipped backwards out of sight to a final resting place on the floor of the North Sea.

During the year 1917 the aircraft employed on submarine-hunting—13 flying boats, 192 aeroplanes and seaplanes and 50 airships—bombed 105 U-boats. Out of this total the flying boats claimed 44 bombings, so that in proportion to their number they were much the most efficient. In short, they proved so painful a thorn in the side of the U-boat commanders, that the Germans produced special light seaplanes for fighting them, and on several occasions some very interesting "scraps" took place in the eastern reaches of the North Sea, in which the British craft held their own.

Besides hunting for submarines, the flying boats convoyed the fleets of cargo boats that moved between Harwich and the Hook of Holland—the Beef Trip, as the pilots called it unofficially. The day before a convoy was due to start the FB's patrolled the route, and when the fleet put out they kept it company, circling about like a sheep dog round its charge, and keeping a sharp lookout for lurking submarines, enemy seaplanes, or hostile destroyers.

Occasionally the flying boats were detailed to make long-distance reconnaissances in the Heligoland Bight, and find out what was going on there. Now, from Felixstowe to Heligoland is 350 miles, and the return trip would demand more fuel than could be carried, without any allowance for scouting in the Bight itself. The flying boats were therefore taken across the North Sea on special steel lighters towed by destroyers at a very high speed. To embark a flying boat, the stern of the lighter was submerged by flooding the after tanks, and the "cargo" was then drawn aboard on a cradle. The tanks having then been blown clear, the lighter rose into towing trim. The flying boat's engines were kept warm, and in condition to start up at a moment's notice, by being muffled in electrically-heated padded covers, supplied with current from the destroyer through an insulated cable. On reaching the slipping point, —generally near enough to the enemy's bases to be decidedly "unhealthy"—the flying boat was quickly put into the water and the destroyer steamed away with the lighter, leaving its former load to carry out the job in hand.

By the end of the war some enormous flying boats were in existence—for example, the Porte "Baby," which weighed over 15 tons and carried a small aeroplane. Under test it took a load of 24 men, seven hours' fuel, and 2 tons of sand. Five engines, totalling 1,800 horsepower, propelled it. The "answer" to this prepared by the Germans, but never used, was the great monoplane flying boat designed by Count von Zeppelin just before his death, after he had realised his great airships to be a failure. Its single plane measured 130 feet from tip to tip, and between 15 and 20 feet from front to back edge. At a height of 13 feet above the water its designer anticipated the plane would be out of reach of the waves. The enclosed boat body was large enough to stand upright in; and in addition to it there was an enclosed cabin for the pilot and wireless operator between the wings.

CONQUERING THE AIR

Military Airships

For war purposes the airship had a much more restricted field than the aeroplane, on account of its lower speed and its vulnerability to attack; and it was confined mainly to patrolling operations over the sea, and, in the case of the German Zeppelins, to night raiding of enemy towns. On the British side flying boats and seaplanes, as has been noticed, were much used for patrol work, but the airship, being able to keep the air much longer, proved itself invaluable for extended observation, and in hunting submarines or convoying merchant ships.

The most popular type on the British side was the small non-rigid sea scout (S.S.) which first appeared in February, 1915. The "Blimp," as it was ribaldly named, became a very familiar object along British coasts. It may be described as a combination of a gas envelope and an aeroplane body. The crew of a Blimp consisted of the pilot, an engineer, and a wireless operator. The first navigated the ship and was responsible for its movements; the engineer looked after the motor and other mechanical equipment; while "Sparks" kept the airship in touch with the base, reported any discoveries or suspicious circumstances, and signalled for help when needed. The original Blimps were such a success that many more were ordered. In 1916 a second type, with a boat-shaped car, capable of floating in the water and being towed, appeared under the official designation of S.S.2. This type also made good and was multiplied.

In the following year the Admiralty got out the S.S.T. (Sea Scout Twin), a larger Blimp with two engines. It had a speed of anything up to 50 miles an hour, and could patrol for 50 hours at a stretch. A single-engined Blimp was in bad case should its motor break down a long way from land in an off-shore wind. The only thing to be done then was to throw out the drogue (sea anchor),—a great canvas bucket which performs the same function in water that a parachute does in air—and send out signals of distress. The provision of a second engine did away with the likelihood of a S.S.T. finding itself in such a predicament.

The Coastal Patrol (C.P.) airship, introduced in 1915, was a much larger ship than the Blimp, having a gas capacity of 200,000 cubic feet. It was a success, and carried out a great deal of long-range patrol and escort duty. The "C-Star" class which appeared in 1918, was an improved C.P., of rather larger capacity. The N.S. (North Sea) class ran much larger than the C.P.'s, being able to hold 360,000 cubic feet of gas, and having a maximum speed of 55 miles an hour. These ships often remained 50 hours away from their base in attendance on the Grand Fleet.

These various classes of non-rigid airships among them made things very uncomfortable for submarines, which were easily "spotted" from the air even when travelling well below the surface. In such a case the airship would drop a depth charge or two, and, if these failed, keep the submarine in sight, if possible, while calling up destroyers to join in the hunt. To attack a submarine while on the surface had its risks, due to the gun carried by the boat, and the correct procedure was then to keep out of range to windward until the craft began to submerge. Now came the time to rush down-wind at top speed, and launch bombs before the hull had quite disappeared under the water.

Among other duties that fell to the patrol airships were the spotting of mines—destroyed on the spot by rifle-fire if floating—and taking names and descriptions of all ships passing through the area patrolled.

CONQUERING THE AIR

When war broke out Britain had no rigid airships, and the first to be completed did not leave the building shed till April, 1917. This was the R9, which had a gas capacity of 800,000 feet and could maintain a speed of 45 miles an hour for 18 hours continuously. Her propellers were arranged to swivel, so that they could be turned into a horizontal plane when she was about to land and so control the rate of descent. This feature made her very useful as a training ship for the crews of later vessels; though she did spells of patrolling the North Sea. The R23 class ships were longer than the R9, faster, and capable of longer flights, and saw a good deal of service in patrolling and convoying. The R26, which made a record flight of 41 hours, took part in the surrender of the German submarines off Harwich after the Armistice. In 1916 the German L33 was brought down in fairly good condition near Colchester, and served as model from which the R33 and R34 were built. These two great ships, however, had not been completed when hostilities ceased, so they took no part in the War.

The airship is more handicapped by strong winds than is an aeroplane with its much smaller surface relatively to horse-power. Yet in 1918 only nine days passed on which British airships did not fly; and at the Armistice they had been in the air 53,534 hours since the beginning of the year.

The German Zeppelins were easily the most notorious of the airships used in the War. Before the last was a few weeks old they had shared the German advance and dropped bombs on to Belgian towns. Their great carrying capacity, high speed, and large radius of action clearly marked them out as the craft to use for raiding England, hundreds of miles from their base. Stealing across the North Sea, at a great height on calm, clear nights, they did very effective work in proving to the inhabitants of these islands that they were not isolated from the War by a navy controlling the intervening sea.

The first Zeppelin raid occurred on January 19, 1915, when certain parts of Norfolk were attacked. From that time onwards for two and a half years, Zeppelins based on Nordholz (near Cuxhaven), Fuhlsbuttel, Heligoland, and Belgian centres, continued to raid important British cities, notably London, at intervals. The number of airship raids totalled 57, out of which 12 were directed at London. The damage done to life and property was great, though perhaps hardly commensurate with the enormous cost of the raids to the Germans. At first the Zeppelins ran little risk, as anti-aircraft defences had not been organised. But soon conditions became increasingly difficult for them, compelling the ships to keep to higher and higher levels, to avoid gun fire and the even more deadly attentions of aeroplanes. When an aeroplane, suitably armed, got within range of a Zeppelin it was a case of the swordfish and the whale, with the odds heavily in favour of the first.

The honour of first bringing down a Zeppelin in an aerial flight belongs to Flight Sub-Lieut. R. A. J. Warneford, a member of the R. N. A. S. squadron operating from Dunkirk. One morning in 1915 he was flying along the Belgian coast to bomb an airship shed, when he sighted a Zeppelin flying at a great height on its return from a raid on England. He promptly made for it and, after much manœuvring, succeeded in getting above it near Ghent. Six bombs were dropped in quick succession, and one or more of these did their work, for the ship took fire and fell on to a convent, killing two of the inmates as well as the whole of the crew. The explosion turned Warneford's machine upside down and stopped the engine; but the pilot managed to get it right way up again and land behind the enemy's lines. Before any of the troops in the vicinity could catch him he re-started his engine, took off, and made for Dunkirk, which he reached safely. For this feat he was awarded the V.C.

Attacking Zeppelins by night was a much more difficult matter, for they had to be sighted first, and to do this was practically impossible unless the ship were picked up by searchlights. On September 2, 1916, thirteen Zeppelins raided the Eastern counties and some of them penetrated to London. The searchlights located one, and, unfortunately for the crew, Lieut. W. L. Robinson happened to be flying not far away. He made for his quarry, lost it, found it again, and flew alongside, raking it with incendiary bullets.

To use the gallant airman's own description as given in his official report: "I flew about 800 feet below it from bow to stern, and distributed one drum along it [from his Lewis gun] alternate new Brock and Pomeroy [incendiary bullets]. It seemed to have no effect: I therefore moved to one side and gave it another drum distributed along its side—without apparent effect. I then got behind it (by this time I was very close—500 feet or less below) and concentrated one drum on one part (underneath rear). I was then at a height of 11,500 feet when attacking the Zeppelin. I hardly finished the drum before I saw the part fired at glow. In a few seconds the whole rear part was blazing. When the third drum was fired there were no searchlights on the Zeppelin and no anti-aircraft was firing. I quickly got out of the way of the falling, blazing Zeppelin, and, being very excited, fired off a few red Vérey lights and dropped a parachute flare. Having very little oil and petrol left, I returned to Sutton's Farm, landing at

2.45 a. m.   On landing I found I had shot away the machine gun wire guard, the rear part of the centre section, and had pierced the rear main spar several times."

The airship fell in flames at Cuffley, all the crew being killed. The huge blazing structure diving headlong to earth was an awe-inspiring sight.   The writer, who witnessed it, can vouch for this.   Lieutenant Robinson received the Victoria Cross for his bravery.

Several similar disasters overtook the raiders, besides losses by storms and gun fire.   Raiding became more and more dangerous, and eventually the airships had to fly at a great height, where the cold was so intense as to cause acute discomfort to the crew and make the engines freeze if they stopped. The last Zeppelin raid proved a terrible fiasco, for the ships got frozen up and drifted helplessly back over France and Belgium, several of them being destroyed.   After that, raiding was left to the "Gotha" and "Giant" bombing aeroplanes.

Bomb raiding by night and day on towns was by no means a speciality of the Germans, as many people may think.   The Germans started it, but they had reason to regret that they had done so.   German aircraft dropped about 280 tons of bombs in Britain from start to finish.   In 1918 alone 5,500 tons were dropped by British machines behind the German lines ; and air raids on German towns numbered more than five times those made by German airships and aeroplanes on Great Britain during the whole of the war.

The failure of their Zeppelins, in which the Germans at first had an implicit faith as being invulnerable and able to do untold damage to an enemy's country, was a terrible disappointment to our opponents and contributed in no small degree to the depression which eventually led to their military collapse.

CONQUERING THE AIR

The Kite-Balloon

The ordinary spherical balloon is suitable for use as a "captive" only in still air or very light breezes. Should a wind arise, the balloon describes arcs of circles about the lower end of the cable restraining it, to the great discomfort of its passengers, and at the same time it spins round. Consequently, though such balloons have been used in warfare for purposes of observation, they are far from ideal.

Not long before the outbreak of war two German army officers invented what they called a kite-balloon, because it resembled a kite in its behaviour in the air. The balloon is sausage-shaped, and attached near its forward end to the mooring cable. It slopes downward towards the rear at an angle of about 40 degrees; and a car for the observer is attached by cords to a fabric belt running along the sides from end to end. When struck by a gust of wind it merely lifts its tail a little, like a kite, until equilibrium is restored. Inside the balloon at the rear, is a ballonet communicating with a kind of open-ended snout facing the wind. The pressure of the air blowing into the ballonet acts against the pressure of the gas, allowing the ballonet to swell, if the gas contracts; or contract, if the gas swells. The wall of the ballonet is connected with an escape valve, which opens automatically when the ballonet has been emptied to a certain extent, and so prevents any possibility of bursting.

To keep the balloon head to wind a small auxiliary sausage is fixed round the rear end and along part of the bottom. It too is open to the air at the forward extremity, and the harder the wind blows the tauter the tail becomes.

During the war the kite-balloon was adopted by all the combatants, as it could be run up quickly to 3,000 or 4,000 feet, at which height the observers in the car could keep an eye on a great deal of country, and do useful work in directing artillery fire. A telephone cable included in the mooring cable kept them in continuous touch with their comrades below.

The kite balloons—"Ruperts," the British called them—were very weatherly affairs, and could be used in winds blowing at any speed up to 40 miles an hour. Observing from them was not very pleasant work, especially in a strong, cold wind: and the chief excitement it provided was when hostile aircraft attacked the balloon with incendiary bullets. Unless the power-driven winches could haul the "Rupert" down out of danger in time, the observer had to take to his parachute before the attack developed. If he waited until the balloon were actually on fire, he ran a serious risk of having his parachute caught by it while it fell.

This kind of balloon proved very useful as a watchdog over ships being convoyed. Towed by one of the protecting vessels, it frightened submarines away or spotted them if they tried an attack. It is said that not a single ship was lost where there was a "Rupert" in attendance.

Aircraft Carriers

The great usefulness of aircraft in war naturally led to their accompanying the British fleets, not in the sense of merely flying in the air near them, but as part of the fighting equipment carried aboard. The first step taken in this direction was the conversion of certain merchant ships—among them the famous old *Campania,* once a transatlantic "crack" liner—into aircraft carriers. This involved considerable alteration of the hulls, and the addition of special tackle for transferring seaplanes from the sea to the ship or in the other direction. Some ships were devoted to carrying observation balloons as well.

Later on, in 1917, *H.M.S. Furious*, a large and fast cruiser, had her fore turret removed and replaced by a large hangar able to accommodate ten machines. The roof served as a platform from which aeroplanes could take off, for it was 160 feet long. When the ship steamed up-wind at her full speed, a very short run sufficed to give the aeroplane lift enough to rise from the deck. There remained the more difficult problem of enabling an aeroplane to land on the ship. So later on the after turret also was removed, and a 300-foot deck constructed behind the funnels. It was now possible for an aeroplane to land by chasing the ship when the latter was steaming "up-wind," though the operation required a good deal of skill on the part of the pilot.

H.M.S. Vindictive subsequently underwent similar conversion into an aeroplane carrier. But, like her companion, she was only a makeshift, as the funnels broke up the floating "aerodrome" into two separate parts. Towards the end of the War the *Argus*, begun as a merchant ship, was completed as a carrier of a more effective kind. She had no upstanding funnels at all, the smoke from her boilers being discharged through a horizontal pipe at the stern, below the level of a great deck which ran unimpeded by any kind of superstructure from one end of the ship to the other, and was 500 feet long. A very queer vessel to look at, but well suited for her particular job.

When the German battleships were being escorted to Scapa Flow for internment after the Armistice, the *Argus* was running her trials in the Firth of Forth, and passed close to the German ships. The surrendered crews were astonished when there suddenly appeared out of a fog bank a large vessel with extraor-

dinarily high sides and an upper deck which had apparently
been swept clean by a hurricane. They had never seen such
a thing before. To add to their amazement, an aeroplane
dived down and landed on the deck of the carrier.

H.M.S. Hermes, a post-war ship of 10,400 tons displace-
ment, was the first vessel to be specially designed as an aircraft carrier. Her predecessors were all modifications. She
certainly is a curious object with her mast and funnel set on
the extreme starboard side. This arrangement, however, gives
a fine sweep of clear flight deck over 500 feet long, and 70-80
feet wide. Below the flight deck are the hangars to house the
aeroplanes, and seaplanes, lifts for raising them on to the deck,
workshops, stores, and so on. The "mother" ship is not merely
a landing place, but a repair depot as well.

The largest warships in the world, the U.S.S. *Lexington*
and *Saratoga,* were originally intended to be battle-cruisers.
But under the terms of the Washington Convention they
could not be completed as such. Accordingly, they were made
into aircraft carriers, for which they are admirably suited by
their huge size and great speed (33 1/3 knots = 39 miles an
hour). A ship with a deck between 800 and 900 feet long
is indeed worthy of the name "floating aerodrome," since the
space available for landing on runs into acres.

Eventually the aircraft carrier will become an extremely important unit of any fleet—perhaps the most important, since
its cargo will be the "eyes of the fleet" much more efficiently
than the scouting destroyers and cruisers of the past. The
bombing aeroplanes carried are in effect heavy guns having
a range running into hundreds of miles.

Aeroplanes will be found also on many ships other than special carriers. To get over the difficulty of launching from
confined spaces, a species of catapult—which in idea is the

same as that used by the Wrights to launch their first aeroplane—has been used successfully. A device of this kind, operated by compressed air, gave a flying boat a speed of 62 miles an hour in a distance of 45 feet, without doing any harm to the pilot.

CHAPTER 25

AIRWAYS

An airway differs from a roadway or a railway in that it has no visible track, since the vehicles using it travel on and through the air. It is, in fact, merely a line or route; but in its full significance it includes also the aerodromes with their buildings at its ends and at intermediate points, the aeroplanes used in the service, the staff and organisation, and all apparatus and devices for assisting regular and safe transport.

Unless you happen to live near Croydon, or on certain lines between Croydon and the sea coast, or at Southampton, you may be quite unaware of the existence of airways, apart from what you read about them in the papers. In England the railway services are so good and the distances to be covered so short comparatively, that the saving of time made possible by aerial transport is hardly worth the expense involved, except under special conditions such as would not justify the establishment of regular services.

When it comes to crossing the sea or mountainous districts, or where train travel is slow, the case is very different. A peep at the map of the European airways would surprise many people by the number of routes it shows. From Croydon, Imperial Airways, Ltd. runs services to Amsterdam, to Cologne, *via* Brussels, and to Zurich, *via* Paris and Basle. There is also a flying boat service between Southampton and the Channel Islands.

Coming to airways operated by foreign companies, if you

care to spend the money you can travel many thousands of miles over organised routes. Thus, from Zurich you may fly *via* Munich, Vienna, Budapest, and Belgrade to Bukharest. Or if you desired a "round" trip, you might proceed by air from Vienna to Prague, Breslau, Warsaw and Danzig. Turning westwards here, you go past Stettin to Berlin, whence a service runs to Copenhagen. From Copenhagen you may cross to Malmö, in Sweden, and from Malmö fly to Hamburg and Amsterdam, and so back to London. Inside the route thus outlined there are many other services, as from Munich to Berlin; Munich to Essen; Brussels to Paris; Paris to Amsterdam; and so on.

In the south of France an airway extends from Toulouse to Perpignan, on the Gulf of Lyons, thence to Barcelona and across the Mediterranean Sea to Alicante. This port is a centre from which airways radiate to Algiers, Oran, and Malaga, the last being on the route to Tangier, Rabat, Capablanca and Dakar, all on the African Atlantic coast. Perpignan is connected by air with Marseilles; Nice with Ajaccio, in Corsica; and Rabat with Oran.

The convenience of air travel may be illustrated by comparing a train-and-steamer journey from London to Paris with one made by aeroplane. In the first case the journey takes seven hours or more, and involves a train journey, embarkation on a steamer, a sea voyage, customs formalities, and another train journey. The trains, as likely as not, will be crowded and uncomfortable.

The traveller by air embarks on the air liner at noon at Croydon, and less than three hours later lands at Le Bourget aerodrome, outside Paris, and thus is in the French metropolis an hour sooner than had he taken the 9 a. m. train from London. The travelling is as comfortable as it is speedy. The air liner's cabin is entirely enclosed,—though the windows on each side may be opened if necessary—and contains two rows of comfortable seats, one on each side of a central gangway by which the passengers may move about. Overhead are racks for small luggage, and behind the cabin is a lavatory. Nothing, in fact, is omitted that makes for comfort. As for the travelling itself, it is under ordinary conditions much smoother than that on the best laid railway; and even in the worst weather the motion is very preferable to that of a Channel steamer.

The time tables of the Imperial Airways, Ltd., give the following times for the journey between Croydon Aerodrome and various continental towns.

Croydon	to Brussels	2 hours 45 minutes.
"	to Cologne	5 hours.
"	to Amsterdam	2 hours 45 minutes.
"	to Bremen	5 hours 30 minutes.
"	to Hamburg	6 hours 45 minutes.

By another line you can reach Berlin in 7¾ hours. Berlin is as far from London as are the Orkney Islands. If you leave Croydon at 8 a. m. you can be in Leipsig at 4 o'clock the same afternoon. In going by air to any part of Germany you thus save yourself a very tedious journey, including a night spent on shipboard or on a train. The longer the voyage, the greater is the relative economy in time given by air travel.

As public appreciation of air travel grows, the airways will be extended. Before long it will be possible to breakfast in London and dine the same day on the Riviera. An aeroplane route from Cairo to India has been surveyed and will soon be in operation. It will run from Kantara, on the banks of the Suez Canal, to Ramleh, in Palestine; thence to Ammon, in Trans-Jordania; and across the Syrian desert to Rutbar Wells. The next halting-place is Bagdad; and after that town come in succession Basra, Bushire, Bandar Abbas, Charbar and Karachi. Assuming the mails to be taken to Port Said by the present system of rail and steamer, six days would be saved, eight days being substituted for a fortnight. Passengers travelling to Bagdad would save a great deal more time, as an aeroplane would transport them from Egypt to that town in a day, as compared with the steamer voyage through the Red Sea and Persian Gulf which takes over a fortnight. There is little doubt that, if this route proves a success, the time will be cut down still more by using mail aeroplanes between London and Marseilles, or even between London and Egypt; and it does not require much imagination to envisage extensions from India to the East Indies and Australia. It is, however, probable that the world's long-distance mail routes will eventually be operated by airships, aeroplanes being used for more local services and to "feed" the main routes as motor vehicles feed the railways.

The liner aeroplanes for the Cairo-Karachi airway are of special design, suitable for hot climates. The cabin has a double fabric covering with intervening air space to protect passengers from the heat, and is provided with electric ventilating fans. Twenty passengers can be accommodated, and each with his luggage may weigh two hundredweight—not more. The framework of a machine is constructed almost entirely of steel, specially enamelled to protect it from corrosion. The wings are built up out of sections of standard size, bolted together, an arrangement which makes it easy to repair damage without sacrificing a whole wing. Three engines, of 400 horse-power each, operate as many tractor screws, and enable the liner to travel at about 100 miles an hour at a height of 10,000 feet. The engines are of the air-cooled type, so dispensing with the radiators and water-jackets which, as we have seen in earlier chapters, are liable to give much trouble in the tropics, and of course add considerably to complication and weight.

Imperial Airways, Limited

This company was constituted early in 1924 to take over the air routes previously operated by four other companies. It now is the only British air line to the Continent.

Its headquarters are at Croydon, where it shares the great Air Port, controlled and operated by the Air Ministry, with certain foreign lines making this their terminus in Britain. The aerodrome is a great flat expanse, covering about two square miles, with a road (Plough Lane) running across it. In the smaller part are a few great hangars and other buildings, and the wireless masts and aerial. This is not used much for landing, and serves as an emergency ground. On the other side of the road we find a large group of hangars and more or less temporary buildings which will presently be replaced by permanent buildings on the far side of the main aerodrome. Beyond the buildings is a concrete-paved space from which the air liners start.

A prospective passenger, on reaching the aerodrome, enters a room where he and his luggage are carefully weighed and his passport is scrutinised. He can then adjourn to the waiting room, restaurant or hotel; or, if the aeroplane be almost due to start, he will take his place in its cabin while his baggage is stowed in the after compartment.

As the pilot has not yet arrived, we may take a peep into the cockpit, reached through doors in the forward end of the cabin. The most prominent object is the "joy-stick," surmounted by a wheel, which does the directing of the great machine. Projecting from the floor is a small binnacle, with compass; and close to it we see a reel on which the wireless aerial is wound when not in use. The wireless transmitting and receiving set is attached either to the side of the cabin near the door, or to the dashboard. The latter carries a whole host of fittings, all of them important. There are the gauges which show the temperature of the cooling water in the radiators and of the lubricating oil, and the pressure of the last while it circulates through the engines. Other dials record height above ground, the number of revolutions per minute of the engines, and the speed of the machine relatively to the air. Then there is a spirit-level to tell the pilot whether he is flying on an even keel or not; and a turn indicator, which shows him when the direction changes to left or right. This last is very useful in fog, for the pilot then finds it as difficult to fly straight ahead as he would find walking in a straight line across a field. We must not overlook the pistol from which he fires coloured signalling lights; and the many switches for breaking various electric circuits. The up-to-date aeroplane's dashboard has a motor-car's soundly beaten, for the number of "gadgets" it wears; and can even give points to the cab of a locomotive.

The pilot is coming, so we must be off. We watch him and his mechanic climb into their seats, warmly clad in their fur-lined leather overalls. They need them, too, for they do not enjoy a snug shelter like the passengers behind them. As the engines are not hot, they are started up by mechanics swinging the propellers; but when warm they can be started mechanically from the cockpit like the engine of a motor car.

The roar of the three great engines—one in the nose of the body, and one on either side between the planes—rises and falls as the pilot moves the throttle. The aeroplane cannot move, for wooden chocks have been placed in front of the wheels. Only five more minutes to go, and the mails have not yet arrived. Here they come! The sacks are tumbled into the "baggage van," and everything is ready. The chocks are now hauled away, and this operation is timed as the official start of the trip. With engines running at but part power, the pilot "taxies" his machine to a place on the aerodrome where it will have a good run up-wind. A mechanic with a big red flag in his hand keeps his eye on the Control Tower—of which more presently—and when a flag is seen to wave there he waves his also as a signal to the pilot that all is clear for him to start.

The great machine begins to move forward, with a thunderous roar, and, gaining speed quickly, rises imperceptibly from the ground and is away with its living and inanimate freights for the lands beyond the Channel.

Armed with special permission, we now adjourn to the Control Tower, where reigns the Traffic Officer at the brain centre of the aerodrome. Climbing a vertical iron ladder some 20 feet high, we arrive at a balcony surrounding the square office, on which a look-out does sentry-go all the day round. Inside the cabin are two officers. One, a wireless operator, is seated at a table with headphones on. The other presides over a large map made of cork, having the airways operated from Croydon plainly marked on it. Every moment, it seems, wireless messages come in or are intercepted, and the official presiding over the map alters the positions of pins with heads and tiny flags of various colours, each relating to some particular aeroplane. Here is the one we have just seen start, well on its way to the sea: there the Paris mail which may be expected shortly. Thus the magic tentacles of wireless make it simple to "keep tab" on all the air liners continuously, though they are moving at a speed of two miles a minute.

Fog is the airman's greatest enemy. The Traffic Officer not only watches the whereabouts of a pilot, but is ready at a moments notice to tell him where he is, should he lose his way. A distant voice is heard in the headphones calling "Mayday, Mayday"—the international appeal for guidance, correctly spelt "m'aidez!" The operator at Croydon tells the pilot to keep on calling for half a minute while he gets a bearing by directional wireless and a colleague at Pulham (Norfolk) does the same. The last 'phones his figures to Croydon. By the Traffic Officer's table is a map with nails driven in it at Croydon and Pulham. A piece of string hangs from each nail, and at some distance from the nails have been drawn parts of circles graduated into degrees. The strings are pulled tight over readings on the circles corresponding to the bearings obtained at Croydon and Pulham, and where they cross is the position of the aeroplane. The pilot is at once informed of his whereabouts relatively to same point shown on his map, and is given the compass bearing of that point. Though the machine may be a hundred miles away, the error seldom exceeds a mile. A third station at Lympne (pronounced Limb) in Kent, sometimes lends a hand to ensure extra accuracy. By means of wireless an aeroplane has on several occasions been guided all the way between Brussels and Croydon without the pilot having seen the earth at all *en route.*

Should an aeroplane be approaching Croydon when the aerodrome is fog-bound, the Traffic Officer gets into touch with other aerodromes and directs the pilot to make for one where the conditions are safe for landing.

On the Traffic Officer's table lies a book containing weather entries. Among other things it records the direction and strength of wind at different levels in various places. Telegrams arrive in quick succession from the Air Ministry's Weather Bureau, so that the Traffic Officer can inform a pilot of what to expect ahead of him till he reaches his destination.

Our attention is next attracted by a board from which project a large number of small electric bulbs. The Traffic Officer moves a switch and then turns a handle on a dial marked with the points of the compass. As the handle is turned round, different combinations of lights are lighted up; each combination forming a double L, like this: ⅃L. On the aerodrome red lights are fixed in the ground, with thick glass windows over them, corresponding in arrangement with those on the board. When a miniature lamp lights up, its "opposite number" on the aerodrome does the same.

The pilot in an aeroplane about to land in mist or bad light sees the two L's, and knows that the long leg of each points down wind. He therefore directs his machine so that it shall run up the right-hand L towards its short leg, which indicates the line at which he must stop. The other L is for machines starting; and the "neutral" strip between the backs of the L's must not be used at all. The Traffic Officer adjusts the position of the L's according to the direction of the wind.

The guiding lamps on the ground, like those fixed on the tops of all buildings to mark them out, are filled with "neon" gas, which emits a red light with remarkable fog-piercing properties. On the further side of Plough Lane is a "neon" beacon, having a large number of neon tubes, 26 feet long, arranged in the form of a cone. This beacon is visible 50 miles away, and its colour renders it quite unmistakable.

The usefulness of aerial transport cannot be turned to full account until flying is made safe by night as well as by day.

CONQUERING THE AIR

The London-Paris airway is already provided with powerful beacons at Tatsfield, Penshurst, Cranbrook, Lympne, Littlestone, and St. Inglevert, besides the terminal ones at Croydon and Le Bourget: and these come in useful for day flying when the light is bad. Night operation of the airway will begin, however, when experiments have shown it to be rendered safe by the various aids provided both on the ground and in the pilot's cockpit. In this connection may be mentioned the great aerial lighthouse recently erected on the summit of Mont Afrique, near Dijon, in France. It has a beam of 1,000,000,-000 candlepower and in clear weather is visible 300 miles away. At present it is the most powerful lighthouse in existence, but eventually others of equal power will be erected in other places on the great continental air routes.

The most powerful of beacons can be nullified by fog. But great help may ultimately be derived from an invention called the "leader" cable. Perhaps you remember the story of the old Greek hero, Theseus, who determined to enter the mazes of the great Labyrinth, in Crete, and slay the Minotaur. Ariadne provided him with a ball of thread which he unrolled as he went in, so that by following it back he should be certain of regaining the entrance. The "leader" cable serves much the same end. For guiding ships through difficult channels into port, it is laid on the sea bottom. Strong electrical impulses are sent through it continuously, and the navigator of a ship provided with the proper wireless receiving apparatus can decide whether he is getting "hotter" or "colder," and so follow the course of the cable, even when a dense fog envelops his vessel. As applied to airways, the cable is buried in the ground along the route. The aeroplane carries sensitive "detectors" on the wings, in circuit with headphones worn by the pilot or with a dial on the dashboard. Should the aeroplane be flying

within reach of the signals—which have a range of some miles—
the pilot can tell where he is relatively to the cable and feel
his way along it. Several of these cables have been laid between Paris and the Channel coast, and eventually no doubt
they will become a regular part of the equipment of airways
liable to obscuration by fog.

People who have never used, nor taken much interest in,
aerial transport may be surprised by figures of what has been
done. British commercial aviation began in August, 1919,
when the London -Paris service was instituted. In the six years
following, British commercial machines flew approximately
5,000,000 miles between London and the continent, carrying
more than 60,000 passengers and many hundreds of tons of
freight. British machines now operate on 1,400 miles of airways as against the original 225 miles.

It is only natural that anyone who has never been in the
air, and gleans his or her knowledge of aviation from the accounts of accidents reported in the papers from time to time—
most of them accidents happening to military pilots learning
how to fly—should think it safer always to "keep one foot on
the ground." As a matter of fact flying in aerial liners is
remarkably safe. The best possible proof of this is given by
the British life assurance offices, which now in most cases have
removed all restrictions from their life policies in regard to
flying as passenger on an aeroplane. This means, in other
words, that they regard the risks of taking a journey by air
as practically *nil*: and you may be sure that their opinions are
based on hard fact.

It may also surprise some people to learn that insurance rates
on freight carried by aeroplane are lower than those applying
to any other form of transport. This because the risks of
breakage and pilferage are smaller. All kinds of things are

now sent by aeroplane. Here are a couple of lists, taken from official sources, which you may find interesting:

London—Paris—Basle—Zurich

Tin ware, gold watch cases, underclothing, newspapers, gold, machine parts, gloves, straw plait, aluminium pistons, tools, slippers, pump sprays, clothing, platinum, gramophone records, live dogs, whalebone, ball bearings, enamelled cowhides, artificial flowers, silk, flowers, books, lenses, cotton, whisky, fish, wall papers, milk, live show pigeons, tennis balls, woollen goods, boots, silver, advertising matter.

London—Amsterdam—Berlin—Copenhagen

Textile goods, machine parts, aero engine parts, china, electric drills, chains, parts of motor cars, cricket bats and balls, live fowls, woollen goods, gold, flannel, roller bearings, radio crystals, watch parts, eggs for hatching, chemicals, printed labels, enamelled cowhide, hats, waterproof garments, lizard skins, water meters, steel tubes.

It is quite customary now to send large consignments of gold by aeroplane: half a million pounds' worth at a time. Among other things a live tiger has been carried. In the ordinary course you may send packages weighing anything up to 250 lbs. apiece. And by special arrangement a package weighing a quarter of a ton may be accepted.

It is certainly a very quick way of sending goods. Organisation has been so perfected that parcels are passed through the Customs in a few moments at the delivery end; and immediately afterwards special Imperial Airways vans are conveying the goods brought by aeroplane to their destination.

PLATE XI

300° CONE OF UNOBSTRUCTED VISION. OBTAINED FROM UPPER & LOWER LOOKOUT POSITIONS & CONTROL COMPARTMENT

UPPER LOOK-OUT POSITION

RUDDER CONTROL
ELEVATOR CONTROL

CONTROL COMPARTMENT

GANGWAY LEADING TO PASSENGERS & CREWS QUARTERS

PORTS FOR ACCESS TO AIRSHIP FROM MOORING MAST

LOWER LOOK-OUT POSITION WITH BOMB SIGHT & DRIFT INDICATOR FOR GROUND OBSERVATION.

GANGWAY TO BOW

SALOON

CABINS & STATEROOMS.

OUTER COVER OF AIRSHIP

GALLEY, DINING SALOON.

CABINS & STATEROOMS

PASSENGER ACCOMMODATION FOR ENGLAND – NEW ZEALAND AIR LINER

VIEW SHOWING GENERAL ARRANGEMENT OF PASSENGERS QUARTERS AND CONTROL COMPARTMENT.

A sectional view of the giant airship designed by Commander C. D. Burney. The airship will have a gas capacity of 5,000,000 cubic feet. The passenger cabins are inside the envelope, and not slung below the framework, as in other airships. [*Photo, Airways.*]

AIRWAYS

Parcels collected in London in the morning are delivered in Amsterdam, Paris, or Brussels the same afternoon; and in Cologne, Zurich, Hamburg, Copenhagen, and Berlin the next morning. And the same with goods taken in the opposite direction.

The Longest Passenger Airway

In no part of the world has the aeroplane proved a greater boon than in Western Australia. This country has a population of about 300,000 people scattered over an area of about 1,000,000 square miles; and the larger part of the population is concentrated in a few towns situated great distances apart on the coast—Perth, Geraldton, Carnarvon among them. North of Geraldton communication was till recently by steamer service operating to and from Singapore and Western Australia, and by other local services calling at all the ports from Derby in the north to Perth in the south. These two places are over 1,400 miles apart, and the steamers took seven days or more to cover the distance between them. There might be intervals of over a fortnight between calls, so that even the coast towns were badly served. Settlers living away from the coast in the "back of beyond" were still worse off, owing to the lack of good roads.

In August, 1921, a company entitled Western Australian Airways, Limited, was formed to run an aeroplane service from Perth to Derby, calling at Geraldton, Carnarvon, Onslow, Roebourne, Whim Creek, Port Hedland, and Broome. The last is inhabited by black people and provides more than three-quarters of the world's supply of pearl shell.

The Airways Company has a Government contract to carry mails once a week from Perth to Derby and from Derby to

Perth, with calls at the intermediate stations. It also carries freight and passengers. At first the mail included but a handful of letters, but now the monthly total is more than 18,000. On many occasions the demand for seats in the aeroplanes has exceeded capacity. The Company at present uses eight machines, all fitted with 240-horsepower engines, piloted by men who have all seen service in the Royal Flying Corps or the Australian Flying Corps, and were chosen for their all-round ability to deal with any kind of emergency that might arise. At regular intervals every machine undergoes rigorous inspection by a Government representative, and has to be given a fresh certificate of airworthiness. Some of the aeroplanes are of Australian manufacture, and have proved equal to the original machines imported by the Company.

During the greater portion of the year ideal flying conditions prevail all along the route, but from December to March violent storms, known locally as "willy-willies," have to be reckoned with. These travel down the coast, causing much havoc in their track. The sky becomes dark, and the wind has a velocity with which an aeroplane can hardly contend. Fortunately, the approach of a willy-willy is heralded by a rapid fall of the barometer for several days, and the Company, acting on the warning given by the mercury, stops the service and makes the aeroplanes snug in their sheds until conditions again become reasonably safe.

The service is operated by relays of machines and pilots, and is carried out in three sections. The machines circulate round the route, and every three weeks reach their main depot at Perth, where they undergo a thorough examination and overhaul. Any job that can possibly need doing can be carried out by the staff of the Company, which is thus quite independent of outside help.

AIRWAYS

Since the service was started it has been conducted with a punctuality which is somewhat remarkable. In very few instances has an aeroplane arrived behind schedule time. All kinds of freight are carried, including a large number of day-old chickens despatched from outlying poultry farms to the towns. The mail planes have also transported motor parts, and shearing machinery and, by the timely and quick delivery of some essential part, averted the closing-down of mining and oil-drilling plants. The mail pilots are often able to render valuable services to settlers and ranchers by warning them in advance of approaching grass fires, sighted during a journey, and so enabling them to get their flocks to safety before the arrival of the conflagration. The aeroplanes on several occasions have saved human life by carrying medical men to patients, or invalids to hospital. Literally flying to the rescue, a Perth surgeon travelled over 500 miles in a day, attended to three patients at different places, and performed a very critical operation.

The Western Australians are already firm believers in the aeroplane. Men and women alike think nothing of an air journey of 1,000 miles. Station-owners are preparing landing-grounds on their properties, and will soon have their own aeroplanes, the speediness whereof will remove the sense of isolation which at present must assail the occupants of a household many miles away from the nearest neighbour.

The coming of the aeroplane has shortened the journey from Perth to Derby from 7 days to 56 hours. The trip can be made for £28, which works out at 4¾d. a mile. In a county where prices generally are higher than here this seems to be a very reasonable rate. Very probably the airway will be extended to Port Darwin, where it will join up with an extension of a service operating in Queensland and so give quick communication between the west and the east coasts.

The Trans-American Airway

In an earlier chapter was described a non-stop flight across the American continent, and in it reference was made to the difficulties attending night flying for want of guiding lights. When, in 1921, the U. S. Post Office authorities inaugurated a trans-continental air-mail service, it was not a "through" service, as the aeroplanes handed the mails over to the railways when they reached the zone of darkness. Thus, a mail plane flying westwards would deliver up its load at Chicago, while an eastbound machine would transfer at Cheyenne. The 900 miles between these two cities had to be traversed at under half aeroplane speed, which meant a delay of from 8 to 9 hours as compared with continuous aerial transport.

To ensure the last being reasonably safe the Post Office Department experimented with powerful beacons and illuminated landing grounds. The upshot has been the establishment, at Chicago, Iowa City, Omaha, North Platte, and Cheyenne, of enormously powerful revolving searchlights emitting beams of 450,000,000 candlepower. The beam is almost horizontal and rotates three times a minute. Its glare has been sighted at a distance of over 130 miles; and 100 miles is quite an ordinary range. As the beacons are only about 200 miles apart, in clear weather the pilot is able to sight one ahead almost before he has got out of range of that next astern.

As an aid in misty weather, and to give the pilot a clear and continuous indication of his route, subsidiary beacons of 4,000,000 candlepower, revolving 6 times a minute, are strung out at intervals of 25 to 30 miles between the main beacons: and between these, again, at every third mile is stationed a 5,000-candlepower gas beacon flashing 150 times a minute. As an extra precaution, all "unattended" beacons are duplicated, and if one fails, its fellow comes into action automatically and a red light shows. The next pilot to pass, seeing the red light, reports the failure, and the beacon is at once attended to.

The main landing grounds are near the main beacons; the emergency fields close to the secondary lights. In all there are 39 places distributed along the night section of the airway in which a landing may safely be made. The grounds and buildings are outlined by electric lights, and the landing strips are illuminated by "flood" lights casting a wide, shallow beam along them. The pilot is aided by a red central marker, illuminated from below, and as a further help he has powerful searchlights attached to the wings of his machine which can be turned on to show him what is ahead of him.

Since July, 1924, the air mails have been traversing the United States by night as well as by day. New York, Bellefonte, Cleveland, Bryan, Chicago, Iowa City, Rock Springs, Salt Lake City, Elko, Reno and San Francisco,—these are the places at which the planes descend and transfer their freights, or fresh pilots take charge. The normal schedule time for the coast-to-coast journey is 33 hours. This compares with 96 to 120 hours by ordinary mail train. In 1860 trains and pony express combined took a letter from New York to San Francisco in 10½ days; and if we go ten years further back, the time is 24 days. In 75 years, therefore, the number of hours needed has been reduced to less than one-seventeenth of its original figure. The business world benefits enormously by the saving of time over even the most rapid transit by train. A bank official has estimated that £20,000 has been saved in a single month on the interest on notes which otherwise would be kept longer in mail sacks between New York and Chicago; and a relatively larger saving must result on the full journey to the Pacific coast.

The service is carried on more or less regardless of weather conditions, with wonderful regularity and punctuality. The pilots often have great difficulty in fighting their way through storms to their destination. We may take the case of a pilot who, not far from Salt Lake City, ran into a terrific blizzard while crossing mountain peaks. Before he could do anything his machine was hurled against a mountain side, and the landing carriage collapsed. The position of a man stranded amid deep snow on a peak 9,400 feet above sea level is not enviable. Our pilot, shouldering his travelling bag, started down the slope, steering a course by compass. He was soon waist-deep in the snow, but he fought his way down the mountain all the rest of the day and through the following night. As day dawned he reached the timber line, and when on the point of succumbing to the fatal sleepiness brought on by great exertion and bitter cold he spied a barn, and a mile further on reached a house, at six in the morning. Two days later he had recovered sufficiently to ride to the nearest post office and telephone to Salt Lake City, when he learned that for days past all the aeroplanes of that Division of the Air Mail Service had been hunting for him.

Another pilot had a somewhat similar experience in the same neighbourhood. He struck a mountain at 8,200 feet, charging through trees which wrecked his machine completely. He was flung out and had his left shoulder dislocated. While descending the mountain he fell heavily, and by a happy stroke of luck the fall replaced the dislocated shoulder. Crossing a railway track, he held up the next train and got aboard.

Some other pilots who went out to retrieve the mails reported that the aeroplane had simply ploughed its way through the trees, and that one of those snapped off measured more than 16 inches in diameter! It must have been a mighty crash!

CHAPTER 26

USES FOR AIRCRAFT

THE main activities of aircraft will, so far as we can forsee, always centre on the transport of passengers and cargo. But it is certain that new uses will be found for aircraft as time goes on, some of them very likely of a kind such as now we cannot even guess at. If you study the newspapers you will occasionally come across instances of the unexpected usefulness of aeroplanes. For example, a large number of ships were some time ago frozen up in the Gulf of Finland, far from land. The position of the crews would have been critical but for the dropping of provisions and other supplies by aeroplane. Then again, some fishing vessels were lost off the western coast of Ireland. Aeroplanes hunted the islands in search of survivors and dropped food on to those islands where none existed.

The high speed of aircraft, the great range of view given by them, and their ubiquity, combine to open up many possible avenues of usefulness. Aircraft have rendered every point on the earth's surface accessible at least to the vision, if not to the foot. The unreachable valley of the imaginative story will have to disappear from fiction, as the airman would make short work of a mountain range that defies the foot traveller, and soon be knocking at the doors of King Solomon's Mines or any other repository of hidden treasure. The air leads everywhere.

In this chapter we will notice a few of the byways of commercial flying, some of them being explored tentatively, maybe, while along others considerable progress has been made.

In Canada and the United States, where enormous damage is done annually to forests by fire, the aeroplane has shown itself ideal for patrolling great areas. In its early stages a fire can be extinguished easily, or at least vastly more easily than after it has got a fair hold. Aeroplanes patrolling at a good height soon detect any signs of fire, and signal or carry news of it to the fire-fighting stations. In case of need they can transport men and appliances to the neighbourhood of the fire, thus saving a great deal of precious time. The large number of lakes scattered about in the lumber-growing regions of Canada make the use of seaplanes convenient in many districts where the difficulty of finding landing places practically rules out the employment of wheeled aeroplanes. In one season an aerial patrol has spotted over six hundred fires and, by timely warning, saved timber worth many millions of dollars.

Aerial photography can and does give valuable assistance to forest-wardens, by showing the location of diseased areas needing treatment, or places whence timber has been removed illegally, and where replanting is necessary. In Burma large forests have been photographed completely from the air, and the information gathered by the camera has proved a great help to the forest officers. This subject is referred to again a few pages further on.

Fighting Insects with Aeroplanes

Mankind's greatest foe is the insect in its larval and winged stages. If a continuous and relentless fight were not constantly waged against the insect we should be in a bad way. Even as things are, insects ravage our vegetable and corn crops, our fruit trees, our forests, cotton and other plantations, and in the course of a year do damage to the extent of many tens of millions of pounds. The price of cotton goods—and every one of us needs a lot of these—depends largely upon the extent to which the boll-weevil has affected the year's cotton crop. Similarly, the cost of timber is in no small degree governed by the activity of certain destructive caterpillars.

The only way of checking the evil-doing of these tiny foes is to kill them by means of poisonous chemicals. In the past these have been applied mainly by hand or mechanical spraying or dusting from the ground. When even small trees, such as apple-trees, have to be treated it is a laborious and expensive business: and of course spraying forest trees is quite out of the question. Then again, spraying, to be effective, must be done under certain weather conditions which may be short-lived, and unless a large labour force be employed a favourable opportunity may be missed.

The aeroplane has proved itself very useful in distributing the chemicals. It can fly over tree-tops as easily as over corn crops, and what it drops is scattered far and wide. Also, it moves so fast that it gets the work done at an amazing speed. The cotton planter can hire an aeroplane to "dust" large areas just after the dew has fallen, when the chemical will stick well. The pilot flies low over the fields, leaving in his wake a poison cloud which soon settles on the plants, and in due course penetrates to the weevils in the cotton bolls.

As an example of what the aeroplane can do for infested plantations we may quote the "dusting" of a certain grove of catalpa trees, grown for posts and fence rails. This grove was being badly punished by the caterpillars of a moth which lays its eggs all over the leaves. Within little more than a month of the eggs being deposited the caterpillars have done their devouring work, gone into the ground, turned into pupæ, and hatched out into moths, which carry on the egg-laying. Consequently three or four broods may successively commit their ravages on the same trees in a single season.

The grove in question had an area of about six acres. An aeroplane was detailed to dress it with about a hundredweight and a half of arsenate of lead, which is very deadly if absorbed into the system of any living creature. The hopper containing the chemical had an automatic gear to liberate the powder in a continuous stream into the blast of air from the propeller. In a few minutes the aeroplane had flown three or four times up and down to windward of the grove, and discharged its load, which was wafted among the trees by the breeze. The mortality among the millions of caterpillars was tremendous; not one out of a hundred escaped the deadly effects of the poison. Their corpses covered the ground, the branches, the tree trunks. Some cloths spread under the trees collected fifty or more dead caterpillars to the square foot, though doubtless many of the creatures that fell on them had crawled off to die.

The caterpillar which delights in the tender "leading" shoots of fir trees has destroyed immense numbers of fine conifers. Carrying on its depredations far above ground, it has been practically immune from attack, as well as from observation. But nowadays it is safe no longer, for observers in aircraft can quickly "spot" ravaged areas and take the measures necessary to free them from their myriad invaders.

The aeroplane lends itself admirably to the sowing of seeds which may be scattered broadcast. It literally runs away from any other contrivance designed to do the job. In twenty minutes an aeroplane has sown a whole square mile of ground with grass seed. This work would have occupied a couple of men for two or three weeks—and they would have had to keep busy to get it done even in that time.

"Spotting" Fish and Seals

The submarine-hunting activities of aircraft during the War have their peaceful counterpart in hunting for shoals of fish and watching the movements of seals during the fishing and sealing seasons. These creatures are governed by laws not yet understood, and the boats that go out in search of them may waste a great deal of time before the quarry is sighted. The fleet that has a dirigible balloon or a few seaplanes in attendance to do scouting for it enjoys a great advantage, since on the one hand it is saved much useless steaming and on the other is much less likely to miss good chances.

Houses on Wings

The aerial counterpart of the motor caravan has already appeared for the use of ranch managers, the directors of companies, and others making tours of inspection. One particular aeroplane constructed in America has a telescopic undercarriage, which allows the body to be lowered till it rests on the ground after it has landed. The body contains living accommodation for six people, including an electric kitchen. There is also a small office equipped with typewriter and desk. The crew and passengers are thus rendered independent of hotels and other shelter while "on tour." In the future commercial travellers will no doubt make increasing use of this type of machine to carry and house themselves and their samples, and to serve as show-rooms.

USES FOR AIRCRAFT

Advertising Uses

The most effective application of aviation as an advertising medium is what is known as sky-writing, invented by Major J. C. Savage who has, both personally and through a staff of specially trained pilots, given demonstrations of it in several countries. An aeroplane employed in sky-writing carries smoke-emitting apparatus under the close control of the pilot, so that he may turn on or cut off the smoke instantaneously. On a day when the wind is not strong enough to obliterate the writing before the words have been traced, the pilot ascends to a great height. Whatever he "writes" in the sky has, from his point of view, to be written backwards, that is, from right to left, instead of from left to right, in order that it may appear right way up to people below. What is meant will be obvious if you write some words on a piece of transparent paper, turn the sheet over, and examine the words from above. In the course of tracing out a dozen letters or so the aeroplane may have to fly several miles. Under favourable conditions the results are very effective; and the advertising value of sky-writing is high because the spectator is fascinated and keeps on looking to watch the development of letter after letter.

Major Savage tells an interesting little story of the way in which he introduced sky-writing to the notice of New York. One day at lunch time the millions of inhabitants were electrified by seeing the words "Hello U. S. A. !" appear in the sky. The evening papers were full of the phenomenon. The morning papers of the day following said very little indeed on the subject, for their proprietors had had time to scent a rival form of advertising that might prove dangerous. But the enterprising Englishman got into touch with the head of a great tobacco firm and secured a very valuable advertising contract.

The appearance in the sky of the name of the special "line" advertised proved an immense attraction and increased sales so enormously that further big contracts were at once fixed up.

Bird's-eye Views

Quite a large business is now done in photographs taken from aircraft of towns, objects of special interest in town or country, factories, private property, and so on. Firms which specialise in this kind of work have come into existence to meet the demand for the bird's-eye view, which in many cases gives a far better idea of the subject photographed than any number of views taken at or near ground level. Photographs of this kind are usually taken in perspective, that is, obliquely; but for certain purposes the vertical photograph is preferred, a number of photographs being pieced together to form a map of docks, railway premises, drainage schemes, or what not. The more we travel by air the greater will be the demand for views taken from the air, since on our journeys we shall see countries and towns from above.

The aerial view can also be of great use to the engineer in making preliminary surveys for roads or railways, since the aeroplane and camera combined can gather in a few hours information which would occupy a field surveying party for weeks. The saving of time is greatest in flat swamps or heavily wooded country where months would have to be spent in merely cutting a line from one observation point to another.

Aerial Map-making

The elaborate maps made of the battle fronts by means of aircraft during the War (see p. 256) prepared the way for the aerial survey which is rapidly gaining importance as a substitute for or complement to the map made by surveying parties using instruments on the earth's surface. Aerial map-making may take the place of ordinary survey methods for country which is hardly explored or at best very thinly settled. It provides a record full of details by which particular areas can be identified. The camera is being used widely for surveying, many thousands of square miles being "taken" annually. Canada has probably been the scene of more aerial surveying than any other country, the Royal Canadian Air Force being very active in mapping all kinds of country. In 1925 the R. C. A. F. photographed 47,700 square miles. Town surveyors find aerial maps valuable in many ways, for these show at a glance the density of settlement in a new district, improvements made, drainage schemes, railways, footpaths, roads, and so on, the plotting of which on hand-compiled maps would be a long and expensive business.

A great deal of aerial survey work had been done also in Burma, where an area of 1,400 square miles in the Irrawaddy Delta was mapped by camera. From the photographic map a drawn map was prepared. The total cost of mapping was less than half that of mapping by "ground" methods, and the work was carried out in a very much shorter time. The contract for this survey entailed taking nearly 4,000 photographs from a height of 9,800 feet.

The same company has since mapped Rangoon and surrounding country to the extent of 70 square miles, and the Burma Oil Company's oil fields on the Irrawaddy.

Air surveying will never replace other methods entirely. For example, a photograph cannot give names, nor can it show contour lines. But it is becoming invaluable for preliminary surveys of more or less unknown country; and provides a useful check on surveys carried out by other methods.

Hunting by Aeroplane

It goes almost without saying that the best big-game hunting is to be found in districts remote from large centres of population and not easily got at by ordinary means of locomotion. Take Canada for example. Here you have a magnificent sporting country through large areas of which no roads nor railways pass. Dense forests, innumerable rushing streams, and deep ravines render it very difficult to traverse. Crossing this game country requires plenty of time, much patience, and considerable physical toughness. Many a busy man has been debarred from hunting by the lack of sufficient leisure. If he is to hunt at all he must be able to get quickly to where the game is. Hence the enlistment of the aeroplane as a means of transporting hunting parties to the scene of action. A seaplane, based on some lake handy to a railway, will in a few hours cover as much ground as would require weeks of toilsome struggling by boat or on foot. It alights on one of the many small lakes and disembarks its passengers and their equipment, and returns to its base. When the hunting holiday ends it calls again to pick up the party and convey it back to the base. In other places the aeroplane is used for day hunting trips, just as a motor car elsewhere. It can hardly be doubted that, by means of aircraft, the backlands of Canada and other countries will be opened up for sport and holiday-making long before they are accessible by road or rail.

PLATE XII

The "Autogiro," invented by Señor Juan de la Cierva, is the latest thing in successful flying-machines. Instead of fixed planes, it has a horizontal windmill, which is kept in rotation by the machine's passage through the air, gives extraordinary stability, and renders almost vertical descents possible and safe.

(Photo. Topical Press.

CHAPTER 27

THE FUTURE OF FLYING

THERE are still vast numbers of folk who have never seen a dirigible balloon or an aeroplane. There are many people who, having seen both, do not yet realise what they portend, and, for lack of having had any personal experience of either, are somewhat indifferent, and even sceptical, as to the future of aerial transport. This condition of mind is not to be wondered at among populations which, a few years ago, saw the air full of war-planes and balloons, whereas now the passage of aircraft is by no means frequent. The natural deduction would, to the person who does not look below the surface of things, seem to be that a means of locomotion which has great value for war is a failure when applied to commercial and peaceful uses, just like submarine navigation.

It is, however, quite certain that the human race, having once been put in possession of practical aircraft, affording quicker movement than anything preceding, will never quit the air again. We might as reasonably expect to see the abandonment of rail and road transport. What will happen is that aerial locomotion will steadily make its way, overcoming prejudice and misunderstanding until, having proved itself indispensable, it will be used by everybody.

It is the fashion to say that human flight is as yet in its infancy. In regard to the extent to which it is used this is true enough. The percentage of the world's population which takes an aerial trip even once a year is at present infinitesimal.

CONQUERING THE AIR

On the mechanical side, however, it is evident that great progress has been made. Speeds of up to 270 miles an hour, altitude climbs of up to nearly 40,000 feet, aeroplane flights lasting nearly two days and covering thousands of miles, and the many great exploits performed by airmen during the War and since, would seem to show that the flying-machine as we know it has reached a stage of considerable development. As regards safety, the percentage of accidents occuring in commercial air services is remarkably small. It is wonderful that we should have got as far in conquering the air as we have in so short a time. For this we have to thank the basis of mechanical experience provided by the motor-car industry and the "forcing" influence of the War in improving design.

This is not to say that our present-day dirigibles and aeroplanes will not appear crude, small, and dangerous to people who, thirty or forty years hence, may examine photographic and printed representations of them or study examples stored in the national museums. Perhaps they will admire the air pilots of today much as we admire the early navigators who braved the perils of unknown oceans in tiny ships. Immense improvements must come. That these will mean a complete alteration in constructional principles and outward shape does not follow, for, after all, the "Flying Scotsman" of today is the same as the "Rocket" in essentials. In any case there is likely to be a great increase in the size and carrying capacity of commercial aircraft, as has been the case with mercantile and other ships, since great size makes for economical running. On the other hand, the private and "sporting" machine will, we may conclude, be built small, for in this case smallness gives economy in another way. And no doubt there will be intermediate sizes, which will be reduced in number as the result of experience. Perhaps we, or our descendants, will see machines able to travel on the road, on the water, or in the air indifferently.

Air Travel in the Future

The popularising of aerial travel depends on a great deal more than the capacity of the machines to be used. Good locomotives do not by themselves make a good railway; and the aerial services of the future will entail an enormous ground organisation. Peeping into the magic mirror which shows the future, we see alighting-places provided, either in open spaces or on the flat roofs of large buildings, in all large cities, so that local traffic at least may begin and end in the very heart of things. The great airports on the long-distance airway routes may still lie some way out, as at present, for convenience sake; but the aerial taxi or private machine now has its parking-place among bricks and mortar, handy to the person who uses it. From these comparatively restricted areas the flying-machine rises more or less vertically by its own power, or is catapulted into the air. Our mirror shows us, by the bye, that the city of the future is free from the smoky pall which in existing times obscures the atmosphere over so many of our great towns.

Betaking ourselves by lift to an air-station, we speed away across country, and note the large number of craft sharing the air with us. These seem to be following ordered routes; and the reason for this is seen in the strings of landing grounds and signs which stretch away in all directions. There is now no difficulty either by day or by night in making a safe landing and finding the way from point to point, even in countries where the population is sparse. For the international airways all over the world have become a very important factor of civilization, and the idea of mechanical flight being confined to daylight hours was discarded long ago. Thanks to the lighting of the routes, the liberal provision of aerodromes, and the wonderful instruments in front of him, the pilot flies through even the worst weather in the reasonable certainty of reaching his destination, or at least a place of refuge, in safety.

Many rivers of the world have become identified with important airways, operated by craft suitable for alighting on water; and lakes everywhere serve as ready-made local airports, from which, in undeveloped countries, aircraft run to outlying and widely scattered homesteads. Isolation is a thing of the past, even in the "back of beyond," for every large ranch or farm has its landing ground and flying-machine. Aerial transport is now greatly assisting the opening up of new territory ahead of roads and railways; it being less expensive, and vastly quicker, to bring in even heavy goods of certain kinds by air than to haul them overland, if indeed it be possible. Of course, in countries where there are roads and railways heavy traffic still moves over them, except in cases where speed is of prime importance; and air transport is in the main limited to passengers and to freight—such as mails,—able to stand a high rate relatively to weight.

Heavy-fuel Engines

Turning from the future to the present, it is interesting to notice some of the lines along which improvement tends to move. High efficiency is particularly needed in aircraft, as their fuel costs are high as compared with those of other means of locomotion. So far as one can see, unless revolutionary improvements be made, commercial speeds will remain much as at present, since extreme speed, whether on land, on sea, or in the air, is very expensive, and the future of aerial transport must depend in no small measure on its being reasonably cheap. Motor spirit—petrol, gasolene, "gas"—is costly, besides being very dangerous. Many deaths have been caused by aircraft taking fire in the air or after a crash which of itself might have led to no fatal results. Therefore experimenters are busy with aero engines of the Diesel type, able to burn a heavy fuel oil of a cheap kind and to dispense with electrical ignition apparatus, as engines of this kind have their gas charges ignited spontaneously by the heat of the high compression to which they are subjected. Such engines will give greater safety and simplicity, and will be run at a much lower fuel cost than ordinary aero engines. They will be especially well suited for dirigible balloons, where—except in the very few cases in which the very expensive non-inflammable helium gas is used——the proximity of large volumes of hydrogen gas is a danger. One need hardly point out the advantage of substituting a fuel costing threepence or fourpence a gallon for one the price of which ranges from a shilling upward.

Saving Wastage of Gas

The weight of fuel that a large airship has to carry for long non-stop journeys runs into many tons—accounts perhaps for a quarter of the total loaded weight. It stands to reason that, as the fuel supply is used up, the airship must rise higher and higher unless sufficient gas be allowed to escape to maintain equilibrium. By the end of the voyage tens of thousands of cubic feet will have been valved and need replacing at a considerable cost. Owing to changes of temperature some wastage is unavoidable, quite apart from that due to alteration of load, but this is comparatively small. If the load could be kept fairly constant throughout a voyage much less gas would be needed to maintain an airship in a properly inflated condition. This involves counteracting the loss of weight caused by the consumption of fuel. But how is this to be done?

You have no doubt often noticed that, when a motor car is started-up on a cold day, quite a lot of water drips from the silencer discharge pipe. Petrol is a combination of hydrogen and carbon, and when it "burns" in the engine's cylinders the hydrogen unites with the oxygen of some of the air drawn in to give a suitable explosive mixture, and water vapour is formed. Why not then, pass the exhaust gases through a condenser and capture the water? This has actually been done, and it has been found possible to accumulate an even greater weight of water than that of the fuel consumed. At first sight this may appear impossible, but it must be remembered that the larger part of the water's weight is contributed by the air which the engine took in as the airship went on her way. The apparatus required is not costly, and soon pays for itself in the saving of gas effected.

While on the subject of airships, reference may be made to the two huge craft being built for the British Government. They will be of 5,000,000 cubic feet capacity, and so be twice as large in this respect as any airships constructed previously. Each will accommodate 140 passengers and their luggage, having a "useful lift" of about 90 tons, or three times that of the R34. A cruising speed of 70 miles an hour is expected. The control and passenger cabins will be inside the hull instead of suspended from it as in earlier ships. These vessels are intended for service between England and New Zealand. It is anticipated that Australia will be reached from London in eleven days, as compared with five weeks by ship. Should the liners prove a success, it is quite possible that still larger vessels will be built.

The Autogiro

For many years past inventors have been trying to produce a practical "helicopter"—a flying-machine supported by large screws on vertical shafts, enabling it to rise and descend vertically, besides moving horizontally or obliquely like an ordinary aeroplane. An apparatus that could start from or alight safely in an area no larger than a suburban back garden or a big roof would have certain obvious advantages over the aeroplane as we know it, for this requires a lot of room both when getting off or landing. How useful, too, it would be in a fog or darkness to be able to feel one's way to land very slowly!

The helicopter has not appeared yet in what may be called a practical form. Specimens tested have acquitted themselves in a decidedly discouraging manner. The Autogiro, the invention of a Spanish engineer, Señor Juan de la Cierva, which *is* practical, does, however, resemble the helicopter in so far as it is supported by what may be likened to a windmill with four sweeps rotating round a vertical mast. It has no fixed "wings." At the time when these words were written the Autogiro was in an experimental stage, though its performances had aroused great interest in aeronautical circles.

Towards the end of 1925 the British Air Ministry invited the inventor to demonstrate his machine at Farnborough. The Autogiro used on that occasion consisted of an ordinary Avro aeroplane body with an 120-h.p. motor and tractor screw. The wings had been removed, and their place was taken by a long spar sticking out to right and left and carrying two small balancing planes. In the forward part of the body rose a short, stumpy mast, supporting a windmill with four sails, attached to a central hub which was free to revolve on the top of the mast. The connection between a sail and the hub permitted the sail to alter its angle automatically as the "mill" revolved, and adjust itself to alterations of pressure. Preparatory to a flight the mill was set in motion by hauling on a rope. As the machine ran along the ground the speed of rotation increased under the pressure of the air, and the mill continued spinning until after the end of the flight. The Autogiro took-off in the usual way, rising quickly, and attained a speed of 70 miles an hour. It turned easily in any direction. A remarkable feature of the performance was that, when the speed was reduced to a figure at which an ordinary aeroplane would "stall" and nose-dive, the Autogiro merely descended on an even keel. This quality renders it easily mastered by a novice and very safe to handle,—for a nose-dive is one of the greatest dangers awaiting the embryo pilot. The Autogiro is able to fly very slowly, at not more than 20 miles an hour, and it cannot lose its balance because the supporting surfaces are high above the centre of gravity of the whole. It may be landed almost vertically without damaging itself—in other words, can alight in a very restricted space.

All this refers to the experimental machine. The inventor claims that, when his ideas have been fully worked out, the Autogiro, on account of its stability, vertical descent and high speed will revolutionise flight. He may claim too much, but at any rate his apparatus has been taken up by aircraft constructors all over the world, and before these words appear in print many Autogiros may be in the air, some of them driven by engines of very low power. It may be that its stability may make the Autogiro the "popular" private machine. The possibility of buying a mount which is practically crashproof and may be mastered in one or two lessons will appeal to many people who are not prepared to risk their necks learning how to pilot an aeroplane.

High Speed at Great Heights

The density of the air decreases with increase in altitude, and at great heights offers very little resistance to anything moving through it. The Germans took advantage of this fact in 1918, when they bombarded Paris with their "Berthas" from points 70 miles away. The guns had sufficient power to make the shells take a path which lay largely through air so tenuous that it checked the projectiles hardly at all.

This falling-off in density limits the height to which an aeroplane can climb. For its weight remains more or less constant, whereas the supporting power of the air decreases unless the aeroplane is driven through it at speed increasing with height. The difficulty is that the power of an engine is limited by the amount of fuel it can consume in a given time, and at a certain speed of revolution this power will fall off as the air becomes thinner and a given volume of it therefore means lower compression in the cylinders. The trouble can be got over in a considerable degree by means of a "super-charger," which mechanically forces into the cylinders a larger volume of air than they would suck in of themselves. Assuming an aeroplane to be able to reach a great height, it should also travel at a much higher speed than at low altitudes on the same expenditure of fuel. We therefore may some day see commercial machines, with bodies specially strengthened so that a normal air pressure may be maintained inside them, hurtling along at great heights and at speeds much in excess of what could economically be used in dense air.

There is good reason to suppose that in the upper regions of the atmosphere air-currents move at enormous speeds and in more or less fixed directions, like the trade winds at sea level. Assuming these winds to have been "mapped," they could be taken advantage of to increase the speed of travel greatly without any increase in the fuel bill.

Wireless Control

That aircraft will ever be driven by power radiated from the ground seems very improbable, as the power required at the transmitting point would have to be enormous. *Control* by wireless, however, is in quite a different category, for delicate relays—electrical triggers—can be operated by a minute amount of energy. Successful experiments in distant control have been made in France and elsewhere. In one instance an aeroplane with nobody aboard was sent up, steered by wireless during a flight of 125 miles, and landed again safely. Other experiments have proved it possible to launch large mail planes from the ground, cause them to drop mails at specified places, and return to the starting point. The terrible possibilities of this form of control during war are evident, and one can only hope that they will never be put to the test; just as we may trust, perhaps vainly, that aircraft will never again be used on a large scale for warlike purposes. For, with cost no object, planes of great size, able to travel at 300 or more miles an hour, could be built and made to sow bombs of enormous destructive power, with devastating results.

It is far pleasanter to envisage the peace-fostering capacities of aircraft. When the ends of the earth are linked together and communication between continents has been made as swift as now between countries, the spirit of aggressive nationalism will, let us hope, be dissipated by the freer intercourse of nations, so that the era of universal flight shall also be one of universal peace.

OTHER BOOKS FROM CGR PUBLISHING AT CGRPUBLISHING.COM

1939 New York World's Fair: The World of Tomorrow in Photographs

San Francisco 1915 World's Fair: The Panama-Pacific International Expo.

1904 St. Louis World's Fair: The Louisiana Purchase Exposition in Photographs

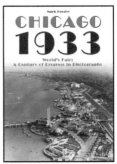

Chicago 1933 World's Fair: A Century of Progress in Photographs

19th Century New York: A Dramatic Collection of Images

The American Railway: The Trains, Railroads, and People Who Ran the Rails

The Aeroplane Speaks: Illustrated Historical Guide to Airplanes

The World's Fair of 1893 Ultra Massive Photographic Adventure Vol. 1

The World's Fair of 1893 Ultra Massive Photographic Adventure Vol. 2

The World's Fair of 1893 Ultra Massive Photographic Adventure Vol. 3

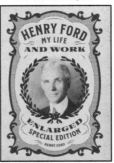

Henry Ford: My Life and Work - Enlarged Special Edition

Magnum Skywolf #1

Ethel the Cyborg Ninja Book 1

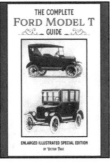

The Complete Ford Model T Guide: Enlarged Illustrated Special Edition

How To Draw Digital by Mark Bussler

Best of Gustave Doré Volume 1: Illustrations from History's Most Versatile...

OTHER BOOKS FROM CGR PUBLISHING AT CGRPUBLISHING.COM

Ultra Massive Video Game Console Guide Volume 1

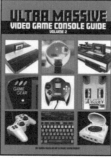

Ultra Massive Video Game Console Guide Volume 2

Ultra Massive Video Game Console Guide Volume 3

Ultra Massive Sega Genesis Guide

Antique Cars and Motor Vehicles: Illustrated Guide to Operation...

Chicago's White City Cookbook

The Clock Book: A Detailed Illustrated Collection of Classic Clocks

The Complete Book of Birds: Illustrated Enlarged Special Edition

1901 Buffalo World's Fair: The Pan-American Exposition in Photographs

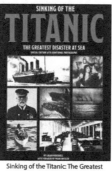

Sinking of the Titanic: The Greatest Disaster at Sea

Gustave Doré's London: A Pilgrimage: Retro Restored Special Edition

Milton's Paradise Lost: Gustave Doré Retro Restored Edition

The Art of World War 1

The Kaiser's Memoirs: Illustrated Enlarged Special Edition

Captain William Kidd and the Pirates and Buccaneers Who Ravaged the Seas

The Complete Butterfly Book: Enlarged Illustrated Special Edition

- MAILING LIST -
JOIN FOR EXCLUSIVE OFFERS

www.CGRpublishing.com/subscribe